SUPPLEMENT TO

A CALIFORNIA FLORA

SUPPLEMENT TO
A CALIFORNIA
FLORA

PHILIP A. MUNZ

RANCHO SANTA ANA BOTANIC GARDEN

CLAREMONT, CALIFORNIA

UNIVERSITY OF CALIFORNIA PRESS

BERKELEY AND LOS ANGELES

1968

ISSUED DECEMBER 16, 1968
UNIVERSITY OF CALIFORNIA PRESS
BERKELEY AND LOS ANGELES, CALIFORNIA
CAMBRIDGE UNIVERSITY PRESS
LONDON, ENGLAND

Contents

Contents

Introduction

A CALIFORNIA FLORA by Munz and Keck appeared in 1959, and ten years have now passed since the book was actually written. Very active floristic work has been underway in California since then and as many revisions and monographs have appeared for groups having species in the state, an attempt should now be made to present as many changes and corrections as possible. Furthermore, with the critical work being done at present on the flora of Europe, reexamination of many types has meant new appraisal of many Linnaean and other older specific names, and changes therefore have to be made for some of the Old World species which have become established here.

Since 1959 I have attempted to record such changes and corrections as I have found, but many others have been made available to me through the kindness of friends to whom I am most grateful. I refer particularly to John Thomas Howell and Thomas C. Fuller, as well as Rimo Bacigalupi, Clare B. Hardham, Al Hobart, Beatrice Howitt, L. L. Kiefer, Peter H. Raven, James L. Reveal, Robert F. Thorne, Ernest C. Twisselmann, H. L. Wedberg, L. C. Wheeler and Louis B. Ziegler. Their names and those of others who have helped appear in italics for individual bits of information in the present treatise. In some cases names represent the collector on whose specimen the record is based; in others the person who published or made known the information in other ways.

In organizing this *Supplement,* page numbers refer of course to the page in the FLORA. In discussing a plant the genus will ordinarily be given, then the number that the species bears in the FLORA:

p. 631. PENSTEMON
    4. P. heterodoxus Gray.

The above two lines indicate that *Penstemon heterodoxus* Gray is treated on page 631 in the FLORA and that it is the fourth species discussed in the genus. Thus the reference

1

is easily made to the FLORA and the information presented in the *Supplement* can be correlated with that in the FLORA. Abbreviations used in the *Supplement* are the same as those in the FLORA.

It is hoped that persons possessing a copy of the FLORA can insert in the margins notes to treatment in the *Supplement*. Since some corrections were made in the second and subsequent printings of the FLORA, occasional references are given for the original 1959 printing and apply only to it, but in such cases this fact is indicated.

p. 14. Sixth paragraph beginning "Deep pervious soil," insert "Cascade Mountains and" before "Sierra Nevada."

p. 17. Fifth paragraph from top of page, beginning "Foothills," insert after "inner Coast Ranges" the words "and some eastern slopes of outer Coast Ranges."

Line 3 from bottom of page, change San Luis Obispo County to Monterey County.

p. 18. Paragraph 1 of "26. Alpine Fell-fields." Change *Astrágalus tegetàrius* to *A. Kentrophÿta.*

In paragraph 2 of "27. Northern Juniper Woodland" insert "Cascade Mountains and the" before "Sierra Nevada."

p. 19. Change for the 1959 printing:

Line 11, Arthur R. Cronquist to Arthur J. Cronquist.

Line 15, Edward R. Balls to Edward K. Balls.

Line 18, Steven S. Tillett to Stephen S. Tillett.

p. 22. For 1959 printing, under LYCOPODIUM add:

1. **L. clavàtum** L. $2n = 68$ (Löve & Löve, 1958); $2n = 34$ (Mehra & Verma, 1957).

2. **L. inundàtum** L. at Humboldt Bay, Humboldt Co.; to Canada and New England. In it the sporophylls scarcely differ in general appearance from the foliage lvs.

p. 24. SELAGINELLA

7. **S. densa** Rydb. var. **scopulòrum** (Maxon) Tryon. Change to **S. Engelmannii** Hieron. var. **s.** (Maxon) Reed.

10. **S. asprélla** Maxon. Reported from Kern R. Canyon, Tulare Co. at 2800 ft., *J. T. Howell*; also in Kern Co., *Twisselmann.*

p. 25. ISOETES

For 1959 printing transpose lines 4 and 5 of generic description.

3. **I. muricàta** Durieu var.**hespéria** Reed. Add to synonymy: *I. echinosperma* Dur. var. *hesperia* (Reed) Löve.

p. 27. EQUISÈTUM

1. and 2. *E. Funstònii* and *E. kansànum* are considered to be the same and are reduced to synonymy under 3. E. laevigàtum by R. L. Hauke (Beihefte zur Nova Hedwigia 8: 1–123. 1963).

4. *E. hyemàle* var. *califórnicum* Milde and var. *robústum* (A. Br.) A. A. Eat. are put in synonymy under var. affìne (Engelm.) A. A. Eat. by Hauke.

4a. E. × Ferríssii Clute [*E. hyemale* var. *affine* × *E. laevigatum*]. It approaches complete intermediacy between its parents and is said to occur in Calif., as in n. Monterey Co., San Gabriel Mts., etc.

p. 28. In Key to Orders, change first line as follows:

A. Plants mostly fernlike, terrestrial or erect on mud, not floating or prostrate on mud; producing one kind of spore in sporangia.

p. 29. BOTRYCHIUM

1. **B. multífidum** ssp. **silaifòlium** (Presl) Clausen. In paragraph 2 transfer sentence "More common in Calif." etc. to 2. **B. símplex** var. **compósitum** (Lasch) Milde as a second paragraph.

2. **B. símplex** E. Hitchc. $n = 5$ (Wagner, 1955). The sp. has been collected at elevs. up to 11,000 ft., *Howell.*

2a. **B. pumícola** Cov.; an Oregon sp. has possibly been collected on Mt. Shasta by *W. B. Cooke* near the s. wall of Diller Canyon. It differs from *B. simplex* as follows:

Sterile blade simple or pinnate, sometimes subternately divided, stalked, inserted at various heights. . . . . *B. simplex*
Sterile blade pinnately divided, with the basal divisions again divided, giving a ternate appearance; the blade sessile, inserted above the middle of the plant. . . . . *B. pumicola*

p. 30. **B. Lunària** var. **minganénse** (Victorin) Dole is treated as a subsp. by Calder and Taylor.

3

p. 31.   PTERIDÀCEAE
In Key to Genera, delete "1. *Pteridium*" at end of "C" and insert after "C":

> D.   Fronds usually 3 times pinnate in lower part. Common native. . . . . . . 1. *Pteridium*
> DD. Fronds once pinnate. Natur. in canyons on s. face of San Gabriel Mts. . . 1a. *Pteris*

p. 32.   PTERIDIUM
1. **P. aquilinum** (L.) Kuhn var. **pubescens** Underwood is the correct name.

1a. Ptèris L.

A large genus of warmer parts of the world, the plants of medium or large size. Sori on a narrow receptacle connected in a marginal line under a simple indusium formed of the revolute margin of the frond, mostly connecting the ends of the free veins. Our sp. with once-pinnate lvs.
1. **P. vittàta** L. LADDER-BRAKE. Rootstock stout; lvs. dark green, erect or nearly so, 2–5 dm. long, clustered; petioles green, scaly; lfts. firm, lanceolate, ± acuminate; $n = 58$ (Kurita, 1963).—Natur. from cult. at ca. 1500 ft., Eaton Canyon, *Kiefer*, San Dimas Canyon, *Beach*, Big Dalton Canyon, *Beach*, San Gabriel Canyon, *Hutt* (all in San Gabriel Mts.). Native of China.

p. 32.   CHEILANTHES
p. 33.   6. **C. Coóperae** D. C. Eat. ranges n. in Coast Ranges to Santa Cruz and San Luis Obispo cos. and in Sierra Nevada is in Fresno and Tulare cos.
8. **C. Paríshii** Davenp. near Quail Springs, Little San Bernardino Mts. and in Anza-Borrego State Park, San Diego Co., *L. L. Kiefer*.
p. 34.   12. **C. intertéxta** (Maxon) Maxon. Near Lake Arrowhead and Big Bear City, *L. L. Kiefer*; Cienega Seca Creek, *Munz*; Bluff Lake, *Johnston*; all in San Bernardino Mts.
13. **C. Covíllei** Maxon in Marin Co., *Howell, Raven*; Mendocino Co., *Kiefer*.
15. **C. Carlótta-Hálliae** Wagner & Gilbert. Tufted, 6–27 cm. tall; rhizome 1–5 cm. long, clothed with old petioles; lvs. wiry, coriaceous, deltoid, 4 times divided, the ultimate segms. linear- to lance-acuminate, 2–8 mm. long; petioles dark brown.—Dry rocky places, Marin, Monterey, San Benito and San Luis Obispo cos. Howell (Am. Fern J. 5 : 19. 1960) finds it growing with *Cheilanthes siliquosa* Maxon (*Onychium densum* of the FLORA) and *C. californica* Mett. (*Aspidotis c.* of the FLORA) and feels that it is probably a hybrid between them.
ALEURITÓPTERIS
1. **A. cretàcea** (Liebm.) Fourn. It has been pointed out that this name is not applicable to our California plants (Howell, Am. Fern J. 50: 22. 1960). Rather than make a new combination in this genus, it is suggested that they be included under *Notholaèna* with N. califórnica D. C. Eat. and ssp. **nigréscens** Ewan as the names.
p. 35.   PELLAÈA
In Key to Species, *P. compácta* ranges n. to Placer Co. and in addition to that correction there can be inserted after "Fronds 2–3 times pinnate" etc.:

> Pinnules with greenish or undifferentiated borders. 3. *P. mucronata*
> Pinnules with opaque whitish borders. . . . . 3a. *P. longimucronata*

p. 36.   2. **P. brachýptera** (T. Moore) Baker; occurs in Placer Co., *Howell*.
3. **P. longimucronàta** Hook. Resembling *P. mucronata*, but with broader pinnules with opaque whitish borders (instead of greenish or undifferentiated borders) and by longer sporangium-stalks.—In the Providence and New York mts., e. San Bernardino Co., *L. Kiefer*; to Colo., New Mex.
3. **P. mucronàta** (D. C. Eat.) D. C. Eat. Delete the paragraph on var. *californica* (Lemmon) M. & J. and place it in synonymy under species no. 1. P. compacta.
3. **P. mucronàta** and 5. **P. Bridgèsii**. Kiefer feels that these hybridize in the Sierra Nevada.
4. **P. andromedifòlia** (Kaulf.) Fée. $n = 29, 87$ (Tryon, 1965). Var. **pubéscens**

Baker. L. Kiefer writes that this var. is quite distinct in its narrow blade, dense pubescence, heavy stipe, large glossy green (not blue-green pinnae which are never in threes. He reports it from Point Mugu (Ventura Co.) and the Channel Ids.

6. **P. Brèweri** D. C. Eat. $n = 29$ (Tryon & Britton, 1958).

p. 37. CRYPTOGRÁMMA

1. **C. acrostichoìdes** R. Br. $2n = 60$ (Löve & Löve, 1965).

PITYROGRÁMMA

Alt and Grant (Brittonia 12: 153–170. 1960) recognize **P. triangulàris** (Kaulf.) Maxon with $n = 30$, 45 or 60 chromosomes and **P. t.** var. **Maxònii** Weath. They treat as species: *P. pállida* (Weath.) Alt & Grant with $n = 30$ and *P. viscòsa* (D. C. Eat.) Maxon with $n = 30$.

J. T. Howell (Leafl. W. Bot. 9: 223. 1962) describes **P. triangulàris** var. **semi-pállida** from Butte Co. as resembling var. *pállida,* but the fronds green and glandless above and the stipes dark green.

p. 38. Hoover (Am. Fern J. 56: 19. 1966) proposes **P. triangulàris** var. **víridis** as lacking evident waxy powder on the lvs. so as to be green underneath.—Santa Cruz Id.; San Luis Obispo, Santa Cruz, Lake and Tuolumne cos.

ADIÁNTUM

1. After **A. pedàtum** L. var. **aleùticum** Rupr. [A. *p.* L. ssp. *a.* Calder and Taylor.] $2n = 58$ (Löve, 1964), insert paragraph:

A. Tràcyi C. C. Hall ex Wagner. Near *A. pedatum,* but with 3 major divisions to each frond instead of 5–9 and with a broader frond than in *A. Jordanii.*—Range, Humboldt to Marin cos.

2. **A. Jórdanii** K. Mull., not C. Muell.

p. 39. Top of page, change Polystichum to Adiantum.

ASPIDIÀCEAE

In Key to Genera, drop "2. *Polystichum*" from end of "B" and after "B" insert:

C.   Veins free. . . . . 2.   *Polystichum*
CC.   Veins anastomosing. . . . . 2a.   *Cyrtomium*

WOÓDSIA

3. **W. Plúmmerae** Lemmon. Differs from *W. oregana* in the indusium having non-ciliated instead of ciliated lobes. Reported by Dodge (Nova Hedwigia 16: 107. 1964) from "Colorado Desert," San Diego Co., *Orcutt.* Since Dodge cites a number of Orcutt collections from Cantillas Mts., etc. in L. Calif., one wonders whether this label is faulty.

p. 40. POLYSTICHUM

2. **P. munìtum** (Kaulf.) Presl. $n = 41$ (Löve, 1964).

Var. **ímbricans** (D. C. Eat.) Maxon. Kiefer feels that this is distinct enough to rank as a sp. He reports finding hybrids between *P. munitum* and *P. scopulinum* at White Mt., n. Siskiyou Co.

3. **P. Lemmònii** Underw. Kruckeberg (Am. Fern J. 54: 123. 1964) questions its occurrence on granite, believing it a plant of serpentine.

4a. **P. Kruckebérgii** Wagner. Like *P. scopulinum,* but lvs. smaller (8–30 cm. long); pinnae largely triangular (5–15 mm. long) and deeply and sharply toothed, the teeth smaller than in *scopulinum;* primary veins fewer (ca. 3–9 pairs); stipe mostly shorter.—Tuolumne and Siskiyou cos.; to B.C., Utah.

5. **P. califórnicum** (D. C. Eat.) Underw. Wagner (Am. Fern J. 53: 7. 1963) writes that this is probably hybrid between *P. Dudleyi* and *P. munitum.* In the description of *P. californicum* in the FLORA transpose lines 6 and 7.

p. 41.   **2a. Cyrtòmium** Presl.

Near to *Polystichum,* but differing in its anastomosing veins. Several spp., Old World. (Name Greek, a *bow*).

1. **C. falcàtum** (L.f.) Presl. [*Polypodium f.* L. f.] HOLLY-FERN. Stiff, erect,

the stipes shaggy; fronds dark green, 3–6 dm. long, 10–20 cm. wide, pinnate; pinnae alternate, 7–10 cm. long, ± ovate; $n = 82$ (Mitui, 1965).—Reported as natur. at La Jolla, San Diego, Big Dalton Canyon (Los Angeles Co.), *Kiefer*. Native of E. Asia, S. Afr., Polynesia.

DRYÓPTERIS

1. **D. dilatàta** (Hoffm.) Gray changed to **D. austrìaca** (Jacq.) Woynar by Morton. $n = 41$ (Löve, 1964).

p. 42.   2. **D. argùta** (Kaulf.) Watt. $n = 41$ (Löve, 1964).

3. **D. Filix-más** (L.) Schott. $n = 82$ (Löve, 1964).

LASTRÈA

Morton (Am. Fern J. 48: 136–141. 1958) uses **Thelýpteris** and

1. **T. pubérula** (Baker) Morton. Reported as in Santa Monica Mts., *Kiefer*.

2. **T. nevadénsis** (Baker) Clute. Apparently the Tuolumne Co. reference in the last line of the description in the FLORA refers to *Athyrium Filix-femina*, not this sp.

p. 44.   BLÉCHNUM

1. **B. Spicant** (L.) Roth, not With. Löve and Löve (Bot. Tidsskr. 62: 94. 1966) refer Pacific N. Am. material to ssp. **nippónicum** (Kunze) Löve & Löve.

WOODWÁRDIA

1. **W. fimbriàta** Sm. in Rees. $n = 34$ (Manton & Sledge, 1954).

ASPLÈNIUM

Change Key to Species to:

Fronds fernlike, the blade with 5–30 pairs of pinnae.
   Stipe and rachis dark chestnut or purplish brown throughout.
     S. California. . . . . 1. *A. vespertinum*
   Stipe red-brown, the upper part and rachis green. . . . . 2. *A. viride*
Fronds grasslike, the blade consisting of 2–3 alternate linear segms. Rare, Tulare Co. in Sierra
Nevada. . . . . 3. *A. septentrionale*

p. 45.   1. **A. vespertìnum** Maxon. At Sherwood Lake, Santa Monica Mts., *B. Joe*.

2. **A. víride** Huds. $2n = 72$. (Meyer, 1958).

3. **A. septentrionàle** (L.) Hoffm. [*Acrostichum s.* L.] Fronds grasslike, the stipe much longer than the blade, the latter consisting of 2–3 alternate linear segms.—Columbine Lake above Sawtooth Pass, Tulare Co., *Howell*; to S. Dak., Okla., New Mex.; Eurasia.

POLYPÒDIUM

1. **P. Scoùleri** Harv. & Grev. $n = 37$ (Manton, 1951).

2. **P. hespérium** Maxon the preferable name. Kiefer (in letter) reports hybrids between *P. h.* and *P. californicum* and between *P. c.* and *P. Scouleri*.

3. **P. califórnicum** Kaulf. Lloyd and Lang report 2 races; one diploid ($n = 37$) from San Francisco s., the other tetraploid ($n = 74$) from Monterey Co. to Humboldt Co. and in Sierran foothills.

p. 46.   4. **P. Glycyrrhìza** D. C. Eat. Reported from Yankee Hill, Butte Co., *Howell*.

p. 47.   MARSÍLEA

1. **M. vestìta** auth., not Hook. & Grev. should be changed to **M. mucronàta** R. Br.

PILULÀRIA

1. **P. americàna** A. Br., not R. Br.

p. 49.   ÀBIES

1. **A. bracteata** D. Don ex Poiteau not (D. Don) Nutt.

2a. **A. amábilis** (Dougl.) Forbes. LOVELY FIR. [*Picea amabilis Dougl.*] Like *A. grandis* in having the lvs. dark green above and with stomates only on the silvery white under surface, but differs in having the bracts gradually narrowed into a slender tip instead of abruptly so; the cones oblong and purple instead of cylindric and green; lvs. erect on the branches instead of in flatter sprays.— Ranging from the Crater Lake region in Ore. to Alaska, but occurs above Diamond Lake, Marble Mts., Siskiyou Co., *Philip A. Lewis*.

p. 51.   PÌNUS
In Key to Species AA, BB, CC, D, change EE. to:

> EE.   Lvs. dull gray-green, 12–28 cm. long; branchlets glaucous; cones 15–35 cm.
> long. .... 16. *P. Jeffreyi*
> EEE. Lvs. dull gray-green, 10–15 cm. long; cones 10–12 cm. long.
> 16a. *P. washoensis*

p. 53.   11. **P. remoràta** Mason. Reported from Marin Co., *Howell*.
13. **P. Murrayàna** Grev. & Balf. is considered to be a ssp. of *P. contorta Dougl.*
by Critchfield (Maria Moors Cabot Foundation Publ. 3: 1–118. 1957).
15. **P. ponderòsa** Lawson according to Little.

p. 54.   16a. **P. washoénsis** Mason & Stockwell. Lvs. gray-green, 10–15 cm. long; cones
10–12 cm. long, reddish purple to purplish black.—Warner Mts., Modoc Co.;
Mt. Rose, w. Nev., Blue Mts., ne. Ore. *Haller* (Madroño 16: 126–132) and
Critchfield & Allenbaugh (Madroño 18: 63–64. 1965).
17. **P. radiàta** D. Don. line 3, insert "mostly" before the last word "in." Becoming established in Marin Co., as seedlings from cult. trees, *Howell.*
18. **P. attenuàta** Lemmon. In n. Tulare Co. on road to Mineral King, *G. A.
Sanger.*

p. 55.   19. **P. Sabiniàna** Dougl. At 5200 ft. in Yosemite.

PÌCEA
In description of genus given as lvs. sometimes stomatiferous on upper side; this
may be misleading since lvs. may twist and the upper side turns down.
1. **P. Engelmánnii** Parry ex Engelm. treated as *P. glauca* ssp. *E.* T. M. C. Taylor (Madroño 15: 144. 1959).

p. 56.   TSUGA
1. **T. Mertensiàna** (Bong.) Carr. s. to Silliman Lake, Tulare Co., at 10,000 ft.,
Kaune.

p. 57.   PSEUDOTSÙGA
1. **P. Menzièsii** (Mirb.) Franco. Reported from near Lompoc, Santa Barbara
Co., *Howell.*

p. 59.   LIBOCÈDRUS
Mostly being broken up into genera for n. and s. hemispheres and for our sp.
the best name is probably **Calocèdrus decúrrens** (Torr.) Florin (Cf. Taxon 5:
192. 1956). Calocèdrus Kurz is a genus of the n. hemis. and has 3 spp.

p. 61.   CUPRÉSSUS
1. **C. Macnabiàna** A. Murr. reported by W. W. Wagener from e. of Amador
City in Sect. 20, T. 7N, R. 11E on Sutter Creek Quadrangle. A review of data
on distribution is by Griffin & Stone (Madroño 19: 19–27. 1967).
2. **C. Bàkeri** Jeps. In Plumas Co., *Wagener & Quick* (Aliso 5: 351. 1963).
3. **C. nevadénsis** Abrams. Reported from e. slope of Greenhorn Range and n.
slope of Breckenridge Mt., Kern Co., *Twisselmann.* E. L. Little, Jr. makes new
combinations: *C. arizónica* Greene var. *nevadénsis* (Abrams) Little and var.
Stephensònii (Wolf) Little (Madroño 18: 164. 1966).
6. **C. macrocárpa** Hartw. ex Gord. $2n = 22$ (Hunziker, 1958). Occurs at Point
Lobos, Monterey Co. and colonizing in Marin Co., *Howell.*

p. 63.   JUNÍPERUS

> Lvs. usually in 3's, etc. .... 2. *J. californica*
> Lvs. usually in 2's, etc. .... 3. *J. osteosperma*

3. **J. osteospérma** (Torr.) Little reported from n. side of San Gabriel Mts.,
Vasek.

p. 64.   4. **J. occidentàlis** Hook. F. C. Vasek (Brittonia 18: 350–372. 1967) restricts
ssp. **occidentàlis** to area from Susanville, Lassen Co. n. to Wash., Ida. Submonoe-
cious with brownish bark; lvs. in 2's or 3's; cotyledons usually 2 in young seedlings. Subsp. **austràlis** Vasek occurs from Lassen Co. and the Yolla Bolly Mts. s.
to San Bernardino Co. A larger tree, mostly dioecious, with reddish brown bark;
lvs. usually in 3's; cotyledons 2–4 in seedlings.

p. 65. TÓRREYA

      1. **T. califórnica** Torr. ranges s. to Fremont Peak, Monterey and San Benito cos., *P. Arnaud.*

p. 67. EPHEDRA

      6. **E. víridis** Cov. $n = 14$ (Raven, Kyhos & Hill, 1965).

p. 68. For 1959 printing, in the upper key, invert the page numbers after Groups 3, 4, 5.

p. 69. For 1959 printing, in AA, B, C move DD down 3 lines to be after the first EE. Line 11 from the bottom of the page and following lines, change to:

> EE. Fls. hypogynous, the ovary not so inclosed.
>   F. Style and stigma single.
>   G. Calyx not tubular.
>   H. Lvs. subulate, squarrose-spreading, 3–6 mm. long.
>   *Caryophyllaceae* (Loeflingia) p. 285
>   HH. Lvs. not subulate.
>   I. Plants perennial; lvs. oblong, 8–18 mm. long. Saline marshes.
>   *Gláux* p. 404
>   II. Plants annual; lvs. ovate.
>   J. Calyx 5–6-parted; stamens 6–7 .. *Eremocarpus* p. 162
>   JJ. Calyx largely 4-parted; stamens. . . 4. *Urticaceae* p. 920
>   GG. Calyx tubular, corolla-like, subtended by bracts often forming a calyx-like invol. .... *Nyctaginaceae* p. 388

p. 71. In CC, D at top of page, after "Sepals 2," insert "sometimes 3."
In CC, DD, etc., below "II. Lvs. alternate" insert:

> I'. Lvs. reduced to small scales; petals 4; thorny shrubs.
>   *Koeberliniaceae* p. 174
> I'I'. Lvs. well developed; plants not thorny shrubs.

Then proceed to "J. Lf.-blades compound," etc.
About middle of page, after CC, DD, EE, FF, GG, H, II, JJ change K to:

> K. Ovary 3–5-loculed.
>   L. Styles 3, bilobed; stamens united in ranks of 5. .... *Ditaxis* p. 162
>   LL. Style 1, with 3 stigmas; stamens not so united. .... *Helianthemum* p. 173
> KK. Ovary or ovaries 1-loculed, etc. as in text.

p. 72. About middle of page, after "J. Lvs. for most part alternate," change to:

> K. Sepals 2, or if more, the lvs. fleshy.
>   L. Sepals 2; plants not large vines; stamens 1–3.
>   *Portulacaceae* p. 295
>   LL. Sepals 5; plants large vines; stamens 5.
>   *Basellaceae* p. 306
> KK. Sepals 3-flowered, etc.

About middle of page, after "M. Fls. regular," etc. insert:

> N. Ovary 1-celled
>   *Caryophyllaceae* p. 273
> NN. Ovary 2–5-celled. . *Linaceae* p. 152

Insert on lower part of page, after CC, D. "Ovary inferior":

> D'. Plant scabrous with short barbed hairs; fr. dry. .... *Petalonyx* p. 177
> D'D'. Plants not scabrous with short barbed hairs.

p. 73. Line 6 from top of page, change to read:

> G. Lvs. compound, consisting of 2 or more lfts. (separately deciduous)

and toward middle of page change GG. to:

> GG. Lvs. simple, but sometimes simply divided, looking like lfts., but not separately deciduous.

About middle of page, insert after "II. The fr. not a legume":

Ia. Lvs. pellucid-punctate (gland-dotted); petals 4, white; lvs. linear; stamens 8. ... *Rutaceae* (Cneoridium) p. 992

IaIa. Lvs. not as above; stamens not 8; petals not 4.

then proceed to "J. Trees with large palmately" etc. and change:

JJ. Trees or shrubs, the lvs. not large and palmately lobed.
J'. Lvs. small, scalelike, linear, caducous; branchlets rigid, spine-tipped. Colo. Desert.
Koeberliniaceae p. 17
J'J'. Lvs. large, pinnately veined.
K. Stamens 4–5, etc.

p. 74. Near top of page, change II to "Lvs. simple and entire or divided, but not compound (including *Geraniaceae* and *Cruciferae* with divided lvs.)."
In middle of page under "II. The fls. not papilionaceous; fr. not a legume," change to:

J. Lvs. not peltate.
K. Fr. a 1-loculed, 3-valved caps.; plants not over 3 dm. high. .... *Violaceae* p. 183
KK. Fr. a 5-loculed, elastically dehiscent, explosive caps.; plants to 1 m. high. *Balsaminaceae* p. 970
JJ. Lvs. peltate; fr. 3-lobed, 3-loculed, each locule 1-seeded. .... *Tropaeolaceae* p. 151

p. 75. In middle of page, "JJ. Stamens 4–7; fr. not opening by a lid."
A few lines farther down, change to:

NN. Ovary 2-loculed; stigma usually 1.
O. Lvs. opposite; fls. in dense axillary clusters, these forming interrupted leafy spikes.
Loganiaceae p. 590
OO. Lvs. alternate; infl. never spicate. ..... *Solanaceae* p. 590

p. 76. Change G and GG as follows:

G. Lvs. opposite and evidently stipulate, or whorled and not stipulate.
Rubiaceae p. 1037
GG. Lvs. opposite or perfoliate, rarely stipulate and when so, the stipules minute .... *Caprifoliaceae* p. 1046

p. 77. CALYCÁNTHUS
At end of generic description insert as reference "Nicely, K. A. A monographic study of the Calycanthaceae." (Castanea 30: 38–80. 1965.) Two spp. of *Calycanthus* are recognized.

p. 79. RANUNCULÀCEAE
In Key to Genera, after "Petals present" and "Sepals not spurred," add

Petals with a nectariferous pit or scale at base; ovule and seed erect or ascending.
6. *Ranunculus*
Petals unappendaged; ovule and seed suspended. .... 6a. *Adonis*

CÁLTHA
2. C. palústris L. Lf.-blades 5–20 cm. wide, crenate or dentate; sepals yellow, 10–15 mm. long.—Marsh near Forestville, Sonoma Co., *Rubtzoff*. A sp. of the e. U.S. and Eu.

p. 83. DELPHÍNIUM
Key to Species G, H, II, J, change to:

KK. Petioles glabrous to puberulent or strigose.
L. Follicles 14–28 mm. long, etc.
31. *D. Andersonii*
LL. Follicles 6–15 mm. long.
M. The follicles puberulent, 10–15 mm. long; fls. lavender to blue-purple. Monterey and San Luis Obispo cos.
28. *D. umbraculorum*

MM. The follicles sparsely hairy, 6–10 mm.
long; fls. dark blue-purple. W. edge of
Colo. Desert.
24. *D. Parishii* ssp. *subglobosum*

Key to Species GG, H, II, JJ, delete "24. *D. Parishii*" and insert:

K. Fls. mostly bluish; sepals 8–12 mm. long; follicles 8–14 mm. long. . . . . 24. *D. Parishii*
KK. Fls. white; sepals 6–7 mm. long; follicles 7–9
mm. long. . . . . 25. *D. inopinum*

In last line of key, change 29 to 22, for the 1959 printing.

1. **D. Ajàcis** L. It is becoming prevalent to separate the annual spp. of *Delphinium* in which the 2 upper petals fuse, the 2 laterals disappear, and the carpel is 1, and recognize the genus **Consólida** (DC) S. F. Gray. The present sp. is the only one treated in this FLORA to which this would apply and it should bear the name Consólida ambígua (L) Ball & Heywood.

p. 84.   2. **D. Purpùsii** Bdg. In Tulare Co., *Thorne*.
4. **D. decòrum** F. & M. is reported from as far s. as Monterey Co., *Howitt & Howell*.
p. 89.   26. **D. Párryi** Gray reported from Monterey Co., *Howitt & Howell*.
p. 90.   29. **D. variegàtum** T. & G. Plants from Carmel and Monterey constitute **D. Hutchinsònae** Ewàn. Stems fistulose, 4.5–6 dm. tall, ± pubescent; lvs. with 5 broadly cuneate-obovate segms., each of which is trifid; fls. dark purple; sepals 15–20 mm. long; spur 10–12 mm. long; petals dark, the laminae ca. 6 mm. long; follicles purple-veined, strigulose; seeds winged on angles.—Monterey coast.

p. 91.   ACONÌTUM
1e. **A. columbiànum** Nutt. in Greenhorn Range, Kern Co., *Twisselmann*.
p. 92.   RANÚNCULUS
In Key, AA, BB, C, DD, EE, after line F insert a line:

F'.   Plants with stems; perennials.

and proceed to G. and GG. After the line GG, insert the line:

F'F'. Plants stemless annuals. Ne. Calif. . . . . 27a. *R. testiculatus*

p. 94.   3. **R. àcris** L. $2n = 14$ (Jørgensen et al., 1958). In Nevada Co., *True & Howell*.
p. 96.   6. **R. cànus** Benth. Reported from as far south as Monterey Co., *Howitt & Howell*.
8. **R. Macoùnii** Britton. $2n = 42$ (Löve & Kapoor, 1968).
p. 98.   13. **R. muricàtus** L. Reported from Madera and Fresno cos., *Weiler*.
15. **R. Eschscholtzii** Schlecht. $2n =$ ca. 56 (Löve & Kapoor, 1968).
p. 99.   17. **R. alismifòlius** Geyer ex Benth. In line 1 of Key, correct to read:

"Receptacle 3–5 mm. long in fr." $2n = 16$ (Löve & Kapoor, 1968).

p. 100.   23. Change to **R. bonariénsis** Poir var. **trisépalus** (Gill.) Lourteig. [*R. t.* Gill. *R. alveolatus* Carter.] Add to range: Chile and Argentina.
p. 101.   26. **R. Cymbalària** Pursh var. **saximontànus** Fern.; at elevs. up to 10,500 ft. in White Mts., *Blakley & Muller*.
27a. **R. testiculàtus** Crantz. [*Ceratocephalus t.* A. Kern.] On p. 92 it keys out with spp. 7 and 8, but is easily recognized as a stemless annual, 4–7 cm. tall, the lvs. basal, divided into linear parts; petals 3–5 mm. long; stamens 10–20; each ak. with a beak twice as long as the body.—Reported from Lassen and Modoc cos., *Fuller*. Native of Old World.
p. 102.   31. **R. subrígidus** W. Drew. Reported from Fulmor Lake, San Jacinto Mts., *Raven*.

6a. Adònis L. PHEASANT'S EYE

A small Eurasian genus like *Ranunculus*, but lacking a nectariferous scale or pit at the base of each petal. Cauline lvs. dissected into numerous linear segms. Fls. solitary at ends of stem or branches.

1. **A. aestivàlis** L. Annual, 2–5 dm. high; fls. solitary, 15–35 mm. across;

petals 6–8, yellow to reddish, 10–17 mm. long.—Reported from Canby, Modoc Co., *Fuller,* and Lassen Co., *Sweeney.* Native of Eurasia.

ANEMÒNE

p. 103.   6. A. quinquefòlia L. var. Gràyii (Behr. & Kell.) Jeps. occurs in Monterey Co., *Howitt & Howell.*

p. 104.   ISOPÝRUM

1. I. occidentàle H. & A. occurs in the San Emigdio Range, Kern Co., *Twisselmann.*

p. 106.   THALÍCTRUM

The literature reference at the end of the generic description should read Contr. Gray Herb. 152.

p. 107.   4. T. polycárpon (Torr.) Wats. $2n = 14$ pairs (Raven, Kyhos & Hill, 1965). At end of generic description cite Ahrendt, L. W. A. Berberis and Mahonia. J. Linn. Soc. 57: 1–408. 1961.

p. 110.   8. B. Dictyòta Jeps. Ahrendt separates *B. D.* and *B. californica* Jeps. on basis of former having lvs. lustrous above and lfts. with 4–8 teeth on each side, the latter with lvs. dull above and the lfts. with 8–12 teeth on each side.

9. B. ampléctens (Eastw.) Wheeler. $2n = 14$ pairs (Raven, Kyhos & Hill, 1965).

12. B. Hígginsiae Munz. Add synonym *Mahonia H.* (Munz) Ahrendt.

13. B. Nevínii Gray. Found in San Francisquito Canyon, n. Los Angeles Co., *Mrs. Thompson.*

p. 113.   BRASÈNIA

1. B. Schrèberi J. F. Gmel. $2n = 80$ (Löve, 1964).

p. 114.   CERATOPHÝLLUM

1. C. demérsum L. Insert synonym *C. apiculatum* Cham.

ANEMÓPSIS

1. A. califórnica Hook. $2n = 22$ pairs (Raven, Kyhos & Hill, 1965).

FREMONTODÉNDRON Cov.

This is the correct name for *Fremontia* Torr., since the latter name has not been conserved, although it had been proposed for conservation when the FLORA was being written. Names to be used under *Fremontodendron* are:

p. 115.   1. F. mexicànum A. Davids.

2. F. califórnicum Cov.

p. 116.   Ssp. napénse (Eastw.) Munz. [*F. n.* Lloyd].

Ssp. obispoénse (Eastw.) Munz.

Ssp. crassifòlium (Eastw.) J. H. Thomas.

Ssp. decúmbens (Lloyd) Munz, comb. nov. [*F. d.* Lloyd, Brittonia 17: 382–384. 1965.] Plant 2–4 m. broad, to 1 m. tall; fls. orange to red-brown, 3–3.6 cm. diam. Eldorado Co.

AYÈNIA

1. *A. californica* Jeps. is placed in synonymy under A. compácta Rose in a revision by Cristòbal (Opera Lilloana 4:1–230. 1960).

p. 117.   ABÙTILON

1. A. Theophrásti Medic. $2n = 42$ (E. B. Smith, 1965).—Reported from Monterey Co., *Howitt & Howell.*

4. A. críspum (L.) Sweet is often treated as **Bogenhárdia c.** Kearn., because of the numerous inflated carpels and the fr. not umbilicate apically.

p. 119.   SPHAERÁLCEA

1. S. Orcúttii Rose. $2n = 10$ (Krapovickas, 1957).

3. S. Émoryi ssp. variábilis (Ckll.) Kearn. Add as synonym *S.E.* var. *californica* Shinners. $2n = 20$ (Krapovickas, 1957).

4. S. ambígua Gray. $n = 5$ (Bates, 1967).

Ssp. montícola Kearn. $n = 15$ (Bates, 1967).

Ssp. rugòsa Kearn. $n = 10$ (Bates, 1967).

p. 122.   Eremálche Greene

Use instead of *Malvastrum* for California species and change generic description to

Low annual herbs. Lvs. orbicular or palmately parted, stellate-pubescent. Fls.

solitary or in pairs in the upper lf.-axils. Involucellate bractlets 3, distinct, persistent. Sepals somewhat united at base. Petals white to rose-purple, hairy along the margins of the claws. Stamineal column simple, glabrous. Style-branches from one and one-half to two times as long as the stamineal column, filiform, as many as the carpels. Stigmas capitate. Carpels 10–40, indehiscent, 1-ovulate, glabrous, reticulate or transversely ridged on the back and angles. Embryo of the solitary seed forming an incomplete circle; endosperm scanty. (Greek, referring to the desert habitat.) A genus comprised of the following four species.

    1. **E. rotundifòlia** (Gray) Greene. [*Malvastrum r.* Gray. *Sphaeralcea r.* Jeps.] Description as in the FLORA. $n = 10$ (Bates, 1967).

    2. **E. éxilis** (Gray) Greene. [*Malvastrum e.* Gray. *Sphaeralcea e.* Jeps.] Description in the FLORA. $n = 10$ (Bates, 1967).

    3. **E. kernénsis** Wolf. [*Malvastrum k.* Munz.] $n = 10$ (Bates, 1967).

    4. **E. Párryi** (Greene) Greene. [*Malvastrum P.* Greene. *Sphaeralcea P.* Jeps.] Description as in the FLORA. $n = 10$ (Bates, 1967).

p. 123.   MALACOTHÁMNUS
Line 4 from top of page, insert (Greek, *malakos*, soft, and *thamnos*, shrub).

p. 124.   3. **M. níveus** (Eastw.) Kearn. in Monterey Co., *Howitt & Howell.*

p. 125.   6. **M. orbiculàtus** (Greene) Greene. In Temblor Range, Kern Co., *Twisselmann.*

p. 126.   16. **M. Jònesii** (Munz) Kearn. In Monterey Co., *Howitt & Howell.*

p. 127.   18. **M. fascículatus** (Nutt. in T. & G.) Greene ssp. *catalinénsis* (Eastw.) Thorne. New synonym under var. **catalinensis.**

p. 128.   LAVATERA
    3. **L. crètica** L. Tracy, San Joaquin Co., *Fuller*; Monterey and Ventura cos., *Howell.*

p. 130.   SÌDA
    1. **S. hederàcea** Torr. I. D. Clement (Contr. Gray Herb. 180: 52. 1957) uses **S. lepròsa** (Ort.) K. Schum. var. **hederàcea** K. Schum.
    2. **S. rhombifòlia** L. at Orland, Glenn Co., *Fuller.*

p. 132.   SIDALCEA
    5. **S. calycòsa** ssp. **rhizómata** (Jeps.) Munz in Mendocino Co., *Howell.*

p. 133.   In Key, AA, BB, CC, DD, EE, FF, G, HH, insert "Sierra Nevada" before "Humboldt."

p. 135.   13. **S. oregàna** (Nutt.) Gray ssp. **spicàta** (Regel) C. L. Hitchc. not Greene.

p. 136.   17. **S. Hickmánii** ssp. **Paríshii** (Rob.) C. L. Hitchc. $n = 10$ (Bates, 1967).

p. 137.   HIBÍSCUS
    1. **H. triònum** L. in Imperial Co., *Fuller,* and Plumas Co., *Fuller.*
    2. **H. califórnicus** Kell. is a perennial in the Botanic Garden.

p. 140.   GERÀNIUM
    In Key to Species, after A, B, C insert "C'":

      C'. Peduncles 2-fld.; petals pink to red; root a taproot; caudex branched.
         D. Stems with retrorse-spreading stiff shining hairs; petals scarcely longer than sepals; seeds coarsely reticulate. . . . . 1. *G. pilosum*
        DD. Stems with retrorse appressed dull hairs; petals ca. twice as long as sepals; seeds finely reticulate. . . . . 2. *G. retrorsum*
      C'C'. Peduncles 1-fld.; petals white, with faint pink edging; roots almost tuberous; caudex not branched. . . . . 1a. *G. microphyllum*

    In Key to Species after A, B, CC, insert "C'":

      C'. Carpel-bodies deciduous from the styles at maturity, each with 2 fibrous appendages near the top. . . . . 2a. *G. Robertianum*
      C'C'. Carpel-bodies permanently attached to the styles, unappendaged.

    Then go to D. in the old key.

p. 141.   1a. **G. microphýllum** Hook. f. Stems slender, with long white and shorter hairs; lvs. dark green; fls. ca. 8 mm. in diam.; carpels smooth, strigose.—Olema, etc., Marin Co. Native of New Zealand.
    2a. **G. Robertiànum** L. Annual, commonly branched at base, the branches ± decumbent, 1–5 dm. long, glandular-pubescent; lvs. with ovate divisions 1.5–6

cm. long; sepals 6–8.5 mm. long; petals red-purple, 8–11 mm. long; style-column 1–1.5 cm. long, excluding the slender subulate beak; carpel-bodies 2.5 mm. long, wrinkled.—Established in San Francisco, *Howell.* Native of Eurasia.

3. **G. Bicknéllii** var. **lóngipes** (Wats.) Fern. in Monterey Co., *Hardham.*

p. 144. ERÒDIUM

1. **E. texánum** Gray. Occurs in the El Paso Range, Kern Co., *Twisselmann.*

p. 146. PELARGÒNIUM

6. **P. grossularioìdes** (L.) Ait. Reported from Cambria, San Luis Obispo Co. and from San Mateo Co.

p. 147. ÓXALIS

In Key to Species, under "A. Petals yellow," change to:

> B. Plants from underground bulblets; petals ca. 2 cm. long.
>   C. The plants acaulescent; lfts. 10–25 mm. long. . . . . 1. *O. Pes-caprae*
>   CC. The plants caulescent; lfts. ca. 10 mm. long. . . . . 1a. *O. incarnata*

Under AA, BB, CC, DD omit "11. *O. Martiana*" and add:

> E. Lfts. suborbicular, 2.5–6 cm. wide; petals 12–18 mm. long.
>   11. *O. Martiana*
> EE. Lfts. narrowed toward base, ca. 1 cm. wide; petals 20–23 mm. long.
>   12. *O. purpurea*

After 1. **O. pes-cáprae**, insert:

1a. **O. incarnàta** L. Perennial from a bulb; stems 15–30 cm. high; lfts. glabrous, 10 mm. long, 8 mm. wide; sepals 7 mm. long; petals yellow, 17–20 mm. long.—Natur. in San Francisco, *Howell et al.* Native of S. Afr.

p. 148. 2. **O. láxa** H. & A. Pacific Grove, Monterey Co., *Howitt & Howell.*

3. **O. corniculàta** L. $2n = 24, 36, 42, 48$ (Eiten, 1963).

5. and 6. **O. pilòsa** Nutt. and **O. califórnica** (Abrams) Knuth. Eiten (Am. Midl. Nat. 69: 303. 1963) uses *O. álbicans* ssp. *pilosa* (Nutt.) Eiten and *O. a.* ssp. *califórnica* (Abrams) Eiten, with **O. álbicans** ssp. **álbicans** e. and s. of Calif.

7. **O. hírta** L. Occurs at Elk, Mendocino Co., *Fuller.*

p. 149. 11. **O. Martiàna** Zucc. Found in Monterey Co., *Howitt & Howell.*

12. **O. purpùrea** Thunb. Acaulescent from a rounded bulb; lvs. rosulate, mostly 3–8; lfts. 3, glabrous and green above, impressed-punctate and ± violet beneath, densely ciliate, to ca. 1 cm. long and wide; petioles 1–5 cm. long; peduncles few, 1.5–2 times as long as petioles; sepals 5–7 mm. long, lanceolate; corolla 2–2.3 cm. long, purple on the limb, yellow in throat.—Reported as escape in Santa Cruz, Monterey, Santa Barbara cos. *Howell.* From S. Afr.

p. 149. LIMNANTHÀCEAE

In family description, change "Carpels 3 or 5" to "Carpels 3 to 5."

p. 150. LIMNÁNTHES

3. **L. Doúglasii** R. Br. var. **ròsea** (Hartw.) in Benth. C. T. Mason. Ranges s. to Fresno Co., *Weiler.*

5. **L. montàna** Jeps. Reported from the Greenhorn Mts., Kern Co., *Twisselmann.*

p. 152. LINÀCEAE

C. Marvin Rogers (Madroño 18: 181–184. 1966) recognizes a new genus **Sclerolìnon** for **S. dígynum** and Helen K. Sharsmith (Univ. of Calif. Publ. Bot. 32: 235–314. 1961) separates the other species treated as *Linum* in the FLORA into **Lìnum** and **Hesperolìnon**, the former including spp. 1–4 and 6, the latter 7–15.

LÌNUM

In Key to Species change AA to:

> A. Petals blue or red, 1–20 mm. long; styles 5; caps. 5–10 mm. long.
> AA. Petals white, rose or yellow, 2–8 mm. long (–15 in *puberulum*); styles often 2–3, sometimes quite united; caps. 2–4 mm. long.

AA, B, C for sp. 5 "Coast Ranges and Sierra Nevada."

p. 153. 2. Change *L. angustifòlium* Huds. to **L. biénne** Mill.

4. **L. perénne** L. ssp. **Lewísii** (Pursh.) Hult. H. G. Baker (Huntiana 2: 141–161. 1965) reports strong crossing barriers between Old World *Linum perenne* L. and New World L. Lewísii Pursh and considers them separate spp.

5. **L. dígynum** Gray [*Cathartolinum d.* Small.] is treated as:

2. Sclerolínon Rogers.

Glabrous annual. Lvs. opposite, oblong, lacking stipular glands. Sepals lance-oblong, obtuse, lacerate-denticulate and glandular on the margins. Petals yellow. Teeth between stamens none; styles 2, free; stigmas capitate; caps. 4-loculed. (Greek, *skleros*, hard, and *linos*, flax.)

Sclerolínon dígynum (Gray) Rogers. [*Linum d.* Gray.]

p. 154.   Beginning with sp. no. 7, *Linum drymarioides* Curran, insert:

Hesperolínon Small

Slender-stemmed annual herbs, ± glaucous, essentially glabrous, or with some puberulence above the axils. Lvs. in whorls of 4 at basal nodes, becoming irregularly whorled at upper nodes and opposite or alternate on ultimate branches, usually early caducous, entire, linear or lanceolate to oblong or almost round, sessile, fleshy, progressively reduced up the stems into small bracts. Fls. in cymes; pedicels filiform, pseudocleistogamous. Sepals 5, united below. Petals 5, erect to spreading, white to lavender or pink or yellow, caducous, clawed. Stamens 5; fils. filiform; anthers versatile. Ovary of 2 or 3 carpels; ovules 4 or 6. Styles as many as carpels, with minute stigmas. Seeds triangular, plump, shining, dark tan to brown. (Greek, *hesperos*, western, and *linos*, flax.)

Petal claw pouches in margins of lamella; petal attachment to apex of cup in sinuses between fils.; carpels 2–3; styles 2–3; stigmas minute.

A. Lvs. lanceolate to rounded ± clasping at base, margined with stipitate glands.
  B. Petals yellow; lvs. irregularly whorled to mainly alternate. .... 8. *H. adenophyllum*
  BB. Petals white to lavender or pink; lvs. in whorls of 4. .... 9. *H. drymarioides*
AA. Lvs. linear to narrow-oblong, with narrow, non-clasping base and not prominently glandular on margin.
  B. Main axis of stem usually long, the primary branches little-spreading; pedicels 0.5–2 mm. long in anthesis.
    C. Sepals glabrous; styles 5–7 mm. long.
      D. Petals yellow; dehisced antlers yellow. .... 10. *H. Breweri*
      DD. Petals white or pink; dehisced anthers white or pink. 11. *H. californicum*
    CC. Sepals pubescent; styles 4–4.5 mm. long. .... 12. *H. congestum*
  BB. Main axis of stem usually short, the primary branches widely spreading; pedicels 0.5–25 mm. long at anthesis.
    C. Carpels and styles 2.
      D. Petals and dehisced anthers yellow. .... 4. *H. bicarpellatum*
      DD. Petals and dehisced anthers whitish. .... 7. *H. didymocarpon*
    CC. Carpels and styles 3.
      D. Petals white to pinkish.
        E. Petals 1.5–3.5 mm. long, not or little spreading; fils. included.
                                                            1. *H. micranthum*
        EE. Petals 4–6 mm. long, widely spreading; fils. exserted.
          F. Pedicels 1–5 mm. long in fl., not strongly reflexed, the buds not pendent. .... 6. *H. disjunctum*
          FF. Pedicels 5–15 mm. long in fl., early deflexed from branch, the buds pendent. .... 3. *H. spergulinum*
      DD. Petals yellow.
        E. Pedicels 2–25 mm. long; petals 1.5–2.5 mm. long, not or scarcely spreading. .... 2. *H. Clevelandii*
        EE. Pedicels 0.5–3 mm. long; petals 4–5 mm. long, widely spreading.
                                                            5. *H. tehamense*

1. **H. micránthum** (Gray) Small [*Linum micranthum* Gray.] No. 13 under *Linum* in the FLORA.

2. **H. Clevelándii** (Greene) Small. [*Linum C.* Greene.] No. 14 under *Linum* in the FLORA.

3. **H. spergulínum** (Gray) Small. [*Linum s.* Gray.] No. 12 under *Linum* in the FLORA.

4. **H. bicarpellàtum** (H. K. Sharsm.) H. K. Sharsm. [*Linum b.* H. K. Sharsm.] No. 15 under *Linum* in the FLORA.

5. **H. tehaménse** H. K. Sharsm. Close to *H. bicarpellatum,* but tricarpellate; petals 4–5 mm. long instead of 3–3.5 mm.; plant ± hoary, not relatively glabrous.—Tehama and Glenn cos.

6. **H. disjúnctum** H. K. Sharsm. Near to *H. micranthum,* but with larger fls. and more spreading perianth; fils. and style exserted.—Serpentine, Inner Coast Ranges, Tehama Co. to Fresno and Monterey cos.

7. **H. didymocárpum** H. K. Sharsm. Near *H. bicarpellatum,* but with petals white to pinkish; dehisced anthers, fils. and styles white.—Serpentine w. of Big Canyon Creek, Lake Co.

8. **H. adenophýllum** (Gray) Small. [*Linum a.* Gray.] No. 8 under *Linum* in the FLORA. Humboldt to Lake cos.

9. **H. drymarioìdes** (Curran) Small. [*Linum d.* Curran.] No. 7 under *Linum* in the FLORA.

10. **H. Brèweri** (Gray) Small. [*Linum B.* Gray.] No. 9 under *Linum* in the FLORA.

11. **H. califórnicum** (Benth.) Small. [*Linum c.* Benth.] No. 11 under *Linum* in the FLORA.

12. **H. congéstum** (Gray) Small. [*Linum c.* Gray.] No. 10 under *Linum* in the FLORA.

p. 156.   POLÝGALA

2. **P. subspinòsa** Wats. var. **heterorhýncha** Barneby, $2n = 38$ (Raven, Kyhos & Hill, 1965).

p. 157.   4. **P. cornùta** Kell. var. **Físhiae** Jeps. $2n = 9$ pairs (Raven *et al.,* 1965).

p. 158.   FAGÒNIA

1. **F. laèvis** Standl. Treatment by D. M. Porter (Contr. Gray Herb. 192: 119. 1963). Branches essentially glabrous; pedicels and sepals stipitate-glandular; stipules subulate, reflexed to spreading, 1–6 mm. long.

2. **F. pachyacántha** Rydb. in Vail & Rydb. [*F. californica* var. *glutinosa* Pringle ex Vail.] Ultimate branches densely stipitate-glandular or with subsessile glands; pedicels and sepals glandular to glabrate; stipules linear-subulate, spreading to slightly reflexed, 3–16 mm. long.

LÁRREA

1. **L. tridentata** Sessé & Moçiño for N. Am. plants according to Porter (Contr. Gray Herb. 192: 110–113. 1963). Lft.-veins usually dark, not lined with hairs (lined with white hairs 1–2 mm. long in S. Am.); lfts. obliquely lanceolate to falcate (not obovate to elliptic); stipules obovate, acute to short-acuminate, 1–4 mm. long, free from stem (not broadly ovate, rounded to obtuse at apex, 1–2 mm. long, clasping the stem).

ZYGOPHÝLLUM

1. **Z. Fabàgo** L. var. **brachycárpum** Boiss. Reported from 12 mi. w. of Tipton, Tulare Co., *Fuller.* In the last line the record from Hamlin should read Patterson, Stanislaus Co., collected by *Hamlin.*

p. 159.   KALLSTROÈMIA

1. **K. califórnica** (Wats.) Vail in Calif. and also var. **brachystýlis** (Vail) Kearn. & Peebles, according to Porter (Contr. Gray Herb. 192: 131. 1963). The sp. has 3–6 pairs of lfts. that are to 3 mm. wide and 7 mm. long; petals 1–2 mm. wide, 3–5 mm. long; beak of fr. 1–2 mm. long; nutlets sharply tuberculate.

Var. **brachystýlis** has lfts. 2–4 pairs, 3–10 mm. wide, 6–21 mm. long; petals 2–3 mm. wide, 4–6 mm. long; beak of fr. 2–3 mm. long; nutlets roundedtuberculate.

p. 161.   TETRACÓCCUS

2. **T. ilicifòlius** Cov. & Gilman. Type locality at 3200 ft., *H. T. Harvey.*

3. **T. Hállii** Bdg. ranges into L. Calif. (Sierra San Pedro Martir), *Jaeger.*

p. 162.   CRÒTON

2. **C. califórnicus** Muell-Arg. $n = 14$ (Szweykowski, 1965).

p. 163.   DITÁXIS

5. **D. lanceolàta** (Benth.) Pax & K. Hoffm. The last word in line 1 should be *Argythamnia* (in the 1959 printing).

p. 166.   EUPHÓRBIA

Key A, BB, C, change to:

> D. Floral lvs. broad at base; caps. with tubercles.
>   E. Plant glabrous annual. .... 2. *E. spathulata*
>   EE. Plant pubescent perennial. .... 2a. *E. oblongata*
> DD. Floral lvs. narrowed at base; caps. smooth.
>   E. Lvs. obovate; glands 4, round to elliptical .... 3. *E. Helioscopia*
>   EE. Lvs. linear to ovate; gland 1, flattened-obconic, tangentially bilabiate.
>   3a. *E. dentata*

p. 167.   Key C, change D. to:

> D. Stipules united into a broad white membranous scale.
>   E. Plant perennial; ♂ fls. 12–20. .... 23..*E. albomarginata*
>   EE. Plant annual; ♂ fls. 5–10. .... 23a. *E. serpens*

p. 168.   2a. **E. oblongàta** Griseb. Like *E. spathulata,* but pubescent, perennial with rhizomes; lvs. sessile, oblong-lanceolate, the floral ovate, mucronate; upper stem-lvs. ca. 4–6 cm. long; caps. warty.—Contra Costa and San Joaquin cos., Santa Clara–San Mateo county line, *Thorne & Raven.* Native of e. Medit.

3a. **E. dentàta** Michx. Like *E. Helioscopia,* but stem not tipped by an umbel; stipules glandlike; each invol. with only 1 gland.—San Joaquin Co., *Fuller.* Native annual from e. of Rocky Mts.

4. **E. Ésula** L. $2n = 60$ (R. J. Moore, 1958).

7. **E. crenulàta** Engelm. ascends to 6000 ft., Lassen Park, *Howell.*

p. 170.   16. **E. maculàta** L. Burch (Rhodora 68: 163. 1966) concludes that E. nutáns Lag. is the correct name for our plant. Wheeler in 1960 reported it from near Lodi, San Joaquin Co.

p. 171.   23a. **E. sérpens** HBK. Like *E. albomarginata* in having stipules united, but is a prostrate annual with 5–10 ♂ fls. instead of 12 or more; lf.-blades 2–7 mm. long.—Hunter's Point, Salton Sea, and San Francisco, *Howell.* Widely distributed in N. and S. Am.

p. 172.   32. **E. prostràta** Ait. Alameda Co., *Howell.*

p. 173.   HELIÁNTHEMUM

1. **H. Greènei** Rob. Add *Crocanthemum occidentale* Janchen to synonymy.

p. 174.   4. **H. guttàtum** (L.) Mill. Differs from the 3 spp. treated in the FLORA in being annual, slender, stellate-pubescent and pilose, 6–30 cm. high; lvs. opposite, elliptic-lanceolate. Native of Eu.

CÍSTUS

1. **C. villòsus** L. occurs in cult. in a number of forms, more than one of which has become natur. Var. **taúricus** Grosser is sparsely hairy, not glandular; var. **undulàtus** Grosser is glandular.

Insert: 21a. **Koeberliniàceae.** JUNCO FAMILY

Almost leafless trees or shrubs with pale green, spine-tipped stiff branchlets. Lvs. alternate, minute, scalelike, soon deciduous. Fls. small, in small axillary racemes. Sepals 4–5. Petals 4–5, deciduous. Stamens hypogynous. Ovary of 2–5 united carpels, superior.

1. **Koeberlínia** Zucc.

Branches spinose, interlocking. Sepals 4. Petals 4, greenish white. Stamens 8. Fr. a rounded berry. (*C. L. Köberlin,* German clergyman.)

1. **K. spinòsa** Zucc. Shrubby or arborescent, with thin smooth, green or yellowish bark on the young branches; lvs. 1.5–2 mm. long; racemes 1–6 mm. long; berry 4–5 mm. diam., grayish.—Reported from Chocolate Mts., Imperial Co., *Wiggins;* to Texas, Mex.

p. 174. TAMARÍX

(M. Zohary of Israel in the 1965 Annual Research Report for the U.S.D.A. treats the following spp. as in Calif.) B. R. Baum (Baileya 15: 19–25. 1967) agrees with this listing.

A. Fls. 5-merous.
    B. Lvs. vaginate; bracts not vaginate, but somewhat clasping. . . . . *T. aphylla*
    BB. Lvs. sometimes auriculate, but not vaginate or amplexicaul.
      C. Staminate fls. with fils. inserted below the disc.
        D. Petals obovate, widened distally; bracts ovate, subobtuse.
        In more saline places. (Includes *T. pentandra* auth.)
        T. ramosissima Ledeb.
        DD. Petals oblong-ovate, narrowed distally. Non-saline habitats.
        T. chinensis Lour.
      CC. Staminate fls. with fils. inserted around the disc.
        D. Petals more than 2.25 mm. long, subpersistent, narrowed slightly toward the apex; racemes 5–10 mm. broad. . . . . *T. africana* Poir.
        DD. Petals not more than 2 mm. long, soon deciduous; racemes 4–5 mm. broad.
          E. The petals elliptical, equally wide in both halves; disc with 5 rounded lobes, each between 2 stamens. . . . . *T. aralensis* Bunge
          EE. The petals elliptic-ovate, definitely wider in lower half; disc not lobed, the fils. confluent at base. Rare. . . . . *T. gallica* L.
AA. Fls. 4-merous; petals oblong, scarcely 2 mm. long; bracts diaphanous.
    (Includes *T. tetranda* auth.) . . . . *T. parviflora* DC.

p. 176. FOUQUIÈRIA

1. **F. spléndens** Engelm. $2n = 12$ (Raven, Kyhos & Hill, 1965).

p. 178. PETALÓNYX

After generic description insert (Davis, W. S. and H. J. Thompson. A revision of Petalonyx, etc. Madroño 19: 1–18. 1967).

1. **P. nítidus** Wats. $n = 23$ (Davis & Thompson, 1967).

2. **P. lineàris** Greene. $n = 23$ (Davis & Thompson, 1967).

3. **P. Gilmánii** Munz reduced to **P. Thúrberi** ssp. **Gilmánii** Davis & Thompson. $n = 23$.

4. **P. Thúrberi** Gray. $n = 23$ (Davis & Thompson, 1967).

p. 180. MENTZÈLIA

9. **M. nìtens** Greene. var. **Jònesii** (Urban & Gilg) Darlington. Petals 8–12 mm. long. Owens V., *Wiggins*.

p. 181. 12. **M. Líndleyi** T. & G. in Monterey Co., *Howitt & Howell*.

Ssp. **cròcea** (Kell.) C. B. Wolf maintained as a sp. by H. J. Thompson (Brittonia 12: 81–92. 1960).

p. 183. EÙCNIDE

Thompson, H. J. & W. R. Ernst. Fl. biol. & systematics. (Jour. Arn. Arb. 48: 56–88. 1967.)

1. **E. ùrens** (Gray) Parry reported from the El Paso Range, Kern Co., *Twisselmann*. $n = 21$ (Thompson & Ernst, 1967).

p. 184. VIÒLA

Change A of Key to:

A. Stipules almost as large as lvs., leaflike with large terminal lobe. Introd. annuals.
    B. Petals scarcely longer than sepals; spur ca. equal to appendages. . . 23. *V. arvensis*
    BB. Petals longer than sepals; spur rather longer than appendages. . . . . 24. *V. tricolor*

p. 185. 1. **V. glabélla** Nutt. In Greenhorn Range, Kern Co., *Twisselmann*.

p. 186. 5. **V. Bàkeri** ssp. **shasténsis** M. S. Baker differs from *V. Bakeri* in having pubescent caps. and a few short appressed hairs on the faces of the sepals. Amador, Lassen, Tehama, and Trinity cos.; to Ore. Clausen (Madroño 17: 175) does not maintain this ssp.

7. **V. áurea** Kell. J. Clausen says **V. a.** and ssp. **mohavénsis** Baker & Clausen should be sspp. of **V. purpurea** Kell. (Madroño 17: 175 & 295. 1964).

Ssp. **mohavénsis** Baker & Clausen reported from Monterey Co., *Howitt & Howell*.

p. 188. 8. **V. purpùrea** ssp. **geophỳta** Baker & Clausen occurs in volcanic ash at 4000–6000 ft.

10. **V. pedunculàta** ssp. **tenuifòlia** Baker & Clausen reported from Santa Lucia Mts., Monterey Co., *Howitt & Howell.*

p. 189.   13. **V. Sheltònii** Torr. found in Greenhorn Range, Kern Co., *Twisselmann.*

p. 190.   22. **V. adúnca** Sm. var. **oxýceras** (Wats.) Jeps. is a separate sp. to M. S. Baker and a ssp. to J. Clausen as *V. a.* ssp. *o.* (Wats.) Piper. It has thinner lvs. never cordate at base, sometimes wider than long (not ovate); fls. smaller, with upper 4 petals mostly in 1 plane, but the lower petal in another plane (instead of all in the same plane); seeds with ratio 1.85 to 1 for length to width (*adunca* almost 2:1).

p. 191.   24. **V. trìcolor** L. WILD PANSY. Corolla 15–25 mm. long, blue-violet or yellow or combination of these; spur up to twice as long as appendages.—Established in counties about San Francisco Bay; native to Eu.

HYPÈRICUM

In Key after line beginning "Sepals ovate to obovate," etc. change to:

Lvs. 1–4 cm. long; herbs to 7 dm. tall.
    The lvs. oblong to ovate, mostly flat; sepals mostly without black dots. . . 4. *H. formosum*
    The lvs. linear to lanceolate, mostly folded; sepals with many black marginal dots.
                                           5. *H. concinnum*
Lvs. 5–7 cm. long; shrubs to 5 m. tall. . . . . 6. *H. canariense*

p. 192.   3. **H. perforàtum** L. At Kernville, Kern Co., *Twisselmann.*

5. **H. concínnum** Benth. $2n = 8$ pairs (Raven, Kyhos & Hill, 1965).

6. **H. canariénse** L. Shrub to 5 m. tall; lvs. oblong-lanceolate, narrowed at base, 5–7 cm. long; fls. 2.5–3 cm. diam., in panicles; sepals ovate, acute, ciliate. —Established in colonies along creeks at Montecito and on hill roads n. of Santa Barbara, *Pollard*; native of Old World.

PAPAVERÀCEAE

In Key to Genera, after A, delete B and BB and change to:

    B.   Basal lvs. broadly linear without petiole; plants pubescent.
        C.   Carpels more than 3. . . . . 1. *Platystemon*
        CC. Carpels 3 . . . . 1a. *Hesperomecon*
    BB. Basal lvs. spatulate, narrowed at base; plants essentially glabrous. . . 2. *Meconella*

p. 193.   PLATYSTÈMON

After generic description insert as a reference: Ernst, W. R. Floral morphology and systematics of Platystemon and its allies Hesperomecon and Meconella. Univ. Kans. Sci. Bull. 47: 25–70. 1967.

Change generic description of Platystemon to:

1. Platystèmon Benth. CREAM CUPS

Low villous annuals with lvs. not narrowed at base, ± alternate below, opposite or whorled above. Fls. terminal on long peduncles. Sepals 3. Petals 6, white to yellowish. Stamens hypogynous, many. Carpels more than 3, each forming a locule around a central chamber; carpels at first united, separate in fr., each several-ovuled, breaking transversely into indehiscent 1-seeded joints. Rest of old description valid, but seeds with wall of fr. adherent.

1. **P. califórnicus** Benth.

1a. Hesperomècon Greene
(*Platystigma* Benth., not R. Br.).

Plants villous. Lvs. broadly linear, not narrowed at the base. Stamens usually many. Carpels 3, the ovary forming 1 locule. Seeds free from wall of fr. (Greek, *hesperos*, western, and *mekon*, poppy).

p. 194.   1. **H. lineàris** (Benth.) Greene. [*Platystigma l.* Benth. *Platystemon l.* Curran. *Meconella l.* Nels & Macbr.] Additional synonymy in FLORA at top of p. 194. Description as in FLORA, for *Meconella linearis*.

2. Meconélla Nutt. in T. & G.

Plants glabrous or with a few short hairs on sepals. Basal lvs. spatulate, distinctly narrowed at base, the blades ± deltoid to orbicular, upper lvs. ± linear. Stamens 4–6 in 1 series or ca. 12 in 2 series. Carpels 3, the ovary a single locule. Fr. frequently spirally twisted. Seeds lustrous black, free. Three spp. (Greek, *mekon,* poppy, and *ella,* diminutive.)

A. Receptacle ca. as broad as long, without rim; stamens 6, the anthers frequently as long as or longer than the fils. . . . . *M. denticulata*
AA. Receptacle broader than long, with small rim beneath insertion of sepals; anthers very much shorter than fils.
    B. Stamens mostly ca. 12, biseriate or unequal. . . . . 2. *M. californica*
    BB. Stamens 4–6, in 1 series, ca. equal in length. . . . . 3. *M. oregana*

1. **M. denticulàta** Greene. [*Platystemon d.* (Greene) Greene. *M. kakoethes* Fedde. *M. oregana* var. *denticulata* of the FLORA.]
2. **M. califórnica** Torr. & Frém. of the FLORA.
3. **M. oregàna** Nutt. in T. & G. of the FLORA.

p. 195.   ARCTOMÈCON
1. **A. Merriàmii** Cov. *n* = 12 (Ernst, 1958).

DENDROMÈCON
1. **D. rígida** Benth. *n* = 28 (Ernst, 1958). Add Piute Mts., Kern Co. as extension of range.
2. **D. Harfórdii** Kell. treated by Raven (Aliso 5: 321, 1963) as ssp. of **D. rígida** Benth. with var. **rhamnoides** as a synonym of *D. rigida*. Thorne has *D. rigida* ssp. *rhamnoìdes* (Greene) Thorne.

p. 196.   ESCHSCHÓLZIA
W. Ernst (Madroño 17: 280–294. 1964) shows that certain corrections are necessary: In Key to Species, change A, B to:

    B. Buds nodding, usually with some hairs; herbage ± canescent-hairy.
      C. Sepals 11–21 mm. long; petals 15–32 mm. long. Inner S. Coast Ranges from w. Merced Co. to Ventura Co. and w. San Joaquin Co. . . . . . 5. *E. Lemmonii*
      CC. Sepals 5–13 mm. long; petals 5–16 mm. long. Outer S. Coast Ranges, San Luis Obispo and Monterey cos. . . . . 5a. *E. hypecoides*

Insert after A, BB, CC, DD, E:

      F. Sepals 7–8 mm. long; petals 10–38 mm. long. 1. *E. caespitosa*
      FF. Sepals 3–4 mm. long; petals ca. 4 mm. long. 1a. *E. rhombipetala*

1. **E. caespitòsa** Benth. Delete *E. rhombipetala* and *E. hypecoides* as synonyms. *n* = 6 (Ernst, 1959).
p. 197.   1a. **E. rhombipétala** Greene. Sepals 3–4 mm. long (not 7–18 mm. as in *E. caespitosa*); petals ca. 4 mm. long (not 10–38 mm.); buds erect.—It has been found in Contra Costa, San Joaquin, Alameda, Stanislaus and San Luis Obispo cos.
2. **E. élegans** Greene. *n* = 17 (Ernst, 1959).
3. **E. minutiflòra** Wats. *n* = 18 (Ernst, 1959).
    E. minutiflora Wats. var. *darwinensis* Jones is treated as a sp., **E. Covíllei** Greene by Mosquin (Madroño 16: 91–96. 1961) on the basis of fl.-size, more northern distribution and chromosome number (*n* = 18 in *E. minutiflora* and 12 in *E. Covillei*).
4. **E. Paríshii** Greene. 2*n* = 6 pairs (Raven, Kyhos & Hill, 1965).
5. **E. Lemmònii** Greene. *n* = 6 (Ernst, 1959).
5a. **E. hypecoìdes** Benth. [*E. eximia* Greene. *E. alcicornis* Greene. *E. delitescens* Greene ex Fedde. *E. asprella* Greene?]. Agreeing with *E. Lemmonii* in having nodding buds; differing in sepals 5–13 (not 11–21) mm. long; petals 5–16 (not 15–32) mm. long, bright yellow, often with a diffuse orange spot near the base (not mostly dark orange or red orange).—Outer S. Coast Ranges of San Benito, Monterey, w. Fresno and n. San Luis Obispo cos. (while *E. Lem-*

monii ranges from w. Merced Co. to Ventura Co., in the Coast Ranges and adjacent margin of the San Joaquin V.).

6. **E. Lóbbii** Greene. In the Greenhorn Range, Kern Co. ,*Twisselmann.*

p. 198.   8. **E. califórnica** Cham. $2n = 6$ pairs (Raven, Kyhos & Hill, 1965). Twisselmann recognizes an especially large plant from sand flats n. of Kernville as **E. prócera** Greene.

GLAÙCIUM

1. **G. flàvum** Crantz. $2n = 14$ (Larsen, 1954).

p. 199.   Argemòne

1. **A. corymbòsa** Greene. $n = 14$ (Ernst, 1959).

2. **A. muníta** Dur. & Hilg. In the Temblor Range, Kern Co., *Twisselmann*; Monterey Co., *Howitt & Howell.*

p. 200.   STYLOMÈCON

1. **S. heterophýlla** (Benth.) G. Tayl. $2n = 56$ (Ernst, 1958).

p. 201.   PAPÀVER

2. **P. Rhoèas** L. $2n = 14, 15, 21$ (Koopmans, 1955).

3. **P. califórnicum** Gray. $2n = 28$ (Ernst, 1958).

After 3. **P. califórnicum** Gray insert:

A plant superficially resembling *P. californicum* Gray but with caps. to 2.5 cm. long, obovoid-oblong, more than twice as long as wide, growing spontaneously near Pacific Highlands, Monterey Co., has been identified by Dr. P. F. Yeo as **P. dùbium** L., a European sp.

5. **P. ápulum** Ten. var. **micránthum** (Boreau) Fedde reported from Temblor Range, Kern Co., *Twisselmann.*

6. **P. hýbridum** L. Annual, 2–5 dm. tall, stiff-strigose; lvs. 2–3 times pinnately lobed into bristle-pointed narrow segms.; fls. 2–4 cm. in diam.; sepals bristly; petals round-obovate, crimson with a blackish basal spot; caps. ± globose, 1–1.5 cm. in diam.—A heavy infestation reported in a vineyard 1 mi. w. of Madera, Madera Co., *T. C. Fuller;* w. Kern and e. San Luis Obispo cos., *Twisselmann.* Native of Eurasia.

CÁNBYA

1. **C. cándida** Parry. $n = 8$ (Ernst, 1958).

p. 203.   DICÉNTRA

Chromosome counts reported by Ernst are $n = 12$ for *D. chrysántha* (H. & A.) Walp., $n = 8$ for *D. formòsa* (Andr.) Walp., and $n = 16$ for *D. ochroleùca* Engelm.

3. **D. formòsa** (Andr.) Walp. s. to Monterey Co., *Howitt & Howell.*

Ssp. **nevadénsis** (Eastw.) Munz is treated as a sp. by K. R. Stern (Brittonia 13: 1–57. 1961).

p. 203.   5. **D. pauciflòra** Wats. reported from the Greenhorn Range, Kern Co., *Twisselmann.*

p. 204.   FUMÀRIA

1. **F. officinalis** L. $2n = 32$ (Löve & Löve, 1956).

p. 206.   Capparidaceae spelled "Capparàceae" by Ernst (Jour. Arn. Arb. 44: 81–95. 1963).

p. 207.   ISÓMERIS

1. **I. arbòrea** Nutt. $2n = 20$ pairs (Raven, Kyhos & Hill, 1965).

OXÝSTILIS

1. **O. lùtea** Torr. & Frém. $2n = 20$ pairs (Raven, Kyhos & Hill, 1965).

p. 208.   WISLIZÈNIA

1. **W. refrácta** Engelm. Lvs. trifoliolate, the lfts. mostly broadly obovate; caps. valves at most faintly tuberculate.

Var. **Pálmeri** (Gray) Jtn. Lvs. mostly simple, or if bifoliolate, the lfts. narrower; caps. valves strongly tuberculate to sometimes horned.—From near mouth of Colo. R. to Son.

CLEÒME

1. **C. serrulàta** Pursh. $n = 17$ (Raven, Kyhos & Hill, 1965).

2. **C. lùtea** Hook. $2n = 17$ pairs (Raven, Kyhos & Hill, 1965).

p. 210. CRUCÍFERAE
In Key to Genera, under A, change B to:

    B. Silicles not winged; stems with branched hairs.
        C. Fruiting pedicels slender, 2–6 mm. long, recurved; style shorter than the fr.
                41. *Athysanus*
        CC. Fruiting pedicels stout, ca. 1 mm. long, not recurved; style almost as long as
          the fr. . . . . 41a. *Euclidium*

p. 211. In Key AA, BB, C, DD, EE, FF, GG, HH, I, JJ, change K to:

        K. Lvs. simple, entire or finely serrate.
           L. The lvs. auriculate-clasping; fls. yellow.
                53. *Conringia*
           LL. The lvs. not auriculate-clasping; fls. purple
             to whitish. . . . . 54. *Hesperis*

p. 215. THELYPÒDIUM
    5. **T. flexuòsum** Rob. in Gray. $n = 13$ (Rollins, 1966).
    7. **T. laciniàtum** var. **millefòlium** (A. Nels.) Pays. $n =$ ca. 14 (Rollins, 1966).
    9. **T. flavéscens** (Hook.) Wats. Rollins puts this in the genus *Caulanthus*; $n = 14$ (Rollins, 1966).
p. 216.   10. **T. Lemmònii** Greene. $n = 14$ (Rollins, 1966).
    11. **T. lasiophýllum** (H. & A.) Greene. Rollins has in *Caulanthus*; $n = 14$ (Rollins, 1966).

p. 217. STREPTÁNTHUS
In Key after A, B, change:

        CC. Annual or biennial; sepals usually lacking short stiff terminal hairs; upper
          pair of fils. connate.
          D. Siliques ascending to recurved-spreading, 2.5–7 cm. long; sepals about
            equally broad.
            E. Lower lvs. saliently lobed, spatulate-obovate, long-petioled; plants
              0.5–1.8 dm. high. Marin Co. . . . . 9. *S. batrachopus*
            EE. Lower lvs. toothed or entire, short-petioled; plants mostly 3–7 dm.
              high.
              F. Basal lvs. oblanceolate to ovate or obovate; petals in dissimilar
                pairs.
                G. Sepals alike; petals 7–10 mm. long.
                  H. Plants annual, 3–6 dm. tall; sepals largely purple, not
                    setose; petals white or with purple veins. Glenn Co.
                    to San Benito Co. . . . . 10. *S. Breweri*
                HH. Plants biennial, to 10 dm. tall; sepals greenish-yellow
                  to red-purple, often setose.
                    I. Petals creamy to light salmon with brownish or
                    orange veins. Sonoma and Lake cos.
                    10a. *S. Morrisonii*
                  II. Petals white. Sonoma Co. . . 10b. *S. brachiatus*

GG, FF, and DD as in the FLORA.
After "BB. Infl. with some conspicuous broad leafy bracts among lower fls."
change to:

        C. Middle cauline lvs. oblong to obovate.
          D. Siliques 1.5–3 mm. broad.
            E. The siliques arcuate-spreading; basal lvs. entire or toothed.
                7. *S. tortuosus*
            EE. The siliques ascending; basal lvs. pinnatifid. 18b. *S. Farnsworthianus*
          DD. Siliques 1 mm. broad, erect. . . . . 8. *S. gracilis*
        CC. Middle cauline lvs. linear or pinnate; siliques deflexed.
          D. Fls. generally yellow, rarely with purplish tinge; lvs. entire and linear
            or with linear lobes. . . . . 18. *S. diversifolius*
          DD. Fls. violet or purplish; lvs. not with linear segms.; siliques 1.5–1.7 mm.
            broad. Tehipite V., Fresno Co. . . . . 18a. *S. fenestratus*

AA, etc. remains as in the FLORA.
p. 218.   3. **S. cordàtus** Nutt. Insert:
    Var. **piuténsis** J. T. Howell. Siliques flattened, broad, but stems taller, to 1 m.,
and with woodier base.—Piute Mts., Kern Co.
    7. **S. tortuòsus** Kell. $n = 14$ (Rollins, 1966).
p. 219.   10. **S. Brèweri** Gray. $n = 14$ (Rollins, 1966).

10a. **S. Morrisònii** F. W. Hoffm. Glabrous glaucous biennial, to 10 dm. tall; upper and lower surfaces of juvenile and of lower lvs. usually uniformly green; upper stem-lvs. auriculate-spatulate to -ovate, clasping, entire or few-toothed; calyx greenish-yellow, becoming golden-yellow in age, glabrous or with a few scattered hairs, to 8 mm. long; petals creamy white to light salmon with brownish or orange veins; lower petals 1 cm. long; upper connate fils. orange; siliques erect or divergent, 2–7 cm. long, torulose.—Serpentine, Big and East Austin Creeks, Sonoma Co.

Ssp. **elàtus** F. W. Hoffm. Upper surface of juvenile and of lower lvs. heavily mottled with purple-brown, lower surface uniformly purplish; calyx greenish-yellow to golden-yellow; upper connate fils. yellow.—Serpentine, head of St. Helena and Bucksnort creeks, Lake Co.

Ssp. **hirtiflòrus** F. W. Hoffm. Upper surface of juvenile lvs. mottled with purple-brown, lower surface uniformly purple; calyx red-purple, densely hirsute; upper fils. orange with 2 purple stripes.—Serpentine, head of East Austin Creek, Sonoma Co.

10b. **S. brachiàtus** F. W. Hoffm. More or less woody biennial to 4.5 dm. tall, glabrous, glaucous below; stem lvs. crisped, auriculate, to 5.5 cm. long, 2.5 cm. wide, entire to coarsely serrate; fls. 8 mm. long; calyx purplish, glabrous, usually reticulate; upper fils. orange, with 2 purplish lines; siliques erect, torulose, purplish, to 6.5 cm. long.—Serpentine, east of Pine Flat, Sonoma Co.

p. 220.   12. **S. glandulòsus** Hook. A. R. Kruckeberg (Madroño 14: 217–226. 1958) recognizes in the S. *glandulosus* complex:

(1) **S. glandulòsus** Hook. Plants ± pubescent below, 3–7 dm. tall; infl. secund; fls. lilac-lavender to purple or more often purplish-black, rarely rose; $n = 14$.—Serpentine, San Luis Òbispo Co. to Tehama Co.

Ssp. **pulchéllus** (Greene) Kruckeberg. Plants often dwarfish, 1–4 dm. tall; fls. reddish-purple, usually secund, crowded on the short simple to branched racemes; siliques divaricate or ascending, 4–6 cm. long; $n = 14$.—Serpentine, Marin Co.

Ssp. **secúndus** (Greene) Kruckeberg. Fls. in open or crowded secund racemes; siliques usually arcuate, 5–6 cm. long. Var. **secúndus** (Greene) Kruckeberg. Fls. greenish-yellow, tinged with rose or purple as blotches at the base of the petal laminae; $n = 14$.—Marin Co. Var. **sonoménsis** Kruckeberg. Fls. yellow, white or greenish-white; $n = 14$.—Sonoma Co. Var. **Hoffmánii** Kruckeberg. Fls. rose to rose-purplish; $n = 14$.—East Austin Creek, Sonoma Co.

(2) **S. álbidus** Greene. Plants ± pubescent below, usually 6–10 dm. high; infl. not secund; fls. greenish-white.—S. of San Jose, Santa Clara Co.

Ssp. **peramoènus** (Greene) Kruckeberg. Fls. lilac-lavender.—Alameda, Contra Costa, Santa Clara cos.

(3) **S. nìger** Greene. Plants glabrous throughout; infl. zigzag in outline; fls. purplish-black; $n = 14$.—Tiburon Peninsula, Marin Co.

13. **S. insígnis** Jeps. $n = 14$ (Rollins, 1966).

p. 221.   17. **S. polygaloìdes** Gray. Basal lvs. 4–8 cm. long, pinnately divided to the linear rachis with the divisions ca. 3–8 on each side, spreading, 2–15 mm. long, mostly linear to linear-oblong.

18. **S. diversifòlius** Wats. Lower and middle cauline lvs. entire and linear or pinnately divided with linear lobes; fls. generally yellow, rarely tinged purplish; siliques 1–1.25 mm. broad; seeds brown, 1.5 mm. long; $n = 14$ (Rollins, 1966).—Foothill Wd., Yellow Pine F., below 5000 ft.; Amador and Butte cos. to Tulare Co.

18a. **S. fenestràtus** (Greene) J. T. Howell. [*Pleiocardia f.* Greene.] Lvs. deeply divided, the segms. usually oblongish or broader, not linear-filiform; fls. violet or purplish; siliques 1.5–1.7 mm. broad; seeds blackish-brown, 1.5–2 mm. long.—Yellow Pine F., Tehipite V., Fresno Co.

18b. **S. Farnsworthiànus** J. T. Howell. Basal lvs. pinnatifid, midcauline lvs. deeply pinnately lobed to subentire; pedicels to 5 mm. long; fls. 10–15 mm. long, the petals whitish with purple nerves; siliques ascending, straight or curved, 7–9 (–12) cm. long, 3 mm. wide.—At ca. 3000–4000 ft., Fresno and Kern cos., Sierra Nevada to Glennville.

p. 222. CAULÁNTHUS

    1. C. amplexicaùlis Wats. var. barbárae (J. T. Howell) Munz comb. nov. [*Streptanthus a.* var. *barbarae* J. T. Howell, Leafl. W. Bot. 9: 223. 1962.] Differing from *C. a.* Wats. in having sepals ochroleucous to yellowish; siliques to 15 cm. long.—San Rafael Mts., Santa Barbara Co.

    2. C. Coòperi (Wats.) Pays. $2n = 14$ pairs (Raven, Kyhos & Hill, 1965).

p. 223.   4. C. Coùlteri Wats. $n = 14$ (Rollins, 1966).

    Var. Lemmònii (Wats.) Munz. Rollins treats this as of specific rank, 1966. $n = 14$ (Rollins, 1966).

    5. C. inflàtus Wats. $n = 10$ (Rollins, 1966).

p. 224. STREPTANTHELLA

    1. S. longiróstris (Wats.) Rydb. $n = 14$ (Rollins, 1966).

    Var. derelícta J. T. Howell. $n = 14$ (Rollins, 1966).

p. 225. SUBULÀRIA

    1. S. aquática L. ssp. americàna Mulligan & Calder for American plants which have more persistent sepals than the European; mature silicles more elliptic; lowest pedicel-axil 30°–50° rather than 50°–90°.

CARDÀRIA

    G. A. Mulligan & C. Frankton (Can. Jour. Bot. 40: 1411–1425. 1962) recognize for this genus:

    1. C. Dràba (L.) Desv. Silicles and sepals glabrous; silicles cordate; $n = 32$.

    2. C. chalepénsis (L.) Handel-Mazzetti [*C. Draba* var. *repens* O. E. Schulz.] Silicles and sepals mostly glabrous; silicles subreniform to obovoid; $n = 40$.

    3. C. pubéscens (C. A. Mey.) Jarmolenko. [*C. p.* var. *elongata* Rollins.] Silicles and sepals with short simple hairs; silicles strongly inflated, ovoid or subglobose; $n = 8$.

p. 226. LEPÍDIUM

In Key, in the E. leading to "10. *L. lasiocarpum,*" insert "sometimes" after "Petals."

    1. L. campéstre (L.) R. Br. $2n = 16$ (Mulligan, 1957).—Reported from Monterey Co., *Howitt & Howell.*

p. 227.   3. L. latifòlium L. In Eldorado Co. and n. along w. slope of Sierra Nevada, *Fuller;* in Yolo, Sonoma, Monterey cos., *Howell.*

    4. L. stríctum (Wats.) Rattan. $n = $ ca. 16 (Rollins, 1966).

    7. L. densiflòrum Schrad. In Greenhorn Mts., Kern Co., *Twisselmann.*

    Var. pubicárpum (Nels.) Thell. $2n = 16$ pairs (Raven, Kyhos & Hill, 1965).

    8. L. pinnatifidum Ledeb. In Glenn Co., Santa Barbara Co., *Fuller;* in Monterey and San Francisco cos., *Howell et al.*

p. 228.   9. L. virgínicum var. pubéscens (Greene) Thell., not C. L. Hitchc.

    11. L. nítidum Nutt. is sometimes used for plants with caps. 3–4 mm. long, while var. insígne Greene has caps. 6 mm. long, the var. ranging in e. Monterey and San Luis Obispo cos. and Tehachapi Mts.

    Var. oregànum C. L. Hitchc. is reported from Goose Lake, Kern Co., *Twisselmann.*

p. 230.   18. L. Jarédii Bdg. $n = 8$ (Rollins, 1966).

CORÓNOPUS

    2. Use C. squamàtus (Forskål) Ascherson, not *C. procumbens* Gilib.

THLÁSPI

Substitute the following for the Key in the FLORA:

Plants annual; silicles roundel, deeply notched; seeds with concentric ridges. 1. *T. arvense*
Plants perennial; silicles cuneate-obovate, scarcely or not notched; seeds smooth.
  Silicles conspicuously acute when mature; styles ca. 3 mm. long. At low elevs., Mixed
  Evergreen F., Humboldt Co. to sw. Ore. .... 3. *T. californicum*
  Silicles obovate or obcordate, largely emarginate; styles 1.5–2 mm. long. At 3000–6500
  ft., Yellow Pine F. and above; Siskiyou, Trinity and Modoc cos.; to Wash., Ida.
                                                  2. *T. Fendleri*

p. 231.   **2. T. Féndleri** Gray var. **hespérium** (Pays.) C. L. Hitchc. [*T. glaucum* var. *h.* Pays.] Delete *T. californicum* from synonymy.

3. T. califórnicum Wats. Stems 2–3 dm. high, reddish; lvs. glaucous, the basal petioled, toothed, elliptic-obovate, the cauline oblong-ovate, sessile, clasping, at least some of them as long as the internodes; pedicels spreading, 7–10 mm. long, rather stout; sepals 3 mm. long, white-margined; petals white, 5–6 mm. long; silicles 7–10 mm. long, usually acute; styles 2–3 mm. long.—Serpentine, 400–1200 ft., Mixed Evergreen F., Humboldt Co. to Josephine Co., Ore.

SISÝMBRIUM

3. S. orientàle L. $n = 7$ (Rollins, 1966). Temblor Range and Tehachapi Mts., Kern Co., *Twisselmann*.

4. S. Îrio L. $n = 7, 14, 21 28$ (Koshov, 1955). Reported from many counties in Central V. of Calif., *Weiler*.

p. 232.   ARABIDÓPSIS

1. A. Thaliàna (L.) Heynh. For 1959 printing, the name Gray in the synonymy should be Gay.

p. 234.   CAKÌLE

2. C. marítima Scop. can be reported from Santa Cruz Id., Santa Rosa Id., Point Mugu and near El Segundo, Los Angeles Co.

p. 235.   ISÀTIS

1. I. tinctòria L. In Sierra and Nevada cos., *Fuller*.

p. 236.   BRÁSSICA

In Key change line 1 of this page:

> D.   Petals ca. 3 mm. wide; beak of silique 2–10 mm. long, the apex narrower than the stigma.
> E.   Plants annual; petals 7–8 mm. long; beak 5–8 mm. long. . . . . . .   6. *B. juncea*
> EE. Plants perennial; petals 9–10 mm. long; beak 9–10 mm. long. 6a. *B. fruticulosa*

5. B. geniculàta (Desf.) J. Ball, without a parenthesis, in 1959 printing.

6a. B. fruticulòsa Cyrillo. Lvs. not auriculate, all lyrate or pinnately lobed; sepals shorter than pedicels; beak often 1–2-seeded.—Dunes in Sunset district, San Francisco, *Rubtzoff*.

p. 238.   BARBARÈA

Substitute "Scop." for "R. Br." as authority for genus.

2. B. vérna (Mill.) Asch. Reported from Monterey Co., *Howitt & Howell*.

3. B. orthóceras Ledeb. Found in Monterey Co., *Howitt & Howell. n = 8* (Rollins, 1966).

p. 239.   RORÍPPA

2. R. sinuàta (Nutt.) Hitchc. $n = 8$ (Rollins, 1966).

4. R. subumbellàta Roll. $n = 5$ (Rollins, 1966).

5. R. curvisilíqua (Hook.) Bessey. $n = 8$ (Rollins, 1966).

p. 240.   NASTÚRTIUM

Peter S. Green (Rhodora 64: 32–43. 1962) uses:

1. Roríppa Nastúrtium-aquáticum (L.) Britt. & Rendle instead of *Nasturtium officinale.*

2. Roríppa microphýlla (Boenn.) Hyland. instead of *Nasturtium m.* It is doubtful that this sp. occurs in Calif., the Jonesville record cited in the FLORA being *Cardámine Brèweri.*

p. 242.   CARDÁMINE

3. C. Brèweri Wats. $n = 42–48$ (Rollins, 1966).

p. 243.   DENTÀRIA

In last line of Key at top of page, insert "or simple" after "3–7-foliolate."

2. D. califórnica Nutt. var. *integrifòlia* (Nutt.) Detl. Rollins (1966) has **D. integrifòlia** Nutt. $n = 16$, and var. **califórnica** (Nutt.) Jeps., $n = 8$ or 16.

p. 244.   IDAHÒA

1. I. scapígera (Hook.) Nels. & Macbr. $2n = 16$ (Raven, Kyhos & Hill, 1965). Occurs in Kern Co., at Glennville, *Twisselmann*.

p. 245.   LYROCÁRPA

1. L. Còulteri var. **Pálmeri** (Wats.) Roll. $2n = 20$ (Rollins, 1941).

DITHÝREA

Change *D. califórnica* var. *marítima* to **D. marítima** A. Davids. Perennial from heavy cordlike underground rhizomes; lvs. to 1 dm. long, the blades rounded, 2–5 cm. in diam., fleshy, subentire; silicles 14–15 mm. broad (as opposed to 10 mm. in *D. californica*); $n = 40$ (Thompson orally for count by Miss Bartholomew) as against 10 for *californica* (Rollins, 1966).—Coastal Strand, Los Angeles Co. to San Luis Obispo Co., San Nicolas Id.

p. 246. PHYSÀRIA

1. **P. Chàmbersii** Roll. $2n = 10$ (Rollins, 1966).

LESQUERÉLLA

1. **L. Pálmeri** Wats. $n = 5$ (Rollins, 1966).

3. **L. occidentàlis** Wats. Ascends to 9700 ft., Lassen Park.

p. 247. PHOENICAÙLIS

In line 1 of generic description change "scapes" to "stems" in the 1959 printing.

CAPSÉLLA

1. **C. Búrsa-pastòris** (L.) Medic. $2n = 32$ (Löve & Löve, 1956).

p. 248. DRÀBA

In Key to Species, AA, BB, C, insert "mostly" before "unforked hairs" in the 1959 printing.

Change end of Key to:

FF. Lvs. 2–7 mm. wide.
    G. Silicles lanceolate, 1.3–3.5 mm. wide; seeds not winged, 1–1.4 mm. long.
        H.   Petals yellow, 5–6 mm. long. .... 21. *D. cruciata*
        HH. Petals white, 2.5–5 mm. long. .... 21a. *D. nivalis*
    GG. Silicles ovate, 3–6 mm. wide; seeds winged, ca. 2 mm. long.
                                          22. *D. asterophora*

p. 249. 1. **D. vérna** L. In Monterey Co., *Howitt & Howell*; in Greenhorn Range, Kern Co., *Twisselmann*; Fresno and Kern cos., *Weiler*.

p. 250. 3. **D. réptans** (Lam.) Fern. $n = 15$ (Mulligan, 1956).

5. **D. nemoròsa** L. $n = 8$ (Mulligan, 1966).

p. 251. 10. **D. Lemmònii** Wats. and 12. **D. Brèweri** Wats. Both spp. have been taken at elevations of 14,200 ft.

13. **D. praeálta** Greene. $n = 28$ (Mulligan, 1966).

p. 252. 17. **D. crassifòlia** Grah. $n = 20$ (Mulligan, 1966).

18. **D. oligospérma** Hook. $2n = $ ca. 60 (Rollins, 1966).

p. 253. 21a. **D. nivàlis** Liljebl. var. **elongàta** Wats. Near *D. cruciata* Pays., but has white petals 2.5–5 mm. long; lvs. cinereous with stalked, irregularly branched and stellate trichomes; stems glabrous to cinereous; silicles glabrous to stellate. —Found at Convict Lake Basin, Sierra Nevada, Mono Co., at 10,800 ft., *Major & Bamberg*; Rocky Mts.

41a. Euclídium R. Br.

A monotypic genus of Eurasia.

1. **E. syriàcum** (L.) R. Br. Annual, divaricately branched, 1–3 dm. tall, stellate or with branched hairs; lvs. lanceolate to oblanceolate, entire to subrepand, 1–3 cm. long, with short winged petiole; fls. loosely spicate; pedicels 0.8–1 mm. long, erect; petals 1–1.2 mm. long; silicle ovoid, hispid, 2–3 mm. long.—Reported as weed near Adin, Lassen Co., *McCaskill*; known from Wash., Ida.; native in Eurasia.

p. 254. THYSANOCÁRPUS

2. **T. cúrvipes** Hook. $n = 7$ (Rollins, 1966).

Var. **elegáns** (F. & M.) Rob. Rollins considers this to be a species. $2n = 28$ (Rollins, 1966).

p. 255. 3. **T. laciniàtus** Nutt. var. **crenàtus** (Nutt.) Brew. reported from as far n. as Tehama Co., *Wagnon*.

p. 257. ÁRABIS

In Key BB, CC, D, EE, F, G, H delete "Cauline lvs. auricled" and "Cauline lvs. not auricled" from I and II respectively.

p. 258. In Key to Arabis, for *A. Lemmonii,* change to "cauline lvs. oblong-lanceolate to ovate, mostly glabrous."

p. 259. 3. **A. blepharoyphýlla** H. & A. Occurs in Monterey Co., *Howitt & Howell.*

4. **A. modésta** Roll. On line between Napa and Yolo cos. *Hemphill.*

p. 260. 9. **A. Drummóndii** Gray. $2n = 14$ (Rollins, 1966).

10. **A. divaricárpa** A. Nels. $2n = 14, 22$ (Rollins, 1966).

12. **A. Lemmònii** Wats. $2n = 14$ (Rollins, 1966).

p. 262. 15. **A. sparsiflòra** var. **califórnica** Roll. $2n = 22$ (Raven, Kyhos & Hill, 1965).

p. 263. 21. **A. Holboéllii** var. **pinetòrum** (Tides.) Roll. $2n = 21$ (Rollins, 1966).

Var. **pendulocárpa** (A. Nels.) Roll. $2n = 14$ (Rollins, 1966).

p. 264. 28. **A. repánda** Wats. Occurs in the Greenhorn Range, Kern Co., *Twisselmann.*

p. 265. 34. **A. platyspérma** Gray. Found in the Greenhorn Range, *Twisselmann.*

p. 266. SÍBARA

1. **S. virgínica** (L.) Roll. $2n = 16$ (Rollins, 1966). Occurs in Fresno and Kern cos., *Weiler.*

2. **S. filifòlia** (Greene) Greene. Collected on Catalina Id., *Trask* in 1901.

p. 268. ERÝSIMUM

1. **E. cheiranthoìdes** L. A garden weed in Fresno, *Weiler.*

2. **E. repándum** L. $n = 8$ (Mulligan, 1966).

3. **E. perénne** (Wats. ex Cov.) Abrams. On Kern R. Plateau and in Piute Mts., Kern Co., *Twisselmann.*

4. **E. argillòsum** (Greene) Rydb. At 9725 ft., White Mts., *Blakley & Muller.*

5. **E. capitàtum** (Dougl.) Greene. $2n = 36$ (Mulligan, 1966).

Twisselmann recognizes a var. **stellàtum** with orange to maroon fls. and published by J. T. Howell as *E. asperum* var. *stellatum.* He also separates E. **moníliforme** Eastw. (Temblor, San Emigdio ranges, etc., Kern Co.) with pale fls., entire lvs. and slender pods constricted between the seeds.

p. 269. 7. **E. ammóphilum** Heller. $n = 18$ (Mulligan, 1966).

8. **E. concínnum** Eastw. $n = $ ca. 18 (Rollins, 1966).

p. 270. ALÝSSUM

1. **A. alyssoìdes** L. Reported from Oakland, Alameda Co.; Warner Mts., Modoc Co., *Fuller.*

p. 271. ## 54. Hésperis L. ROCKET

Annual to perennial, caulescent. Lvs. lanceolate or lance-ovate, serrulate, acuminate to acute, sessile or short-petioled, gradually reduced up the stem. Infl. racemose or paniculate, particularly in fr. Fls. purple to white, short-pediceled. Siliques subcylindric, very slender; stigma lobed, erect. Seeds in 1 row in each locule, oblong, marginless. Cotyledons incumbent. (Greek, *hesperos, evening* or *evening-star,* because of the evening fragrance of the fls.)

1. **H. matronàlis** L. Stems 3–8 dm. tall, with simple spreading hairs; lvs. 3–12 cm. long, 1–3.5 cm. wide, mostly on short petioles; calyx ca. 7 mm. long; petals 15–20 mm. long; siliques 5–14 cm. long.—Sparingly natur. as a weed, as at Trinity Center, Trinity Co., and Quincy, Plumas Co., *Howell.* Native of Old World.

p. 271. Illustration for *Elátine* at top of page, the seed drawn is of the *brachysperma-obovata* group.

CHORÍSPORA

1. **C. tenélla** (Pall.) DC. Collected in Lassen Co., *Anderson in 1963.*

MATTHÌOLA

2. **M. bicórnis** DC. Roadside near Tehachapi, Kern Co., *Fuller.* Siliques 8–30 cm. long, branchlike, with 2 long slender hornlike processes from the backs of the stigma-lobes. From the E. Medit.

p. 273. BÉRGIA

At end of generic description, dates for *Bergius* should be 1730–1790.

p. 274.   CARYOPHYLLÀCEAE
Key under AA, B, C, DD insert

E.   Petals bifid or bilobed. Common. . . . . .2. *Cerastium*
EE. Petals entire. Rare. . . . . .2a. *Holosteum*

Key, under AA, BB, CC, D, E, F, insert

G. Calyx-tube lacking white scarious seam between the teeth; plant annual; fls. 10–20 mm. diam. . . . . 12. *Vaccaria*
GG. Calyx-tube with white scarious seam between the teeth; plant perennial; fls. 4–5 mm. diam. . . . . 12a. *Gypsophila*

At end of Key, change the last word "*Tunica*" to *Kaulrauschia*."

p. 275.   STELLÀRIA
1. S. mèdia (L.) Vill. not Cyrill as in 1959 printing.
4. S. Jamesiàna Torr. is treated as *Arenària J.* (Torr.) Shinners in Sida 1: 50.
1962.
5. S. gramínea L. reported from Stanford University campus and San Francisco. $2n = 26$ (Löve & Löve).
6. S. longipès Goldie. $2n = 104$ (Jørgensen et al., 1958).

p. 276.   8. S. sitchàna var. Bongardiàna (Fern.) Hult. in Greenhorn Range, Kern Co.,
Twisselmann.
10. S. críspa C. & S. Kern Co., *Twisselmann.*
11. S. obtùsa Engelm. In Nevada Co. and on Lassen Peak, *Howell.*

CERÁSTIUM
Key, change last line to "Annual without persistent basal sterile offsets" and
add:

Caps.-teeth revolute; sepals 4–6 mm. long; caps. 5–9 mm. long. . . . . 3. *C. glomeratum*
Caps.-teeth plane on the margin; sepals 8–10 mm. long; caps. 18 mm. long.
3a. *C. dichotomum*

p. 277.   2. C. vulgàtum L. $2n = 72, 126, 144, 180$ (Blackburn & Morton, 1956).
3. Change *C. viscòsum* to C. glomeràtum Thuill. [*C. v.* many auth.] $n = 36$
(Huynk., 1965).
3a. C. dichótomum L. Annual, differing from *C. viscosum* in having sepals
8–10 mm. long; caps. 18 mm. long, the caps.-teeth plane on the margin (not
revolute).—Reported from 5 mi. e. of Montague, Siskiyou Co., *Fuller*; native
Medit. to Iran.

p. 277.   2a. Holósteum L. JAGGED CHICKWEED

Annuals or biennials, with several fls. borne in an umbel on a long terminal
peduncle. Sepals 5. Petals 5, usually jagged or denticulate to the point. Stamens
mostly 3–5. Styles mostly 3. Pod ovoid, 1-celled, many-seeded.
1. H. umbellàtum L. Glaucous, glandular-pubescent annual, 5–20 cm. tall;
lvs. oblong; fls. white or pink, small; styles 3; caps. cylindric, deeply 6-toothed.
—Grenada, Siskiyou Co., *Howell*; from Old World.

p. 278.   ARENÀRIA
In Key after A, BB, under C. delete "3. *A. californica*" and insert:

D. Plant 2–5 cm. high; branches decumbent; seeds smooth. . . 4. *A. pusilla* var. *diffusa*
DD. Plant 3–10 cm. high; branches erect; seeds rough. . . . . 3. *A. californica*

p. 279.   4. A. pusílla Wats. In Greenhorn Range, Kern Co., *Twisselmann* and in San
Luis Obispo Co., *Hardham.*
p. 280.   8. A. obtusilòba (Rydb.) Fern. $n = 13$ (Wiens & Halleck, 1963).
p. 282.   16. A. macradènia Wats. Kern Plateau, Kern Co., *Twisselmann.*
Var. Parishiòrum Rob. In Tehachapi Mts., Kern Co., *Twisselmann.*
18. A. macrophýlla Hook. In Santa Lucia Mts., *Howitt & Howell.*
p. 283.   SPERGULÀRIA
2. S. atrospérma R. P. Rossb. in Plumas Co. and sw. Kern Co., *Howell.*
p. 284.   4. S. Boccònii (Scheele) Foucaud. $2n = 36$ (Blackburn & Morton, 1957).
p. 285.   **Polycárpon**

1. **P. tetraphýllum** (L.) L. $2n = 54$ (Blackburn & Morton, 1957).

LOEFLÍNGIA

1. **L. squarròsa** Nutt. At 4000 ft. in Plumas Co., *Howell.*

SILÈNE

Fls. solitary or more often cymose, some spp. (*S. californica, S. Lemmonii* and *S. Sargentii*) are diurnal, others (*S. montana, S. Grayi, S. verecunda*) vespertine (letter from *H. L. Buckalew*).

p. 287.   Key under OO, change to:

> P.   Calyx usually plainly constricted below the ovary, 10–12 mm. long; appendages of petals 1–2 mm. long; infl. tending to have more than 1 fl. in a cymule. Lake and Mono cos. s. . . . . 22. *S. verecunda*
>
> PP.   Calyx slightly constricted below the ovary, ca. 13 mm. long; appendages of petals scarcely 1 mm. long; infl. with a single fl. in a cymule. Siskiyou Co. 22a. *S. marmorensis*

2. **S. conoìdea** L. Collected at Greenville, Plumas Co., *Budaj.*

p. 288.   4. **S. gállica** L. $2n = 24$ (Blackburn & Morton, 1957).

7. **S. califórnica** Durand. $2n = 72$ (Kruckeberg, 1960).

p. 289.   10. **S. invìsa** Hitchc. & Maguire. $2n = 48$ (Kruckeberg, 1960). Reported from Lassen Park.

11. **S. campanulàta** Wats. $2n = 48$ (Kruckeberg, 1960).

12. **S. apérta** Greene. $2n = 48$ (Kruckeberg, 1960).

15. **S. montàna** Wats. G. Bocquet (Candollea 20: 49–50, 1965) shows that *Silene montana* Wats. is antedated by *S. m.* Arrondeau. The next name available is **S. bernardìna** Wats., of which ssp. **bernardìna** is *S. montana* var. *b.* of the FLORA; ssp. **Maguìrei** Bocquet is *S. montana* of the FLORA; and ssp. **Maguìrei** var. **siérrae** (Hitchc. & Maguire) Bocquet is *S. montana* var. *sierrae* of the FLORA. For *S. bernardina* ssp. *Maguirei* $2n = 48$ (Kruckeberg, 1960). Both *S. bernardina* and var. *sierrae* have been reported from the Greenhorn Mts., Kern Co., *Twisselmann.*

p. 290.   17. **S. Lemmònii** Wats. $2n = 48$ (Kruckeberg, 1960).

18. **S. occidentàlis** Wats. $2n = 48$ (Kruckeberg, 1960).

19. **S. Gràyii** Wats. $2n = 48$ (Kruckeberg, 1960).

p. 291.   22. **S. verecúnda** Wats. $2n = 48$ (Kruckeberg, 1960).

Ssp. **Andersònii** (Clokey) Hitchc. & Maguire. $2n = 48$ (Kruckeberg, 1960).

22a. **S. marmorénsis** Kruckeberg. Stems slender, 2.5–4 dm. long, simple, retrorsely glandular-pubescent above; cauline lvs. 5–7 pairs, lanceolate, 3–4.5 cm. long, 3–5 mm. wide; infl. 1–2 dm. long; pedicels 7–10 mm. long, glandular; calyx ca. 13 mm. long, glandular, the lobes 3 mm. long; petals pale pink above, 12–16 mm. long, the blade 4–6 mm. long, bilobed over half its length, the lobes oblong, appendages 2, oblong, scarcely 1 mm. long.—Near Somes Bar, Siskiyou Co., in Yellow Pine F.

p. 292.   LÝCHNIS

2. **L. álba** Mill. $2n = 24$ (Mulligan, 1957).

p. 293.   12a. **Gypsóphila** L.

Herbs, branched or diffuse, glaucous, scanty-leafy when in bloom; fls. small, many, cymose-paniculate; calyx 5-toothed, scarious between the nerves; petals 5, entire or emarginate; stamens 10; styles 2 (3). Over 100 spp. in Old World.

1. **G. paniculàta** L. Perennial, 6–9 dm. high; lvs. lanceolate; fls. numerous,

white, 4–5 mm. diam., in crowded corymbs in panicles.—Near Janesville, Lassen Co. and Macdoel and Weed, Siskiyou Co., *Fuller*; Eurasia.

DIÁNTHUS

Insert Key:

Fls. in heads or clusters surrounded by invol.-like bracts.
    Tufted perennial; involucral bracts glabrous. . . . . 1. *D. barbatus*
    Annual or biennial; involucral bracts hairy. . . . . 2. *D. Armeria*
Fls. 1-2-3, not in heads. . . . . 3. *D. deltoides*

2. **D. Armèria** L. Hairy involucres; plant annual or biennial in duration; lvs. linear; fls. bright red with pale dots.—Magalla, Butte Co., *Howell*; introd. from Eu.

3. **D. deltoìdes** L. Fls. 1, rarely 2–3, not in involucral heads; petals rose or white with pale spots and a dark basal band.—Reported from se. Siskiyou Co. and Huntington Lake, Fresno Co., *Howell.* Introd. from Eu.

TÙNICA

1. Change *T. prolífera* (L.) Scop. to **Kohlráuschia velùtina** (Guss.) Reichb. because of misdetermination and add Shasta and Sacramento cos. for occurrence.

p. 295.   SCLERÁNTHUS

1. **S. ánnuus** L. $2n = 48$ (Blackburn & Morton, 1957).

p. 295.   35a. **Basellàceae.** BASÉLLA FAMILY

Climbing fleshy perennial herbs with ca. 20 spp., mostly native in trop. Am. Rootstocks tuberous; lvs. alternate, usually petioled, entire, mostly fleshy, broad, glabrous. Fls. bisexual, regular, racemose, small, with 2 bracts, 2 sepals, 5 persistent petals remaining closed. Stamens 5, opposite the petals. Ovary superior, 1-loculed, 1-ovuled; styles usually 3, with cleft or entire stigmas. Fr. indehiscent, fleshy, inclosed by the persistent corolla.

1. **Boussingaúltia** HBK.

Stems much branched. Fls. in axillary and terminal spikelike racemes. Sepals nearly flat, not winged. Ca. 14 spp.

1. **B. grácilis** Miers var. **pseùdo-baselloìdes** Bailey. MADEIRA VINE. MIGNON-ETTE VINE. A twining vine 3–6 m. tall, producing little tubercles in the lf.-axils by means of which propagation occurs; lvs. ovate, 2.5–7.5 cm. long, subcordate at base, short-petioled; racemes to 3 dm. long, many-fld.; fls. white, aging black, fragrant.—Late summer. Occasional escape from cult., as in San Francisco.

p. 296.   PORTULÁCA

1. **P. oleràcea** L. $2n = 36$ (Sharma & Bhatt, 1956).

p. 297.   LEWÍSIA

2. and 5. **L. Leàna** and **L. Cotylèdon.** Tucker et al. (Cactus & Succ. Soc. Am., March, 1964) report a hybrid between these species.

3. **L. Congdònii** (Rydb.) J. T. Howell. In Foothill Wd., Yellow Pine F., at 2000–7000 ft., *J. T. Howell.*

p. 298.   7. **L. pygmaèa** (Gray) Rob. in Gray. $n = $ ca. 33 (Wiens & Halleck, 1962).

13. **L. redivìva** Pursh. At sea level in San Francisco Bay area.

Var. **mìnor** (Rydb.) Munz. In Greenhorn Range, Kern Co., *Twisselmann*; and 1.5 mi. n. of Kenworthy Ranger Station, San Jacinto Mts., Riverside Co., *Ziegler.*

p. 300.   CLAYTÒNIA

R. J. Davis (The N. Am. perennial spp. of Claytonia, Brittonia 18: 285–300. 1967) recognizes the taxa I have in the FLORA and includes also in *Claytonia*, with the same specific names: **Móntia parvifòlia** and **M. Chamíssoi.**

1. **C. umbellàta** Wats. $2n = 16$ (Davis, 1967).

2. **C. lanceolàta** Pursh. $2n = 16$ (Davis, 1967); $n = 8$ (Wiens & Halleck, 1962).

3. and 4. **C. bellidifòlia** Rydb. and **C. nevadénsis** Wats. reported by Buckalew (letter) as having lvs. entirely red when they push out of the ground and
remaining so for some time, turning green on upper surface by anthesis but
remaining red beneath and on a vein around the perimeter.

4. **C. nevadénsis** Wats. Occurs in Shasta Co., Calif. and Harney Co., Ore.,
Chambers.

p. 301.   MÓNTIA

1. **M. parvifòlia** (Moç. ex DC.) Greene. $2n = 20$ (Nilsson, 1966).

4. **M. lineáris** (Dougl. ex Hook.) Greene, not (Dougl.) Greene.

p. 302.   6, 7, and 8. D. Moore (Bot. Notiser 116: 16. 1963) for the *M. fontana*
group gives 3 spp. for California:

6. **M. mìnor** Gmel. [*M. verna* Neck.] Seeds (0.8) 1–1.2 (–1.4) mm. diam.,
dull, entirely covered with rather broad tubercles.—Monterey Co. to s. Ore.

7. **M. Hállii** (Gray) Greene. Seeds 0.6–1.2 mm. diam., rather shiny with
7–11 rows of slender tubercles around the keel.—L. Calif. to B.C.

8. **M. Funstònii** Rydb. Seeds 0.7–1.2 mm. diam., somewhat shiny, with keel
tubercles generally low, sometimes none.—Scattered locations (in Calif. at
above 6000 ft.), n. L. Calif. to B.C.

p. 303.   12. **M. perfolista** (Donn) Howell. $n = 6, 12, 18$ (Raven, 1962); 18 (W. H.
Lewis, 1963).

13. **M. spathulàta** (Dougl.) Howell. In Temblor Range, Kern Co., *Twisselmann.* $2n = 48$ (Nilsson, 1966).

p. 304.   Var. **víridis** A. Davids. Also in Greenhorn Range, *Twisselmann.*

14. **M. gypsophiloìdes** (F. & M.) Howell. $2n = 16$ (Nilsson, 1966). In Temblor Range, *Twisselmann.*

15. **M. sibírica** (L.) Howell. $n = 12$ (Raven, 1962; W. H. Lewis, 1963);
$2n = 18$ pairs (D. E. Anderson, 1963).

p. 305.   CALYPTRÍDIUM

2. **C. Párryi** var. **Hésseae** Thomas. In the Santa Lucia Mts., *Howitt &
Howell.*

p. 306.   6. **C. umbellàtum** var. **caudicíferum** (Gray) Jeps. at elevs. up to 14,200 ft.,
Mr. Whitney, *Raven.*

p. 307.   GLÌNUS

1. **G. lotoìdes** L. In San Luis Obispo Co., *Hardham*; Kern Co., *Twisselmann.*

CYPSELÈA

1. **C. humifùsa** Turp. Northeast of Graton, Sonoma Co., *Rubtzoff*; Clear
Lake, Lake Co., *M. S. Baker, Mason.*

TRIÁNTHEMA

1. **T. Portulacástrum** L. Occurs in Kern and Tulare cos., *Twisselmann.*

p. 308.   TETRAGÒNIA

1. Change *T. expansa* to **T. tetragonioìdes** (Pall.) O. Kuntze.

p. 309.   MESEMBRYÁNTHEMUM

1. **M. nodiflòrum** L. $n = 18$ (Reese, 1957).

4. **M. cordifòlium** L. f. In Monterey Co., *Howitt & Howell.*

p. 311.   OPÚNTIA

In Key, change last line by deleting "19. *O. occidentalis.*" Add:

E.   Joints ± elongate; petals 1.5 times as long as wide; stigma often longer than
     wide; fr. not with a deeply impressed umbilicus. . . . . 19. *O. littoralis*
EE. Joints nearly round; petals narrow, twice as long as wide; stigma often wider
     than long; fr. rounded, with deeply depressed umbilicus. . . . . . . 20. *O. oricola*

p. 313.   11. **O. Wrightiàna** (Baxter) Peeb. extends into L. Calif.
p. 315.   19. **O. occidentàlis** Engelm. & Bigel. Benson & Walkington (Ann. Mo. Bot.
Gard. 52: 262–273. 1965) discuss the *O. occidentalis* group and report that:

(1) *O. occidentalis* was based on a type from Cucamonga, San Bernardino
Co. which proves to be the Mission Cactus, **O. megacántha** Salm-Dyck and
not a native California plant.

(2) **O. littoràlis** (Engelm.) Ckll. is the specific name to be used and consists of several vars. which can be keyed out as follows:

A. Spines none or a few along the top of the joint; spines 6–12 (–20) mm. long; fls. magenta. From Glendora, Los Angeles Co. to Riverside Co., at low elevs. (mostly below 2000 ft.) .... var. *austrocalifórnica*
AA. Spines usually on most of the joint; spines 25–69 mm. long; fls. yellow or the center reddish.
  B. Joints green, not glaucous; spines 5–11 per areole. Near the coast from Santa Barbara Co. to L. Calif. .... var. *littoràlis*
  BB. Joints moderately glaucous; spines 1–4 (–6) per areole. Away from the coast.
    C. Spines brown or dark gray. Newhall, Los Angeles Co., to San Bernardino and Riverside cos. at mostly below 2000 ft. .... var. *Vàseyi*
    CC. Spines reddish to gray.
      D. The spines reddish with yellow-white tips; fls. yellow. Largely at 3000–7000 ft., San Gabriel, San Bernardino and San Jacinto mts. var. *Pièrcei*
      DD. The spines red and yellow to gray; fls. often with a reddish center. Mts. of e. Mojave Desert. .... var. *Martiniàna*

In the above, **O. littoràlis** (Engelm.) Ckll. var. **littoràlis** excludes **O. orícola** Philbrick.

O. l. var. **Vàseyi** (Coulter) Benson & Walkington includes *O. occidentalis* var. *V.* and var. *Covillei* of p. 316 of the FLORA.

O. l. var. **austrocalifórnica** Benson & Walkington. Low, the joints elongate-obovate, ca. 12.5–20 cm. long; petals pale purple.

O. l. var. **Pièrcei** (Fosberg) Benson & Walkington much as *O. o.* var. *P.* in the FLORA.

O. l. var. **Martiniàna** (L. Benson) L. Benson. At 2000–8000 ft., e. San Bernardino Co.; to Nev., Ariz.

p. 316.   20. **O. orícola** Philbrick. A coastal sp. separable from *O. littoralis* in having yellow, subhooked spines to 2 cm. long (instead of white with red-brown base and 1.5–3.5 cm. long); joints nearly round (not elongate); petals narrow, twice as long as wide (not 1.5 times); stigma often wider than long (not longer than wide); and fr. rounded, with deeply depressed umbilicus.—Ranging from Santa Barbara to n. L. Calif.

p. 320.   POLYGONÀCEAE
In description of family, insert after "stipules," the words "sometimes obsolete."

p. 322.   CHORIZÁNTHE
In Key change F. to "Calyx-lobes entire or nearly so."

p. 323.   Line 16 from top, change to:

FF. All the calyx-lobes not entire.
  G. Both outer and inner calyx-lobes deeply bilobed, the divisions sharply acute; fls. white, 5.5–6 mm. long. Sierra Madre, Santa Barbara Co.
      25d. *C. Blakleyi*
  GG. Not both outer and inner calyx-lobes deeply bilobed.
    H. Not all the calyx-lobes erose.
      I. The outer and inner calyx-lobes fimbriate. 24. *C. fimbriata*
      II. The outer calyx-lobes entire to bilobed.
        J. Outer calyx-lobes entire, the inner fimbriate.
          K. Outer calyx-lobes roundish, erect, purplish; inner oblong, erect; fls. 3.5–5 mm. long. Serpentine, Monterey Co. to Santa Barbara Co. 25. *C. Palmeri*
          KK. Outer calyx-lobes obovate, flaring, white; inner oblong, erect; fls. 4–4.5 mm. long. San Benito and Monterey cos. to Santa Barbara Co.
              25c. *C. obovata*
        JJ. The outer calyx-lobes bilobed or erose; inner shallowly bilobed.
          K. Outer calyx-lobes erose; inner shallowly bilobed; fls. 4–4.5 mm. long. E. Monterey Co., San Benito Co., w. Fresno Co., San Luis Obispo Co.
              25b. *C. ventricosa*
          KK. Outer calyx-lobes bilobed; inner fimbriate; fls. 5–6 mm. long. San Benito and Monterey cos. to Santa Barbara Co. .... 25a. *C. biloba*
    HH. All the calyx-lobes ± erose.
      I. Involucral teeth straight. .... 16. *C. valida*
      II. Involucral teeth uncinate. .... 28. *C. Parryi*
EE. Involucral teeth very unequal, the anterior one usually longer than involucral tube, the others relatively short.
  F. Elongate anterior involucral tooth straight.

G. The outer calyx-lobes obovate, shallowly bilobed, well exserted; the inner lobes half as long, fimbriate; fls. ca. 3.5 mm. long, whitish; stamens 9. San Luis Obispo and Monterey cos. . . . 26a. *C. rectispina*

GG. The outer calyx-lobes linear-oblong, obscurely erose, almost included; the inner minutely erose; fls. white, almost 3 mm. long. San Benito, w. Fresno, Monterey, San Luis Obispo and Kern cos. 26. *C. uniaristata*

FF. Elongate anterior involucral tooth uncinate; outer calyx-lobes ovate, minutely erose; inner erose; fls. 3.5 mm. long, pink. Inner Coast Ranges, Mendocino and Lake cos. to Ventura Co., Sierran foothills of Tulare and Kern cos. . . . . 27. *C. Clevelandii*

p. 324.   5. **C. polygonoìdes** T. & G. in Monterey Co., *Howitt & Howell.*

p. 328.   25a. **C. bilòba** Goodm. [*C. Palmeri* Wats. var. *biloba* Munz.]. Annual, to 3.5 dm. tall, appressed curly-pubescent and commonly with some longer spreading hairs toward the infl.; lvs. basal, elliptic and sessile to oblanceolate and petioled, 1–5 cm. long, strigose; bracts at lower branches similar to lvs., but awn-pointed; upper bracts to ca. 8 mm. long; invols. 5–7 mm. long, gray-pubescent and with coarser hairs on ribs, the tube 4–5 mm. long; fls. partly exserted, 5–6 mm. long, the lobes 2 mm. long, the outer obovate, obcordate to bilobed, inner oblong, obtuse, fimbriate in upper third.—San Benito and Monterey cos., to Santa Barbara Co.

25b. **C. ventricòsa** Goodman. [*C. Palmeri* var. *v.* Munz.] Diffuse, 1–3 dm. tall, spreading-pubescent; lvs. basal, oblanceolate, long- or short-petiolate, the blades to 4.5 cm. long, hirsute beneath, less so above; lower bracts like the lvs., the upper subulate; invols. ventricose, the tube ca. 3.5 mm. long, sparsely pubescent except on the ribs (with short ascending hairs), 5 teeth uncinate, the 6th elongate, ca. 2 mm. long, straight or uncinate; perianth partly exserted, 4–4.5 mm. long, the outer lobes broadly obcordate, subentire or erose, ca. 1.5 mm. long, the inner squarish, emarginate, ca. 1 mm. long, fimbriate in distal half.—E. Monterey Co., San Benito Co., w. Fresno Co., San Luis Obispo Co.

25c. **C. obovàta** Goodm. Erect, 1–3 dm. tall, subappressed or spreading pubescent; lvs. oblanceolate, long petioled, the blade 1–2 cm. long, densely soft-hirsute beneath, sparsely so above; lower bracts foliose, strigose, mucronate to awn-pointed, the upper subulate; invols. urceolate, 4.5–5 mm. long, grayish with ascending hairs, sometimes less pubescent, the tube 3–4 mm. long, the teeth divergent, 5 uncinate, the anterior 2 mm. long, straight or curved downward; calyx 4–4.5 mm. long, glabrous, the tube slightly longer than the outer lobes, these obovate, the inner truncate, finely fimbriate.—Santa Barbara Co. to San Benito and Monterey cos.

25d. **C. Blàkleyi** Hardham. Erect, 0.5–2 dm. tall, bright yellow-green, with long spreading hairs throughout; lvs. basal, long-petioled, the petiole and blade ca. 2 cm. long; invols. urceolate-cylindric, the tube 3.5–4 mm. long, glabrous except for long spreading hairs on the ribs of the older invols. and short upcurled hairs on the younger; 5 teeth short, uncinate, the anterior 1.5–2 mm. long, slightly recurved or nearly straight; calyx white, 5.5–6 mm. long, the inner lobes deeply bilobed, with remotely dentate margins, ca. 0.5 mm. long, the outer slightly longer, narrow, similarly bilobed.—Sierra Madre, Santa Barbara Co.

26a. **C. rectispìna** Goodm. Spreading to decumbent, the stems 1–2 dm. long, grayish strigose; lvs. oblanceolate to spatulate, 1.5–3 cm. long, obtuse, villoushirsute; bracts foliose, 0.5–1 cm. long, awn-tipped; invols. urceolate-cylindric, gray-pubescent, the tube 2–2.5 mm. long, 5 teeth, short, uncinate, widely spreading, the anterior 1 as long as or longer than the tube, straight, divergent; calyx partly exserted, ca. 3.5 mm. long, strigulose on outer surface, segms. very unequal, the outer 3 nearly as long as calyx-tooth, broadly obovate to suborbicular, truncate, subentire, the inner 3 half as long, oblong, erose to finely fimbriate, mostly obtuse.—San Luis Obispo and Santa Barbara cos.

p. 329.   30. **C. califórnica** (Benth.) Gray. Monterey Co., *Howitt & Howell.*

p. 331.   OXYTHÈCA

6. **O. caryophylloìdes** Parry. Pine Mt., Ventura Co., *Pollard, Blakley, Twisselmann.*

7. Eriógonum Michx. WILD BUCKWHEAT
This section represents pages 332 through 354 of the FLORA.

Annual or perennial herbs or shrubs with basal or cauline, alternate lvs. and often with alternate or more commonly whorled scalelike or foliaceous bracts, entire and estipitate. Fls. perfect or sometimes also imperfect, borne in invols. Invols. campanulate to turbinate or cylindric, 4–10-lobed or -toothed, awnless, few- to many-fld., sessile or peduncled. Pedicels ± exserted, intermixed with setaceous bractlets and jointed at summit with the base of the perianth or with a slender and stalklike, stipitate base. Perianth commonly called "calyx," 6-parted or -cleft, petaloid, with 2 series of 3 segms. each. Stamens 9, the fils. filiform, often pilose at the base, inserted at base of perianth. Ovary 1-celled, 3-angled or -winged; styles 3; stigmas capitate. Aks. mostly 3-angled, sometimes lenticular. A N. Am. genus of ca. 205 spp., mostly w.; some of importance as bee-plants, others with some horticultural possibility. (Greek, *erion*, wool, and *gonu*, knee or joint, the type of the genus, *E. tomentosum* Michx. being hairy at the nodes.)

(Stokes, Susan G., The genus Eriogonum, 1–132. 1936.)

James L. Reveal, a graduate student at Brigham Young University, Provo, Utah, has spent several years studying the genus *Eriogonum* and has kindly prepared a manuscript with a key to the California species as he now sees them (August, 1967). He has written up various changes in name and status and inserted many new taxa, as well as chromosome counts. Many of the species proposed since January 1, 1958 (the date at which the FLORA had to be closed to changes and new species) were included in the *Supplement* manuscript which I submitted to the University of California Press in June, 1966, however some of these have since received different status in Mr. Reveal's treatment.

I have decided, on looking over his many suggestions and corrections for this complex genus, to include the text from the FLORA for the species he has not changed in order to provide a continuous and usable treatment. Although it is therefore difficult to separate our contributions my work mostly consisted of filling in gaps from the FLORA and dividing up *Eriogonum latifolium* as here treated. I wish to make it clear that the new interpretations, corrections arising from the study of types, and many other important suggestions are by Mr. Reveal and he should receive the credit for the improvement over the FLORA. Since he has used the varietal rank instead of the subspecific rank employed by Miss Stokes in her revision, for the sake of uniformity I have followed him in regard to the species which he has not written up.

Philip A. Munz

Mr. Reveal is grateful to the United States National Herbarium and the Smithsonian Institution which sponsored his Predoctoral Internship in Washington, D.C. (from September 1966 to February 1967) where his part of the paper was basically prepared. His field work and herbaria visits were largely supported by an NSF grant to Dr. Arthur Cronquist for studies on the Intermountain Flora through a cooperative program between the New York Botanical Garden and Utah State University. His contributions were submitted to the Department of Botany, Brigham Young University, as partial fulfillment of the requirements for Doctoral Research credit given the Fall Semester of 1966–1967.

A. Calyx stipelike at the attenuated base (see also *E. saxatile* and *E. crocatum*); bracts leafy, indefinite in number (2–several). (Subgenus *Oligogonum* Nutt.)
    B. Invols. with lobes at least half as long as tube and usually reflexed or spreading.
        C. Calyx pubescent externally.
            D. Flowering stems or scapes without subtending bracts and with solitary terminal invols. Inyo Co. to Modoc Co., e. of the Sierra Nevada crest. .... 1. *E. caespitosum*
          DD. Flowering stems with whorled subtending bracts at the base of the umbel or near the middle of the stems.
            E. Invols. solitary, terminal, not immediately subtended by leafy bracts, the flowering stems with whorled bracts near the middle.
                F. Invol. lobes oblong, as long or longer than the tube; calyx densely pilose externally; lvs. mostly tomentose above; aks. densely hairy above the middle. E. slope of Sierra Nevada, Nevada Co. north, ne. Calif. below 8000 ft. . . . . 2. *E. Douglasii*
                FF. Invol. lobes broadly triangular, shorter than the tube; calyx sparsely pilose externally; lvs. subglabrous and green above; aks. glabrous or with few scattered hairs above the middle. Tulare Co. ... 3. *E. Twisselmannii*

EE. Invols. more than 1, umbellate, subtended by 2–several leafy bracts, stems without a whorl of bracts.
  F. Lvs. ± glabrate above; calyx, including the stipe 7–9 mm. long. Above 3000 ft. .... 4. *E. sphaerocephalum*
  FF. Lvs. densely white-tomentose above and below; calyx, including the stipe, 5–7 mm. long. Below 2000 ft. .... 5. *E. tripodum*
CC. Calyx glabrous externally.
  D. Invols. solitary, without subtending bracts immediately below invols., flowering stem with whorled leafy bracts near the middle: fls. yellow.
    E. Lvs. densely tomentose above and below, occasionally glabrate above, (5–) 10–15 mm. long. W. slopes of Sierra Nevada, Nevada Co. to Fresno Co., 3000–5000 ft. .... 6. *E. Prattenianum*
    EE. Lvs. glabrate and green above, ± oval, mostly less than 8 mm. long. Scott Mts., Siskiyou and Trinity cos., 7000–9000 ft. .... 7. *E. siskiyouense*
  DD. Invols. clustered and subtended by 2–several bracts.
    E. Flowering stems with a whorl of leafy bracts at about midlength; lvs. mostly linear-oblanceolate to oblanceolate. Modoc Co. .... 8. *E. heracleoides*
    EE. Flowering stems without a whorl of leafy bracts.
      F. Scapes erect or nearly so; invols. up to 10 mm. long.
        G. Lvs. less than 2 cm. long, not cordate at the base; invols. 3–5 mm. long. Throughout Calif. .... 9. *E. umbellatum*
        GG. Lvs. 2–10 (–20) cm. long, usually cordate at the base; invols. 6–10 mm. long. N. Coast Ranges. .... 10. *E. compositum*
      FF. Scapes usually flat on the ground; invols. 9–12 mm. long; lvs. 2–4 cm. long. N. Coast Ranges and n. Sierra Nevada. .... 11. *E. Lobbii*
BB. Invols. with lobes much shorter than tube, toothlike and suberect.
  C. Calyx pubescent externally.
    D. Infl. capitate, subtended by 5 membranaceous bracts; scapes 8–30 cm. long, erect; calyx yellowish.
      E. Lvs. subglabrous to short-pilose, 1–3 cm. long, calyx cream-colored, 5–6 mm. long. Inyo and Mono cos. .... 12. *E. latens*
      EE. Lvs. hirtellous to glabrescent, 0.5–1.5 cm. long; calyx bright yellow, 3 mm. long. Del Norte and Siskiyou cos. .... 13. *E. hirtellum*
    DD. Infl. subcapitate to umbellate, subtended by 2 membranaceous bracts; scapes 4–8 (–15) cm. long, suberect to nearly prostrate; calyx white to rose. Shasta and Siskiyou cos. .... 14. *E. pyrolifolium*
  CC. Calyx glabrous externally.
    D. Bracts in a whorl near middle of flowering stem which bears a single invol.
      E. Calyx yellow; lvs. densely white-tomentose on both surfaces.
        F. Lvs. elliptic to ovate, 5–15 mm. long; scapes 1–3 dm. long; calyx 5–7 mm. long in fruit. W. slope of Sierra Nevada, Nevada Co. to Fresno Co., 3000–5000 ft. .... 6. *E. Prattenianum*
        FF. Lvs. rounded, 1–3 cm. long; scapes 4–6 cm. long; calyx 3–5 mm. long in fruit. Siskiyou Co., 7500–9000 ft. ....15. *E. alpinum*
      EE. Calyx white or pink; lvs. oblanceolate to spatulate, silky pubescent below, less so above. Mendocino Co. .... 16. *E. Kelloggii*
    DD. Bracts subtending the umbel or head of several invols.
      E. Styles less than 1 mm. long; fils. pilose.
        F. Calyx white to pink with a reddish midrib; style ca. 1 mm. long. Mostly Tulare Co. .... 17. *E. polypodum*
        FF. Calyx yellow; styles 0.5 mm. long.
          G. Lvs. glabrate above, mostly rounded at the base; infl. mostly open. Tuolumne Co. n. to cent. Ore. .... 18. *E. marifolium*
          GG. Lvs. densely white-tomentose on both surfaces, mostly acute at the base; infl. mostly congested. Alpine Co. to Tulare Co. 19. *E. incanum*
      EE. Styles 2–4 mm. long; fils. densely woolly.
        F. Calyx ochroleucous; lvs. broadly ovate, rounded or subcordate at base. N. Sierra Nevada. .... 20. *E. ursinum*
        FF. Calyx yellow; lvs. obovate to spatulate, attenuated at the base. N. Coast Ranges. .... 21. *E. ternatum*
AA. Calyx not stipelike at the base; bracts not leafy, regularly 3 in number.
  B. Stems not jointed internally.
    C. Invols. campanulate to turbinate, not angled or ribbed, 4-or 5-toothed or -lobed, rarely obscurely nerved at the base; mostly peduncled. (Subgenus *Ganysma* [S. Wats.] Greene.)
      D. Lvs. basal and also on the lower nodes, tomentose or floccose except in *E. spergulinum*.
        E. Basal lvs. oblanceolate to oblong-obovate, not revolute for most part, tomentose or floccose.
          F. Invols. ± glandular-puberulent to pubescent externally.
            G. Calyx-segms. dissimilar, the outer segms. ovate, elliptic, or roundish, the inner segms. narrowly lanceolate or oblong, and longer.
              H. Outer segms. obovate to elliptic, not obviously inflated, or if so, only near the base, the inner segms. spatulate; stamens conspicuously exserted. .... 22. *E. angulosum*
              HH. Outer segms. elliptic to roundish or obovate, obviously inflated

at maturity, the inner segms. narrowly lanceolate; stamens included.

    I.   Outer segms. inflated at the base and middle, the sides of segms. incurved below, the inner segms. obtuse to acute; peduncles and invols. glandular-puberulent, with non-capitate hairs. .... 23. *E. maculatum*

    II. Outer segms. inflated above the middle, the apex curved inward, the inner segms. acute to acuminate; peduncles and invols. with capitate-glandular hairs. ... 24. *E. viridescens*

GG. Calyx-segms. similar or nearly so, the outer segms. oblong, not inflated.

    H.   Fls. not concealed by cottonlike tomentum inside the invols.; invols. 2 mm. long. .... 25. *E. gracillimum*

    HH. Fls. concealed by tufts of cottonlike tomentum inside the invols.; invols. 3 mm. long. .... 26. *E. gossypinum*

FF. Invols. glabrous or densely tomentose, not glandular.

    G.   Invols. glabrous.

        H.   Calyx hispid externally; lvs. floccose to glabrous, 2–8 cm. long; plants up to 7 dm. tall. .... 32. *E. Ordii*

        HH. Calyx glabrous externally; lvs. floccose below, less so above, 1.5–2.5 cm. long; plants up to 3 dm. tall. ...... 51. *E. argillosum*

    GG. Invols. tomentose.

        H.   Lvs. mostly basal or subbasal, rarely axillary; calyx smooth, not papillose; ak. beaks granular. W. Kern Co., ne. San Luis Obispo and se. Monterey cos. .... 50. *E. temblorense*

        HH. Lvs. mostly cauline and axillary; calyx papillose; ak. beaks papillose. San Benito Co., w. Fresno Co., and sw. Merced Co.
                              52. *E. vestitum*

EE. Basal lvs. linear, revolute, pilose; invols. 0.5–1 mm. long. 27. *E. spergulinum*

DD. Lvs. strictly basal, pilose or tomentose at least below.

E.   Invols. 4-lobed or -toothed.

    F.   Calyx pubescent with hooked hairs externally.

        G.   Invols. 2-fld.; aks. exserted; calyx ca. 1 mm. long. 28. *E. hirtiflorum*

        GG. Invols. 4–6-fld.; aks. not exserted; calyx ca. 1.5 mm. long.
                              29. *E. inerme*

    FF. Calyx puberulent or hispidulous externally, the hairs not hooked.

        G.   Calyx white, 1.5–2 mm. long, apex notched or apiculate; lvs. spatulate, ciliate or pilose. .... 30. *E. apiculatum*

        GG. Calyx pink or yellow, 0.5–1 mm. long, the segms. not apiculate.

            H.   Calyx pink, 0.5–0.7 mm. long; lvs. spatulate, hirsute; invols. 0.5–0.7 mm. long. Montane. .... 31. *E. Parishii*

            HH. Calyx yellow, 1–2 mm. long; invols. 0.7–2 mm. long. Deserts.

                I.   Lvs. short-hirsute, suborbicular, 1–2.5 cm. long; invols. 0.7–1 mm. long. .... 34. *E. trichopes*

                II. Lvs. floccose or glabrous, obovate to oblanceolate, 2–8 cm. long; invols. 1–2 mm. long. .... 32. *E. Ordii*

EE. Invols. 5-lobed or -toothed.

    F.   Calyx pubescent or puberulent externally.

        G.   Invols. glabrous externally.

            H.   Outer segms. not saccate-dilated.

                I.   Lf.-blades short-hirsute; invols. turbinate.

                    J.   Calyx pink or whitish with reddish midveins; lvs. hirsutulous and slightly glandular. .. 33. *E. glandulosum*

                    JJ. Calyx yellow.

                        K.   Plants strictly annual; branchlets numerous and whorled at each node; invols. usually 4-lobed, occasionally some 5-lobed. .... 34. *E. trichopes*

                        KK. Plants perennial but flowering the first year; branchlets few at each node, not in whorls.
                                35. *E. inflatum*

                II. Lf.-blades woolly; calyx 1 mm. long; invols. broadly campanulate. .... 40. *E. reniforme*

            HH. Outer calyx-segms. saccate-dilated at each side of the cordate base at maturity, sparsely puberulent at the base of the perianth tube, yellow maturing reddish or reddish with white lobes.
                                37. *E. Thomasii*

        GG. Invols. glandular-puberulent externally.

            H.   Calyx white to red, the outer segms. rounded and narrowed abruptly to a narrow clawlike base, slightly glandular externally at the base and with a white tuft of hairs within. 38. *E. Thurberi*

            HH. Calyx yellow, the outer segms. obovate, smooth, glandular on entire outer surface, glabrous within. .... 39. *E. pusillum*

    FF. Calyx glabrous externally.

        G.   Lvs. pilose-hispid, not woolly. Inyo and Mono cos. 36. *E. esmeraldense*

        GG. Lvs. tomentose below.

H. Stems glabrous or glandular, not woolly.
    I. Outer calyx-segms. panduriform, crisped, not cordate; pe-
        duncles slender, 5–25 mm. long. . . . . 41. *E. cernuum*
    II. Outer calyx-segms. not panduriform or crisped.
    J. Outer calyx-segms. cordate at the bases; peduncles
        stoutish.
        K. Peduncles deflexed.
            L. Stems glabrous.
                M. Invols. narrowly-turbinate to turbinate,
                    peduncles 0–15 mm. long; calyx white,
                    oblong.
                    N. Invols. 1.5–3 mm. long; plants
                        variously branched; calyx 1–2.5
                        mm. long, not gibbous at matur-
                        ity. . . . . 43. *E. deflexum*
                    NN. Invols. 1–1.5 mm. long; plants
                        branching in a series of flat-
                        topped layers, pagoda-like; calyx
                        1.5 mm. long, gibbous at the base
                        at maturity. . . . . 44. *E. Rixfordii*
                MM. Invols. hemispheric, sessile; calyx yel-
                    low to reddish-yellow, suborbicular.
                    45. *E. Hookeri*
            LL. Stems glandular, stems short and stout,
                crowns flat-topped. . . . 46. *E. brachypodum*
        KK. Peduncles erect; plants 3–10 dm. high; branches
            erect and whiplike with peduncles 3–5 mm. long;
            calyx 1.5–2 mm. long. . . . . 47. *E. insigne*
    JJ. Outer calyx-segms. obtuse at the base.
        K. Plants glandular; invols. deflexed, sessile or sub-
            sessile above, peduncled to 10 mm. below; calyx
            white becoming reddish. . . . . . . 48. *E. eremicola*
        KK. Plants glabrous.
            L. Peduncles short, straight and erect, less than
                1 mm. long; calyx white to reddish. Inyo Co.
                42. *E. Hoffmannii*
            LL. Peduncles long, curving upwards, 1–3 (–5)
                cm. long; calyx white to yellowish. Nevada
                Co. to Lassen Co. . . . . 49. *E. collinum*
HH. Stems woolly.
    I. Lvs. basal or subbasal, oblong to elliptic; styles 0.7–1 mm.
        long; invols. 2–2.5 mm. long; stamens 2–2.5 mm. long.
        W. Kern Co., se. Monterey Co. and ne. San Luis Obispo
        Co. . . . . 53. *E. temblorense*
    II. Lvs. strictly basal, roundish; styles 0.1–0.3 mm. long; in-
        vols. 2 mm. long; stamens 1–1.5 mm. long. E. Monterey
        Co. and sw. Fresno Co. . . . . 55. *E. Eastwoodianum*
CC. Invols. cylindric or cylindric-turbinate to turbinate or prismatic, often 5–6 nerved,
    angled, or ribbed, mostly sessile, solitary or congested into heads, the teeth usually short.
D. Plants annual; lvs mostly in basal rosettes. (Subgenus *Oregonium* [S. Wats.] Greene.)
    E. Flowering branches with short branchlets, usually of a single internode; invols.
        axillary and terminal.
        F. Calyx 1–1.5 mm. long, yellow to cream-white. Deserts.
            G. Calyx yellow, 1 mm. long, the segms. connate only at the base, calyx
                tube acutish; branches capillary, spreading and open infl. Mojave
                Desert, Inyo Co. to San Bernardino Co. . . . . 50. *E. mohavense*
            GG. Calyx whitish to cream-colored, 1–1.5 mm. long, the segms. connate
                about half the length of the calyx, calyx tube green or reddish,
                campanulate; branches stouter, erect and narrow infl. Mono. Co.
                51. *E. ampullaceum*
    FF. Calyx 1.5–2.5 mm. long, white to rose or red. Coast Ranges.
        G. Stems tomentose.
            H. Invols. glabrous, 2.5 mm. long; calyx 1.5–2.5 mm. long. Santa
                Clara Co. to San Benito and Monterey cos. . . 52. *E. argillosum*
            HH. Invols. tomentose.
                I. Invols. 1.5–2 mm. long.
                    J. Lvs. basal and cauline, oblong to elliptic; styles 0.7–1
                      mm. long; stamens 1.5–2.5 mm. long.
                      K. Lvs. mostly basal or subbasal, rarely axillary;
                        calyx smooth; ak. beaks granular. W. Kern Co.,
                        ne. San Luis Obispo and se. Monterey cos.
                        53. *E. temblorense*
                    KK. Lvs. mostly cauline and axillary; calyx and ak.
                      beaks papillose. San Benito Co., w. Fresno and
                      sw. Merced cos. . . . . 54. *E. vestitum*

JJ. Lvs. strictly basal, roundish; styles 0.1–0.3 mm. long;
stamens 1–1.5 mm. long. E. Monterey Co. and sw.
Fresno Co. . . . . 55. *E. Eastwoodianum*
  II. Invols. 3–4 mm. long; calyx 2 mm. long. Contra Costa Co.
56. *E. truncatum*
GG. Stems glabrous.
  H. Lvs. round to reniform.
    I. Invols. 2.5 mm. long, 5-lobed; calyx 2–2.5 mm. long. Ala-
meda Co. to Kern Co. . . . . 57. *E. Covilleanum*
    II. Invols. 3–4 mm. long, 8-lobed with short teeth; calyx 1.5
mm. long. The Pinnacles, Monterey and San Benito cos.
58. *E. Nortonii*
  HH. Lvs. oblong to oblong-ovate.
    I. Invols. 3–4 mm. long, distinctly 5-lobed; calyx 1.5–2.5 mm.
long. Marin and Contra Costa cos. . . . . . . 59. *E. caninum*
    II. Invols. 2.5–3 mm. long, obscurely 5-lobed; calyx 1.5 mm.
long. Santa Clara Co. to San Benito and Monterey cos.
52. *E. argillosum*
EE. Flowering branches elongate, virgate, and bearing invols. at the nodes, the
lateral ones appressed.
  F. Calyx glabrous or minutely puberulent externally.
    G. Invols. 2–5 mm. long.
      H. Lvs. oblong-obovate to oblanceolate; stems tomentose.
        I. Invols. 4–5 mm. long, cylindric, with minute teeth; outer
calyx segs. narrowly obovate; aks. 2 mm. long.
60. *E. roseum*
        II. Invols. 2–3 mm. long, turbinate, with prominent teeth;
outer calyx-segs. broadly obovate; aks. ca. 1 mm. long.
61. *E. gracile*
      HH. Lvs. rounded or nearly so; stems usually glabrous or only
sparsely floccose.
        I. Stems simple below, glabrous except at the base; outer
calyx-segs. more than twice as long as wide. Mts. of s.
Calif. . . . . 62. *E. Davidsonii*
        II. Stems mostly branched from the base, glabrous or floccose;
outer calyx-segs. less than twice as long as wide. Cent.
and n. Calif. . . . . 63. *E. vimineum*
    GG. Invols. 1–1.5 mm. long.
      H. Outer calyx-segs. fan-shaped, their sides incurved below the
broad truncate apices, yellowish to reddish; branches incurved at the summit in age; invols. few fld. San Bernardino
Co. to Mono Co. . . . . 64. *E. nidularium*
      HH. Outer calyx-segs. not as above.
        I. Outer calyx-segs. not hastate, glabrous or glandular, 1–2
mm. long, white or yellow; lvs. strictly basal.
          J. Calyx-segs. 1.5–2 mm. long.
            K. Stems densely tomentose; fls. 3–10 per invol.;
plants densely branched and spreading. San Bernardino Co. to Inyo Co. . . . 65. *E. Palmerianum*
            KK. Stems glabrous to sparsely floccose; fls. more than
10 per invol.; plants usually sparsely branched
and erect. San Bernardino Co. n. along the e.
side of the Sierra Nevada. . . . . 66. *E. Baileyi*
          JJ. Calyx-segs. 1–1.5 mm. long.
            K. Calyx yellow. Deserts, San Bernardino Co. to
Mono Co. . . . . 67. *E. brachyanthum*
            KK. Calyx white. S. Coast Ranges, Santa Clara Co. to
San Luis Obispo Co. . . . . 68. *E. elegans*
        II. Calyx-segs. hastate at the base when mature, 0.8–1.2
mm. long, white to pink; lvs. basal or also cauline; stems
tomentose. San Bernardino Mts. south. . . . 69. *E. foliosum*
  FF. Calyx densely hairy externally. Inner N. Coast Ranges.
70. *E. dasyanthemum*
DD. Plants perennial; lvs. often cauline as well as basal. (Subgenus *Eucycla* [Nutt.]
Kuntze.)
  E. Invols. solitary at the nodes, the lateral ones appressed to the branches.
    F. Calyx stipitate with long, winged attenuated bases, 5–7 mm. long.
      G. Infl. 1–1.5 dm. across, open and lax; calyx narrowed to a 3-angled
base, pinkish to white or yellowish; aks. ca. 2 mm. long. Mts. of s.
Calif. . . . . 71. *E. saxatile*
      GG. Infl. 0.3–0.8 dm. across, dense; calyx narrowed to a tubular base,
sulphur yellow; aks. ca. 3 mm. long. N. base of Santa Monica Mts.
72. *E. crocatum*
    FF. Calyx astipitate, 2–5 mm. long.
      G. Invols. 2–6 mm. long.

H. Infl. with invols. in cymes or panicles.
    I. Lvs. more than 2 cm. long. . . . . 94. *E. nudum*
    II. Lvs. less than 2 cm. long.
        J. Calyx glabrous.
            K. Lvs. rotund-ovate, 3–5 (–10) mm. long and wide; plants herbaceous, 8–20 cm. high, glabrous. Amador Co. . . . . 73. *E. apricum*
            KK. Lvs. lanceolate, oblong, or elliptic, 8–20 mm. long; plants subshrubs or shrubs.
                L. Infl. a compact terminal cyme; invols. tomentose or glabrous; outer calyx-segms. subcordate at the base. . . . 74. *E. microthecum*
                LL. Infl. a divaricately branched panicle; invols. glabrous.
                    M. Outer calyx-segms. round, subcordate at the base; branches green, dichotomous, ascending. . . 75. *E. Heermannii*
                    MM. Outer calyx-segms. obovate, narrowed at the base; branches grayish, mostly horizontal, tiered. . . 76. *E. Plumatella*
        JJ. Calyx silky-villous, yellowish; plants shrubby, 6–15 dm. high. Imperial Co. . . . . 77. *E. deserticola*
HH. Infl. with invols. placed racemosely along the branches; invols. tomentose.
    I. Plants shrubby, up to 15 dm. high; lvs. elliptic to oblong, 2–3 cm. long; invols. racemosely arranged on the ends of the fragile branches. . . . . 78. *E. Kearneyi*
    II. Plants low subshrubs less than 3 dm. high.
        J. Plants suffrutescent and much branched at the base or densely cespitose; lvs. many, lance-elliptic to oblanceolate, ± revolute.
            K. Invols. 5–6 mm. long; calyx 4–5 mm. long, ochroleucous with red midribs. Santa Lucia Mts.
                          79. *E. Butterworthianum*
            KK. Invols. 2–3 mm. long; calyx 2–4 mm. long, white to pink. Sierra Nevada and mts. of s. Calif.
                          80. *E. Wrightii*
        JJ. Plants not suffrutescent at the base or densely cespitose; basal lvs. few, rounded to broadly ovate.
            K. Basal lvs. roundish to broadly ovate, 1.5–4 cm. long, on petioles 1–5 cm. long; plants from a highly branched, woody, spreading caudex, suberect; invols. and calyx 3–5 mm. long.
                          81. *E. panamintense*
            KK. Basal lvs. oblong, 3–5 cm. long, on petioles 3–5 cm. long; plants arising from a single, woody, little branched caudex, erect; invols. 2–3.5 mm. long; calyx 2.5–3 mm. long. . . 82. *E. racemosum*
GG. Invols. 6–7 mm. long; loosely branched whitish tomentulose herbs 8–18 dm. high. S. Coast Ranges. . . . . 83. *E. elongatum*
EE. Invols. mostly clustered or in heads.
  F. Calyx-segms. dissimilar, the outer segms. often twice as wide as the inner segms., lobes dividing the calyx to the swollen basal joint.
    G. Infl. capitate.
        H. Outer calyx-segms. plane, not inflated; lvs. 6–20 (–60) mm. long. Common in s. and e. Calif. . . . . 84. *E. ovalifolium*
        HH. Outer calyx-segms. rounded and inflated; lvs. 2–4 mm. long. Rare, Panamint Mts., Inyo Co. . . . . 85. *E. Gilmanii*
    GG. Infl. cymose-umbellate with divaricate rays usually more than 2 cm. long. N. Calif. . . . . 86. *E. strictum*
  FF. Calyx-segms. similar or nearly so.
    G. Plants cespitose, matted, herbaceous, the caudex much branched and woody; flowering stems scapelike.
        H. Calyx villous externally and internally; ovary sparsely pilose; lvs. lanate-tomentose. Inyo Co. . . . . 87. *E. Shockleyi*
        HH. Calyx and ovary not as above.
            I. Invol. a distinct rigid tube, 3–4 mm. long.
                J. Infl. compactly cymose-umbellate, the rays up to 5 mm. long; calyx whitish becoming reddish, finely glandular-hairy. Kern and Tulare cos. . . . . . . 88. *E. Breedlovei*
                JJ. Infl. tightly capitate.
                      K. Calyx yellow; lf.-blades 5–35 mm. long.
                          L. Flowering stems 1–2.5 dm. tall, floccose; lf.-blades 2–3.5 cm. long. Below 6000 ft., Nevada Co. north. . . . . 89. *E. ochrocephalum*

LL. Flowering stems less than 1 dm. tall, glabrous or glandular; lf.-blades 4–15 mm. long.
M.   Stems and invols. glandular. Above 9000 ft., Inyo and Fresno cos. north to Placer Co. ... 90. *E. anemophilum*
MM. Stems and invols. glabrous. Below 6000 ft., Modoc Co. north.
91. *E. chrysops*
KK. Calyx white; lf.-blades mostly less than 5 mm. long, densely white-tomentose on both surfaces; stems glabrous to floccose. Mono Co. south.
92. *E. Kennedyi*
II. Invols. membranaceous and indistinctly forming a tube, 2–3 mm. long; calyx rose to red. White Mts... 93. *E. gracilipes*
GG. Plants shrubby, or if herbaceous, then not cespitose.
H.   Plants essentially herbaceous, only the base woody.
I.   Lvs. spreading, oblong-ovate to ovate, obtuse, mostly 2–6 cm. long.
J.   Invols. 2–5 mm. long. Mainland.
K.   Invols. and flowering stems tomentose; heads 1–few, mostly 1.5–3 cm. across. Immediate seacoast.
94. *E. latifolium*
KK. Invols. and flowering stems glabrous, or if tomentose then plants with heads many and plants from interior of n. Calif. .... 95. *E. nudum*
JJ. Invols. 5–6 mm. long. Insular. ...... 96. *E. grande*
II.   Lvs. erect, ± lanceolate, acute.
J.   Flowering stems glabrous or villous, 4–8 dm. long; lf.-blades 4–15 cm. long. ....97. *E. elatum*
JJ. Flowering stems tomentose, 2–5 dm. long; lf.-blades 2–5 cm. long. .... 98. *E. pendulum*
HH. Plants definitely shrubby.
I.   Lvs. narrowly linear or nearly so, the blades less than 2 cm. long, strongly fascicled; shrubs with terminal cymose or subumbellate infl. .... 99. *E. fasciculatum*
II.   Lvs. linear-oblong to orbicular, or if linear, more than 2 cm. long.
J.   Heads in dense compound cymes. Insular.
K.   Lvs. linear or narrowly oblong, ± revolute, 2–3 cm. long. .... 100. *E. arborescens*
KK. Lvs. oblong-ovate, plane, 3–10 cm. long.
101. *E. giganteum*
JJ. Heads terminal on 2-forked peduncles or scattered along the stems. Mostly mainland.
K.   Calyx glabrous externally; lf.-blades 5–15 mm. long. .... 102. *E. parvifolium*
KK. Calyx white-villous; lf.-blades 15–30 mm. long.
103. *E. cinereum*
BB. Stems internally jointed. Death Valley. (Subgenus *Clastomyelon* Cov. & Mort.)
104. *E. intrafractum*

Subgenus **Oligogònum** Nutt.

1. **E. caespitòsum** Nutt. [*E. sericoleucum* Greene ex Tidestr. *E. sphaerocephalum* var. *s.* S. Stokes.] Low compact matted perennial from much-branched woody caudices; lvs. elliptic to oblong-spatulate, densely white-tomentose, 5–15 mm. long, short-petioled, 1–3 mm. wide, crowded on the tips of the short branches, ± revolute; flowering stems scape-like, bractless, slender, 3–8 cm. high, somewhat loosely tomentose; invols. solitary, terminal, the tube turbinate, ca. 3 mm. long, with somewhat longer linear lobes that become reflexed; calyx yellow, 2.5–4 mm. long in anthesis, later reddish and 4–6 (–10) mm. long in fruit, pubescent especially toward the stipelike base, the segms. similar, oblance-oblong; fils. pilose basally; aks. lanceolate in outline, somewhat 3-angled, ca. 3 mm. long, often pubescent at the apex.—Dry gravelly slopes and flats, 5000–8600 ft.; Sagebrush Scrub, N. Juniper Wd., Yellow Pine F.; White Mts., Inyo Co. to Modoc Co.; to Ida., Mont., Colo. May–July.

2. **E. Douglásii** Benth. [*E. caespitosum* var. *D.* Jones. *E. c.* ssp. *D.* S. Stokes.] Rather loosely matted perennials from much-branched woody caudices, the plants to 3–4 dm. across; lvs. mostly linear to linear-spatulate, tomentose on both surfaces, 5–20 mm. long, the petioles often making up ⅓ of this; flowering stems loosely tomentose, 4–12 cm. long,

with a whorl of oblanceolate leafy bracts near the middle and a single terminal invol.; involucral tube turbinate, 3 mm. long, with reflexed oblong lobes ca. as long; calyx yellow, later often reddish, 5–8 mm. long, villous-pubescent on midribs and base, segms. narrowly obovate; fils. pilose basally; aks. lanceolate in outline, 3-angled, pubescent on upper half, ca. 3 mm. long.—Infrequent, dry rocky places, 4500–8000 ft.; Sagebrush Scrub to Yellow Pine F.; e. slope of Sierra Nevada from Nevada Co. to Modoc Co.; s. to Siskiyou Co.; to Wash., Ida., Nev. May–July.

Considerable work is necessary on this species. The type specimen is distinctive and it appears that much of what has passed in California and adjacent southern Oregon as *Eriogonum Douglasii* is actually a capitate form of *E. sphaerocephalum.* The distinguishing feature which separates the two is that *E. Douglasii* has densely tomentose lvs. on both surfaces while the *E. sphaerocephalum* form has lvs. that are subglabrous above and generally larger. In addition the involucre characteristics used in the key may be used to separate the two species.

3. **E. Twisselmánnii** (J. T. Howell) Reveal, stat. & comb. nov. [*E. Douglasii* var. *T. J. T. Howell,* Leafl. West. Bot. 10: 13. 1963.] Loose matted perennials from a much-branched spreading woody caudex, the plants 1–2 dm. high; lvs. oblanceolate or elliptic, tomentose below, subglabrous and green above, 6–10 mm. long, the petioles 2–4 mm. long; flowering stems loosely tomentose, 5–12 cm. long, with a whorl of oblanceolate leafy bracts near the middle and a single terminal invol.; invols. campanulate-cupulate, ca. 5 mm. long, the base of the tube subtruncate to broadly turbinate, with 6–9 triangular lobes, reflexed, about as long as the tube; calyx ochroleuceous, brownish, or yellowish, 5–6 mm. long, with sparse long hairs and numerous minute glandular hairs externally, and numerous minute glandular hairs or long non-glandular hairs internally, segms. subequal, the outer segms. obtuse or emarginate, 5 mm. long and 3.5 mm. wide, the inner segms. broadly oblanceolate, 6 mm. long and 3 mm. wide, the calyx tube about 1.5 mm. long, stipe 1 mm. long; aks. 5.5 mm. long, lanceolate-ovoid in outline, smooth, glabrous or with few scattered hairs.—Dry rocky outcrops, 7900–8200 ft.; Yellow Pine F., near The Needles, s. Tulare Co. July–Sept.

Eriogonum Twisselmannii is closely related to *E. Douglasii* where J. T. Howell placed it, but the latter is found nearly 300 miles to the north and differs in several morphological aspects, growth habit, pubescence, as well as the distinct geographical separation.

4. **E. sphaerocéphalum** Dougl. ex Benth. [*E. s.* var. *brevifolium* S. Stokes ex Jones.] Caudices much branched, woody, with decumbent leafy branches 5–12 cm. long; lvs. mostly oblanceolate, in whorls at the upper nodes, ± glabrate above, grayish-lanate below, 1–3 cm. long including the slender petioles; flowering stems ascending to erect, 5–15 cm. long, with a whorl of leafy oblanceolate bracts at the middle, capitate, simple, or umbellate above, each peduncle bearing 1 invol. with broadly turbinate tubes 3–4 mm. long, the lobes ca. as long; calyx bright sulphur-yellow, villous-tomentose, 7–8 mm. long, the stipitate base slender and ca. 2 mm. long, the segms. oblong-ovate; aks. lanceolate-ovoid in outline, 3-angled and pubescent above, ca. 3 mm. long.—Dry rocky places, 3000–7000 ft.; Sagebrush Scrub, N. Juniper Wd., Yellow Pine F.; Lassen Co.; to Wash., Ida., Nev. May–July.

Var. **halimioìdes** (Gand.) S. Stokes. [*E. h.* Gand.] Calyx whitish to pale yellow or pinkish; *n* = 20 (Reveal, 1965).—Dry rocky places, 3000–7500 ft.; Sagebrush Scrub, N. Juniper Wd.; Siskiyou, Lassen, and Modoc cos.; E. Ore., w. Nev. to Ida.

The common form of *Eriogonum sphaerocephalum* in California is the var. *halimioides,* and in many cases, this form has been recognized as *E. Douglasii* rather than *E. sphaerocephalum.* As noted under *E. Douglasii,* the two forms may be separated by the pubescence of the lvs., and when the type of *E. Douglasii* is considered, it is possible that to a great degree most of the material called *E. Douglasii* in both California and Oregon is actually a capitate form of *E. sphaerocephalum* var. *halimioides.*

5. **E. tripòdum** Greene. Caudices woody, loosely branched; lvs. in whorls at the tips of branches, narrowly oblanceolate, 1.5–2.5 cm. long, white-tomentose on both surfaces, revolute; flowering stems slender, 2–3 dm. high, bearing a whorl of foliaceous bracts near the middle at the base of a 3-rayed umbel, the rays naked or bracted, glabrous; invols. solitary and tomentose, the spreading or reflexed lobes shorter than the tube; calyx yellow, 4–5 mm. long, villous-tomentose, the stipelike base ca. 2 mm. long; fils. pilose basally; aks. narrow-ovoid, strongly angled, pubescent at the apex, ca. 2 mm. long.—Gravelly

slopes, often on serpentine, below 2000 ft.; Foothill Wd.; inner Coast Ranges and Sierran foothills, Tehama and Lake cos. and Tuolumne and Mariposa cos. June–July.

6. **E. Pratteniànum** Durand. [*E. umbellatum* ssp. *serratum* S. Stokes, as to type, not as to concept.] Low tufted perennials from a branched woody caudex, 10–15 cm. across; lvs. elliptical to ovate, lf.-blades acutish, 5–15 mm. long, 2–7 mm. wide, densely white-felty tomentose on both surfaces, occasionally becoming subglabrous above at maturity, short petioled, 1–5 mm. long, tomentose, densely crowded at the tips of the branches with 5–15 lvs.; scapes slender, erect, (5–) 10–30 cm. high, with a whorl of leafy bracts near the middle, narrowly elliptic, 7–10 mm. long, 2–4 mm. wide, similar to the lvs.; invols. solitary, without bracts at the base, campanulate, the tubes 3–4 mm. long, arach-noid-tomentose externally, glabrous internally, 8–10-lobed, the lobes 1.5–2.5 mm. long, erect or reflexed at maturity, the bractlets linear, 2–3 mm. long, whitish with several long marginal cells, the pedicels glabrous, (3–) 5–7 mm. long; calyx yellow, glabrous, 3–4 mm. long including the stipe in anthesis, the stipe 1–1.5 mm. long, the calyx-segms. similar or nearly so, obovate to spatulate, 2.5–3 mm. long, 1–1.5 mm. wide; stamens ex-serted, fils. 3–4 mm. long, sparsely pilose basally; ovary glabrous, styles (0.5–) 1–1.5 mm. long; calyx 6–7 mm. long in fruit; aks. lance-ovate, 4–5 mm. long, light yellowish-brown to rustic, smooth and glabrous, gradually tapering to the apex, mostly indistinctly 3-angled, embryo straight.—Dry rocky ridges and outcrops, 3000–5000 ft.; Yellow Pine F.; w. slope of the Sierra Nevada from Nevada Co. south to Fresno Co. May–July.

Eriogonum Prattenianum has been totally neglected in all monographs and revisions of the genus, as well as all floristic treatments in California, since the species was published in the *Journ. Acad. Nat. Sci. Phila.* ser. II, 3: 100. 1855. The holotype at the Academy of Natural Sciences in Philadel-phia consists only of a single stem broken off the plant slightly below the whorl of foliaceous bracts near the middle, yet the species is so distinct that even from this fragmentary material it is possible to match it with the present day collections. The original collection was made by Henry Pratten in 1851 from near Nevada City, Nevada Co., California. Although it has been recollected and named *E. umbellatum* ssp. *serratum*, the above description is the first prepared for the species as defined by the type.

Eriogonum Prattenianum has been known for several years to California botanists as the Sierra Nevada form of *E. siskiyouense*. The Siskiyou Buckwheat, however, is known only from its type locality on Mt. Eddy in the Scott Mountains where it occurs on rocky ridges from 7000 to 9000 feet elevation. The Sierran Buckwheat grows on rocky open places from 3000 to 5000 feet in the Yellow Pine Forest belt. The two species also differ in their flowering times. Actually, *E. Prattenianum* seems to be more closely related to *E. tripodum* which occurs in the same general area but always at a lower elevation.

Stokes based her name, *Eriogonum umbellatum* ssp. *serratum*, on *A. A. Heller 13208* from near Grass Valley, Nevada Co., but her resulting concept of the name was applied to specimens of *E. umbellatum* var. *polyanthum*. The specimens of *E. Prattenianum*, from Tehipite Valley, Fresno Co., differ from the others in that the lvs. are subglabrate above and may represent a distinct variety, but the lack of ade-quate material dictates that it remain unnamed at this time.

7. **E. siskiyouénse** Small. [*E. ursinum* var. *s.* S. Stokes.] Low matted or tufted peren-nials from a woody base, with short compact branches 3–7 cm. long; lvs. oval to spatu-late, crowded at ends of branches, 5–8 mm. long, acutish, short-petioled, glabrate above, tomentose below; scapes slender, erect, 3–8 cm. high, with a whorl of leafy bracts near the middle; invol. solitary, without bracts at its base, campanulate, somewhat arachnoid-tomentose, the tube 3.5–4 mm. long, the reflexed lobes ca. as long; calyx yellow, gla-brous, 5 mm. long, short-stipitate, the outer segms. oblong, rounded at the apex, the inner segms. somewhat narrower; fils. pilose basally; aks. narrow-ovoid, glabrous, 3-angled.—Rocky ridges, 7000–9000 ft., in Subalpine F.; Mt. Eddy, Siskiyou and Trinity cos. Aug.–Sept.

8. **E. heracleoìdes** Nutt. var. **angustifòlium** (Nutt.) T. & G. [*E. h.* of most authors. *E. a.* Nutt.] Loosely tufted plants from branched woody caudices; lvs. linear, 2–5 cm. long, 2–6 mm. wide, white-tomentose, especially beneath, short-petioled; flowering stems 2–4 dm. high, tomentose, usually with a whorl of leafy bracts near the middle of the stems and another at the base of the umbel; umbels simple or compound, the rays 2–5 cm. long; invols. solitary, turbinate, woolly-tomentose, the tubes 2.5–3 mm. long, the lobes 3–4 mm. long, spreading or reflexed; calyx glabrous, 4.5–6 mm. long including the stipitate base which is tubular and 1.5–2 mm. long, the segms. oblong-ovate; fils. pilose basally; aks. light brown, narrow, somewhat 3-angled, ca. equally pointed at both ends, pubescent at the apex, ca. 2 mm. long.—Occasional in dry places, 6000–7500 ft.; Sage-

brush Scrub, N. Juniper Wd., Yellow Pine F.; Warner Mts., Modoc Co.; to B.C., Mont., Utah. June–Aug. The var. *heracleoides* occurs chiefly in se. Wash., the Wallowa Mts., Ore. and w. Ida.

9. **E. umbellàtum** Torr. Caudex open or depressed, the plants cespitose to subshrubby; lvs. spatulate to suborbicular, mostly less than 2 cm. long and not more than 3–4 times as long as broad, tomentose to glabrate, the petioles short to long; flowering stems tomentose to glabrous, erect; infl. usually umbellately or cymosely divided, or in reduced forms, often simple or capitate; invols. usually deeply lobed, the lobes erect; calyx cream to yellow, maturing to a rose or red in most, the midribs often large and obvious, up to 10 mm. long; aks. usually sparsely pubescent at the apex, up to 4 mm. long.—In numerous situations throughout much of California.

In the *Eriogonum umbellatum* complex there are about 20 distinct infraspecific populations now currently recognized, and certainly more exist. The treatment given here is an attempt to summarize the species as best as possible at the present time, but no doubt several errors are made or continued here. While not all of the types have been seen, a majority have been and it is hoped from these studies that the nomenclature proposed here is more stable than in the past. Likewise it is hoped that the definition of the various varieties is clearer and more exact than previously presented in any treatment to this date. However, it must be quickly mentioned, that we are perpetuating the past handling of var. *stellatum* which is here defined to include at least two and possibly three distinct types. The holotype of var. *stellatum*, however, has not been seen, and it is not known at this time which part of this overall complex, found throughout much of the western United States, is represented by the type and which which remain to be described or recognized. In California, the following varieties may be tentatively recognized.

KEY TO VARIETIES

A. Primary rays of umbels simple, not branched or bracteate in the middle.
  B. Umbels subcapitate or rays few and scarcely more than 1 cm. long.
    C. Calyx bright yellow, 4–7 mm. long.
      D. Lvs. slightly tomentose below, not dense or matted, subglabrous to glabrous above; scapes slender, 1–3 dm. high. Common Sierra Nevada form mostly below 10,000 ft.
          (a) var. *umbellatum*
      DD. Lvs. densely and thickly matted white-tomentose below, subglabrous to glabrous above; scapes stout, 2–4 dm. high. Common form in n. Calif., Siskiyou and Trinity cos. e. to Modoc Co. .... (g) var. *polyanthum*
    CC. Calyx mostly whitish to red, 3–8 mm. long, occasionally pale yellow, or if yellow, then plants mainly above 9000 ft.; scapes 0.4–1.2 dm. high. Mostly montane.
      D. Lvs. green and glabrate above; calyx mostly whitish to yellow or reddish to purplish.
        E. Calyx yellow or pale yellow, 2–4 mm. long. Sierra Nevada above 10,000 ft. to Mt. Shasta and Warner Range down to 9000 ft. .... (b) var. *Covillei*
        EE. Calyx reddish to purplish or cream-colored, 3–8 mm. long.
          F. Calyx cream-colored to pale yellow with a tannish midrib. E. slope of the Sierra Nevada to San Bernardino Mts.; Nev. .... (c) var. *dicrocephalum*
          FF. Calyx reddish-brown to pink with a large reddish or purplish midrib. Inyo, Panamint, and Grapevine mts.; s. Nev. .... (d) var. *versicolor*
      DD. Lvs. densely white-woolly on both surfaces; calyx deep red, 4–5 mm. long. San Gabriel Mts. .... (e) var. *minus*
  B. Umbels open, the rays mostly 2.5 or more cm. long.
    C. Calyx whitish, cream-colored, or pale yellow; lvs. tomentose (at least sparsely so) on both surfaces. E. slope of the Sierra Nevada to San Bernardino Mts., Nev.
          (c) var. *dicrocephalum*
    CC. Calyx bright yellow, often becoming tinged with red.
      D. Lvs. tomentose, at least below.
        E. Lvs. slightly tomentose below, not dense or matted, subglabrous to glabrous above; scapes slender, 1–3 dm. high. Common form in the Sierra Nevada mostly below 10,000 ft. .... (a) var. *umbellatum*
        EE. Lvs. densely and thickly matted white-tomentose below, subglabrous to glabrous above; scapes stout, 2–4 dm. high. Common form in n. Calif., Siskiyou and Trinity cos. e. to Modoc Co. .... (g) var. *polyanthum*
      DD. Lvs. totally glabrous on both surfaces; calyx 7–10 mm. long. Placer Co. to Modoc Co. .... (f) var. *Torreyanum*
AA. Primary rays of umbels usually branched, or if not, then with bracts near the middle.
  B. Lvs. totally glabrous on both surfaces.
    C. Plants 1.5–3 dm. high, woody only at the base; calyx 7–10 mm. long; infl. with bracts near the middle, rarely divided; lvs. elliptic. Placer Co. to Modoc Co.
          (f) var. *Torreyanum*
    CC. Plants 4–12 dm. high, woody about half the height of the plants; calyx 3–6 mm. long; infl. compoundly divided; lvs. narrowly lanceolate. Mono, Inyo, and Tulare cos.
          (k) var. *chlorothamnus*
  B. Lvs. pubescent, at least below.

C.   Plants 4–12 dm. high, woody about half the height of the plants; calyx 3–6 mm. long; lvs. narrowly lanceolate, subglabrate below. Mono, Inyo, and Tulare cos.

(k) var. *chlorothamnus*

CC. Plants up to 5 dm. high, woody only at the base; lvs. mostly elliptic, tomentose, at least below.

D.   Lvs. sparsely tomentose above and below, the pubescence even on both surfaces. Inyo-White Mts., Panamint Mts. .... (j) var. *subaridum*

DD. Lvs. densely tomentose, at least below.

E.   Calyx 3–7 mm. long, including the stipe.

F.   Lvs. densely tomentose below, subglabrous to glabrous above. Coast Ranges, w. slope of the Sierra Nevada, mts. of s. Calif. (i) var. *stellatum*

FF. Lvs. densely tomentose on both surfaces. Central Coast Ranges, Glenn Co. to San Benito Co. .... (1) var. *bahiiforme*

EE. Calyx 7–10 (–12) mm. long, including the stipe. N. Coast Ranges.

(h) var. *speciosum*

(a) Var. **umbellàtum**. [*E. polyanthum* of California authors, not Benth., in large part. *E. reclinatum* Greene.] Plants 2–6 dm. high; lvs. tomentose below, less so to glabrous above, lf.-blades elliptic to ovate, 1–2 cm. long, petioles slender; scapes slender, mostly 1–3 dm. long, the umbels few rayed, bractless; invol. tubes 2–3.5 mm. long with reflexed lobes as long; calyx yellow, 4–7 mm. long; *n* = 40 (Reveal 1965, 1968).—Rather common on dry slopes and ridges, 2500–10,000 ft.; Sagebrush Scrub to Yellow Pine F. and Subalpine F.; Coast Ranges from Tehama Co. to Humboldt and Siskiyou cos., Sierra Nevada from Tulare Co. n.; to Wash., and e. to Colo. June–Sept.

This variety has been called ssp. *polyanthum* for several years and considered the common California form although the type of *polyanthum* is a different plant entirely. The distinguishing features of the common California form do differ slightly from the Rocky Mountain plants which are true var. *umbellatum*, and especially in the large subshrubby size of the plants found along the eastern slope of the Sierra Nevada which Greene named *E. reclinatum*. In considering the entire range of var. *umbellatum*, however, the California plant gradually blends into the low Rocky Mountain form through northern Nevada and Idaho.

(b) Var. **Covíllei** (Small) Munz & Reveal comb. nov. [*E. C.* Small, *Bull. Torr. Bot. Club* 25: 42. 1898. *E. ursinum* var. *C.* S. Stokes in name. *E. umbellatum* var. *polypodum* of S. Stokes, not *E. p.* Small. *E. umbellatum* ssp. *C.* Munz.] Plants less than 1.5 dm. high; lvs. lightly tomentose on both surfaces, lf.-blades narrowly elliptic, 0.5–1 cm. long, the petioles as long; scapes slender, less than 1 dm. long, the umbels capitate or nearly so; invols. 1.5–3 mm. long with reflexed lobes as long; calyx yellow, 2–4 mm. long.—Dry gravelly rocky soil, above 10,000 ft.; Alpine Fell-fields of Sierra Nevada, Subalpine F., Mt. Shasta and Warner Range above 9000 ft. July–Sept.

The var. *Covillei* is the high alpine form of *Eriogonum umbellatum* which occurs in the Sierra Nevada. It is closely related to var. *Hausknechtii* (Dammer) Jones which occurs in similar habitats in the high mountains of Oregon. These two varieties seem to have evolved from var. *umbellatum*, while the var. *Porteri* (Small) S. Stokes which is found in the high mountains of northeastern Nevada and Utah was derived from the glabrous-leaved form of var. *umbellatum*, the var. *intectum* A. Nels. All of the alpine varieties are characterized by their capitate or subcapitate inflorescences, but differ from each other in leaf pubescence and geographical distribution.

(c) Var. **dicrocephalum** Gand. [*E. aridum* Greene. *E. azaleastrum* Greene. *E. u.* ssp. *aridum* S. Stokes. *E. u.* var. *aridum* C. L. Hitchc.] Lf.-blades tomentose on both surfaces, or subglabrous to glabrous above, 1.5–2 cm. long; scapes 1–2.5 dm. high; rays few, (0.5–) 1–3 cm. long; calyx whitish, cream-colored, or pale yellow, often with a large tannish midrib, 4–8 mm. long including the stipe.—Occasional, below 10,000 ft.; Pinyon-Juniper Wd., Lodgepole F.; e. slope of Sierra Nevada, White Mts., Mono Co. s. to San Gabriel Mts., San Bernardino Co.; n. Nev., w. Utah. June–Aug.

A recent examination of the type of var. *dicrocephalum* shows that this is an earlier name for what has been known as *aridum*.

(d) Var. **versicólor** S. Stokes. Low, matted perennials less than 1.5 dm. high; lvs. lightly tomentose on both surfaces, the lf.-blades elliptic, 0.5–1.5 cm. long, the petioles ca. as long; scapes slender, less than 1.5 dm. long, the umbel rays few, less than 1.5 cm. long; calyx reddish-brown to rose or pink with a large reddish or purplish midrib, 3–6 mm. long.—Occasional, below 9000 ft.; Pinyon-Juniper Wd.; Panamint, Inyo, and Grapevine mts., s. Nev.

The var. *versicolor* is closely related to var. *dicrocephalum* and occasionally the two are difficult to distinguish. The California plants are simply branched in the inflorescence, but in the Charleston Mts. of southern Nevada, biumbellate forms are not infrequently found.

(e) Var. mìnus Jtn. [*E. m.* Ewan.] Low and densely matted; lf.-blades round-ovate, 4–10 mm. long, permanently densely white-woolly on both surfaces; scapes 3–12 cm. long; rays of umbels 1–3, 5–20 mm. long; calyx 4–5 mm. long, often deep red.—Dry stony slopes, 8000–10,000 ft.; Lodgepole F., Subalpine F.; San Gabriel Mts. July–Sept.

(f) Var. Torreyànum (Gray) Jones. [*E. T.* Gray.] Lvs. glabrous, elliptic, 3–6 cm. long; infl. compound, bracteate near the middle of the rays; calyx 7–10 mm. long, bright yellow, numerous in each invol. the heads up to 5 cm. in diam.—Dry gravelly or stony places at ca. 6000 ft.; Placer Co., reported as far n. as Modoc Co. July–Aug.

The var. *Torreyanum* is definitely known only from the Donner Pass area although it has been reported as far north as Modoc Co. This variety is exceedingly distinct and no other forms are known to be near it. The plants from eastern Oregon which have been called var. *Torreyanum* actually represent another variety that may be called var. **glabérrimum** (Gand.) Reveal [based on *E. g.* Gand., *Bull. Soc. Bot. Belg.* 42: 197. 1906]. This variety differs mainly in that the Oregon plant has smaller flowers in equally smaller heads in distinct compoundly umbellate inflorescences.

(g) Var. polyánthum (Benth.) Jones. [*E. p.* Benth. *E. dumosum* Greene. *E. modocense* Greene. *E. u.* sspp. *p.* and *d.* S. Stokes. *E. u.* var. *m.* S. Stokes.] Plants 3–10 dm. high; lvs. densely matted and felty white-tomentose below, ovate to elliptic, 5–30 mm. long, 5–20 mm. wide, short-petioled; scapes stoutish, 1–4 dm. long with large bracts 1–4 cm. long; invols. 4–6 mm. long, 4–10 mm. wide; calyx yellow, 6–7 mm. long.—Dry sandy or gravelly places below 5000 ft.; Sagebrush Scrub, N. Juniper Wd. up to Red Fir F.; Placer Co. n. to Siskiyou and Modoc cos.; s. Ore. July–Aug.

The recognition of var. *polyanthum* as here described differs considerably from the treatments given before in the various state floras. The type of *polyanthum* was collected by John C. Frémont near Mt. Shasta, and is the large, bright yellow-flowered subshrub so often seen on the loose sandy soils of that area. Nearly all of the references to *polyanthum* in California should actually be applied to var. *umbellatum.*

(h) Var. speciòsum (Drew) S. Stokes. [*E. s.* Drew.] Plants 5–10 dm. high; similar to var. *polyanthum* but with compound infl. and larger fls., 7–10 (–12) mm. long.—Dry rocky places mostly below 3000 ft.; Yellow Pine F., Foothill Wd.; N. Coast Ranges from Del Norte Co. to Siskiyou Co. July–Aug.

(i) Var. stellàtum (Benth.) Jones. [*E. s.* Benth. *E. u.* ssp. *s.* S. Stokes.] Basal lvs. spatulate-obovate, glabrate above, densely tomentose below, the petioles often exceeding the blades, the lf.-blades 1.5–2.5 cm. long; rays of the umbels often compoundly branched with foliaceous bracts at the base of each division; calyx usually bright yellow, sometimes with a reddish tinge, mostly 6–8 mm. long.—Dry rocky slopes, 3000–7500 ft.; Yellow Pine F. to Red Fir F.; Trinity to Siskiyou and Del Norte cos., along the w. slope of the Sierra Nevada to Merced Co., mts. of s. Calif.; to Wash., Mont., e. to Utah. July–Sept.

As noted at the beginning of this discussion, the var. *stellatum* is not yet clearly understood. In California, the variety, as here defined, includes not only the northern California element which is probably true var. *stellatum*, but also an element from near Yosemite Valley which differs in its pubescent leaf and shorter and more compact stature, and the plants from the mountains of southern California. This last population is apparently unnamed. It may be distinguished by its densely tomentose stems and leaves and wide spreading low growth. However, in many respects, the southern California plant approaches var. *bahiiforme* of the Coast Ranges, and until this relationship can be investigated, it would be unwise to propose a new variety for this seemingly distinct population.

(j) Var. subáridum S. Stokes. [*E. u.* ssp. *s.* Munz.] Lvs. very finely and closely tomentose on both surfaces, not densely tomentose below, lf.-blades 1–1.5 cm. long; infl. compound; calyx mostly yellow, occasionally pale yellow, 6–7 mm. long.—Dry rocky slopes, 5000–9000 ft.; Pinyon-Juniper Wd.; White, Inyo, Argus, and Panamint mts., across the Mojave Desert to s. Nev., Utah, and sw. Colo. July–Aug.

(k) Var. chlorothámnus Reveal, var. nov. A var. *stellato* differt fruticosis, 5–10 dm. altis, foliis fere subglabris vel glabris, ellipticis vel oblanceolatis, 5–20 mm. longis et 4–6 mm. latis. Plants 5–10 dm. high; lvs. subglabrous or glabrous on both surfaces, narrowly elliptic or oblanceolate, 5–20 mm. long, 4–6 mm. wide, short-petioled; scapes slender,

1–2.5 dm. long; invols. 3–6 mm. long; calyx yellow, 3–6 mm. long.—Dry gravelly places; Sagebrush Scrub, 7000–9000 ft.; Owens V., Inyo and Mono cos., Little Kern River, Tulare Co. July–Sept. TYPE: Summit of Sherwin Grade, 4 miles s. of Tom's Place, on a dirt road 0.5 mile e. of U.S. Hwy. 395, Mono Co., Calif., 23 July 1966, *N. H. Holmgren & J. L. Reveal 2938.* Holotype deposited at the Intermountain Herbarium, Utah State University.

For several years this plant has gone under the name of var. *bahiiforme,* as a syntype collected by Horn is representative of this plant. By typifying var. *bahiiforme* (see below), it becomes necessary to recognize this distinct variety. A part of the overall complex associated with var. *stellatum,* the var. *chlorothamnus* is actually more closely related to var. *subaridum* which occurs nearby on the White Mts.

(1) Var. **bahiifórme** (T. & G.) Jeps. [*E. polyanthum* var. *b.* T. & G. *E. stellatum* var. *b.* Wats. *E. trichotomum* Small. *E. Smallianum* Heller. *E. u.* var. S. S. Stokes. *E. u.* ssp. *b.* Munz.] Lvs. ± felty, white-tomentose on both surfaces, the petioles scarcely as long as the blades, the lf.-blades 1–1.5 cm. long; infl. compound, or at least with bracts on the primary rays; calyx 5–8 mm. long, yellow becoming tinged with red.—Dry rocky places, mostly above 1000 ft.; Yellow Pine F., Foothill Wd.; Coast Ranges from Lake and Glenn cos. s. to San Benito Co. July–Sept. LECTOTYPE: New Idria, San Benito Co., Calif., *Brewer 771* (GH).

By typifying the var. *bahiiforme* with the New Idria collection this allows for the exclusion of the Owens Valley plants which are now named var. *chlorothamnus,* and it also allows for the exclusion of the plants from the mountains of southern California which have, on occasion, been called var. *bahiiforme.* As noted under var. *stellatum,* these southern California plants are presently placed there although it is likely that they represent a distinct group.

10. **E. compósitum** Dougl. ex Benth. [*E. c.* var. *citrinum* S. Stokes.] Perennials with ± branched woody caudices; lvs. basal, ovate to lance-ovate, usually truncate or more commonly cordate at the base, densely white-tomentose below, usually glabrate and greenish above, the lf.-blades 2–10 (–20) cm. long, the petioles as long or longer; scapes stout, 2–4 (–5) dm. long, subglabrous, ascending to erect; infl. simple to compound, umbellate, subtended by narrow foliaceous bracts; invols. campanulate, 6–10 mm. long, mostly pilose-tomentose externally, with 5 linear, finally reflexed lobes; calyx glabrous, ochroleucous to pale yellow, becoming 5–6 mm. long, the stipe 1–1.5 mm. long; calyx-segms. similar, ± oblong-ovate; fils. pilose basally; aks. narrowly triangular-ovoid, pubescent above, light brown, 5–6 mm. long; *n* = 20 (Reveal, 1968).—Dry rocky hills and slopes or ledges, below 7500 ft.; Yellow Pine F., Red Fir F.; Lake Co. to Del Norte and Siskiyou cos.; to Wash., Ida. May–July.

11. **E. Lóbbii** T. & G. [*E. L.* var. *minus* T. & G.] Few-branched from stout woody caudices, covered with hairy bases of dead lvs.; lvs. in tufted rosettes, mostly round-oval, plane, densely tomentose especially below, the lf.-blades 1–4 cm. long, abruptly narrowed into petioles as long or longer; scapes flat on the ground or decumbent, tomentose, 0.5–2 dm. long, with foliaceous bracts subtending the 2- to several-rayed umbels; rays 1–3 cm. long, woolly-hirsute; invols. campanulate, 8–12 mm. long, the lobes reflexed; calyx white to rose (especially in age), 5–7 mm. long, the base scarcely stipitate, the stipe mostly less than 1 mm. long, the calyx-segms. oblong-obovate; fils. hairy basally; aks. lance-ovoid, glabrous, shining, olive-green, 4.5–6 mm. long, 3-angled at the apex.— Gravelly slopes and ridges, 5500–8000 ft.; Red Fir F. to Alpine Fell-fields; Coast Ranges, Lake Co. to Humboldt and Siskiyou cos. and 5500–12,000 ft., Sierra Nevada, from Inyo and Mariposa cos. to Plumas Co.; w. Nev. June–Aug.

In western Nev., var. *robustius* (Greene) Jones [*E. r.* Greene.] occurs and may be distinguished by its larger flowers, leaves, and higher and more robust stature when seen in the field. It is to be expected at low elevations in the foothills of the Sierra Nevada in eastern Placer, Nevada, or Sierra cos.

12. **E. làtens** Jeps. [*E. monticola* S. Stokes.] Caudex woody, with short branches; lvs. basal, round-ovate to elliptic-obovate, subglabrous to short-pilose, paniculate, the lf.-blades 1–3 cm. long, abruptly narrowed to longer petioles; scapes naked, 1.5–3 dm. long; infl. capitate, 2–3.5 cm. in diam., subtended by membranous rose-colored bracts; invols. few, campanulate, sparsely pilose, the lobes oblong-ovate, becoming recurved; calyx cream-colored to pale yellow, strigose near base, 5–6 mm. long at low elevs., 3–4 mm. long in alpine situations, not obviously stipitate at base; fils. pubescent basally; aks. lance-

ovoid, glabrous, 3–4 mm. long.—Dry stony slopes and ridges, 6500–11,000 ft.; Pinyon-Juniper Wd., Red Fir F. to Alpine Fell-fields; e. slope of the Sierra Nevada and White Mts., Inyo and Mono cos.; w. Nev. July–Aug.

13. E. hirtéllum Howell & Bacig. Perennials with woody, long-creeping rhizomes covered with old lf.-bases and with small clusters of lvs.; lvs. basal, ovate, elliptic, or broadly oblanceolate, 0.5–1.5 cm. long, 0.3–0.8 cm. wide, petioles 0.3–2 cm. long, the petioles and lf.-blades hirtellous or the blades sometimes glabrescent; scapes naked, erect and slender, 8–25 cm. long; infl. capitate, subtended by 5 narrowly oblong hirtellous bracts; invols. turbinate, 5–6 mm. long, 5–6 toothed, the teeth 1 mm. long, erect, hirtellous externally; calyx bright yellow, densely white-pilose externally near the base, glabrous within, the calyx-segms. dissimilar, the outer segms. 3 mm. long, much broadened and subrounded above a clawlike base, to 3 mm. wide, the inner segms. 2.5 mm. long, 1 mm. wide, not obviously stipitate at the base; fils. hirsutulous basally; aks. not known.—Dry serpentine ridge-top, Klamath Mts., Del Norte and Siskiyou cos., 5300 ft. July–Sept.

This new species was recently proposed by Howell & Bacigalupi in *Leafl. West. Bot.* 9: 174. 1961, and is most closely related to *Eriogonum latens* Jeps. which is known only from Inyo and Mono counties. These species, along with *E. Lobbii* and *E. pyrolifolium* have indistinctly stipitated bases, but their overall morphological similarities with the other members in the subgenus *Oligogonum* indicate that they fit here rather than elsewhere.

14. E. pyroliifòlium Hook. Caudex woody, stout, few-branched from a strong taproot; lvs. basal, ovate to rounded, the lf.-blades glabrous, 1.5–2 cm. long, abruptly narrowed to the equally long, villous petioles; scapes naked, 4–8 (–15) cm. long; infl. capitate or umbellate, subtended by 2 lanceolate bracts; rays simple, up to 6 mm. long; invols. campanulate, loosely woolly externally, with short, erect, teeth; calyx whitish to rose, loosely villous, 5–6 mm. long, obscurely stipitate, somewhat sparsely pubescent and glandular-puberulent at the base and along the midribs; fils. pilose basally; aks. lance-ovoid, pubescent above, ca. 5 mm. long.—Dry gravelly and sandy slopes, 8500–10,500 ft.; mostly Alpine Fell-fields; Mt. Lassen, Little Mt. Hoffmann, and Mt. Shasta; n. in the typical and in a more common form, var. *coryphaèum* T. & G. which has densely tomentose lvs. below; to Wash. and Mont. July–Aug.

15. E. alpìnum Engelm. Caudices rather slender, with elongate underground branches; lvs. basal, rounded, densely white-tomentose on both surfaces, the lf.-blades 1–3 cm. long; scapes 4–6 cm. long, densely white-tomentose, bracted well above the middle and each bearing a single campanulate invol. with 5–6 or more short erect teeth; calyx yellow, glabrous, 3–5 mm. long, short-stipitate; fils. somewhat pubescent at the base; aks. glabrous.—Loose slopes and ridges, 7500–9000 ft.; Subalpine F., Alpine Fell-fields; Mt. Eddy and Scott Mtn., Siskiyou Co. Aug.–Sept.

16. E. Kellóggii Gray. Caudex cespitose, branched and forming loose mats, the stems branched, loosely tomentose, with rosettes of lvs. at the tips; lvs. oblanceolate to spatulate, silky-tomentose beneath and often less so above, 4–10 mm. long, short-petioled; scapes slender, 4–7 cm. long, with a whorl of leafy bracts near the middle; invols. solitary, turbinate, tomentose, with short erect teeth; calyx whitish or pinkish, glabrous, 5–7 mm. long, stipitate at base; fils. pilose basally; aks. angled-conical, glabrous except for the sparsely pubescent apices, ca. 5 mm. long.—Dry ridges, ca. 4000 ft.; Yellow Pine F.; known definitely only from Red Mt., n. Mendocino Co. Possibly also on Black Butte Mts., Glenn Co.

17. E. polypòdum Small. [*E. umbellatum* var. *p.* S. Stokes, as to name and type. *E. ursinum* var. *Covillei* S. Stokes as to application, not *E. umbellatum* var. *C. E. ursinum* var. *venosum* S. Stokes.] Low spreading perennials from branched woody caudices, forming loose mats; lvs. ovate with rounded or cordate bases, revolute, the lf.-blades less than 1 cm. long, the petioles stout, shorter than blades; scapes erect, 5–15 cm. tall, slender; infl. capitate or few-rayed umbels; invols. turbinate, 3–4 mm. long; calyx chalky white with reddish midribs, 2.5–3 mm. long, calyx-segms. oblong; plants polygamo-dioecious; fils. pilose basally; aks. ca. 3 mm. long, with a wrinkled cellular-papillose adherent basal part which is over half their entire length and free from the seed.—Dry sandy to gravelly flats and slopes often among boulders, ca. 8000–10,500 ft.; Subalpine F.; s. Sierra Nevada, mostly in Tulare Co. July–Aug.

18. E. marifòlium T. & G. [*E. m.* var. *apertum* S. Stokes. *E. cupulatum* S. Stokes.]

Caudex loosely and much branched, forming mats with tomentose branchlets with terminal tufts of lvs.; lvs. ovate to oval, densely white-tomentose below, ± glabrate and green above, 5–15 mm. long, the petioles ca. as long; scapes slender, usually sparsely tomentose, 0.5–2 (–4) dm. long; infl. capitate or more frequently open umbels with subtending linear bracts. the central ray often shorter than the lateral rays, the lateral rays up to 2–3 cm. long; invols. 2–3 mm. long, sparsely pubescent externally, with short erect teeth; plants polygamo-dioecious; calyx yellowish, often tinged with red along the midribs, glabrous, the ♀ fls. 4–5 mm. long with stipes ca. 0.5 mm. long, the ♂ fls. mostly less than 3 mm. long; fils. pilose basally; aks. glabrous except sometimes at the very tip, angled-conic with narrowed bases, greenish, 3.5–4 mm. long; styles ca. 0.4 mm. long; $2n = 32$ (Stokes & Stebbins, 1955).—Dry gravelly or sandy soil on flats or slopes, 3500–11,000 ft.; Red Fir F., Subalpine F.; Sierra Nevada mostly n. of Fresno Co. to Siskiyou Co. and cent. Ore., w. Nev. July–Aug.

19. **E. incànum** T. & G. [*E. marifolium* var. *i.* Jones. *E. rosulatum* Small. *E. ursinum* var. *r.* S. Stokes.] Caudex densely cespitose, forming branched mats 1–3 dm. across; lvs. oblong-ovate, lf.-blades 5–15 mm. long, 3–7 mm. wide, densely tomentose on both surfaces, narrowing to tomentose petioles 5–10 mm. long; scapes tomentose, 0.1–2 dm. high; infl. capitate during early anthesis, subtended by a whorl of 3–6 lanceolate, tomentose bracts, 4–5 mm. long, the infl. becoming umbellate after fertilization with a central sessile invol. and rays 2–20 mm. long especially on the ♀ plants, ♂ infl. remaining subcapitate; invols. broadly turbinate, 2.5–3 mm. long with 5–8 broadly triangular teeth; calyx pale yellow to yellow, glabrous, 2.5–3 mm. long, the ♀ fls. becoming 4–6 mm. long in fruit, polygamo-dioecious; fils. pilose basally; aks. tomentulose at the apex to nearly or quite glabrous, ca. 3 mm. long.—Gravelly and rocky slopes and ridges, 7000–12,000 ft.; Red Fir F. to Alpine Fell-fields; Tulare and Inyo cos. to Tuolumne and Alpine cos. July–Sept.

The recognition of this species which is often associated with the related *Eriogonum marifolium* comes after an intensive study of both in the herbarium and in the field. In the Tioga Pass area the two are distinct even though they can be seen growing together. The male plants of *E. marifolium* are often confused with the unrelated *E. umbellatum*, but this is often due to lack of both sexes being collected or observed.

20. **E. ursìnum** Wats. [*E. ovatum* Greene.] Caudex woody, branched, forming loose mats; lvs. tufted at ends of branchlets, ovate, the lf.-blades 8–14 (–25) mm. long, densely white-tomentose below, often glabrate above, the petiole short; scapes 2–4 dm. long, villous-tomentulose to subglabrate; infls. of compact umbels, the rays often 1–3 cm. long, the infl. subtended by narrow lfy. bracts, the rays often bearing smaller bracts; invols. woolly-villous, subcampanulate, with short broad teeth; calyx ochroleucous, glabrous, 5–6 mm. long, with a stipe 1 mm. long; fils. woolly basally; aks. subconic, subglabrous, ca. 4 mm. long, narrowed at the base; styles ca. 2.5 mm. long.—Dry open gravelly places, 3500–8000 ft.; Yellow Pine F., Red Fir F.; Sierra Nevada from Placer Co. to Butte and Shasta cos. May–Aug.

Var. **nervulòsum** S. Stokes. Plants rhizomatous; scapes erect, 4–6 cm. long; infl. congested, subcapitate.—Stony places; Red Fir F.; Snow Mt., Lake Co. Aug.–Sept.

21. **E. ternàtum** Howell. [*E. ursinum* var. *confine* S. Stokes.] Caudex woody, much-branched, forming mats; lvs. in terminal tufts on the branchlets, obovate to oblong, glabrate to tomentose above, densely tomentose below, the lf.-blades 10–15 mm. long, the petioles ca. as long; scapes 1–3 dm. high, bracted at the summit and also on the rays, the rays 1–2 cm. long; invols. turbinate, 5–8 mm. long, woolly-tomentose externally, the teeth ca. 2 mm. long; calyx sulphur-yellow, glabrous, 3–5 mm. long, stipitate at the base; fils. woolly basally; aks. pilose at the apex; styles 3 mm. long.—Rocky places, 2000–6000 ft.; Yellow Pine F., Red Fir F.; Del Norte and Siskiyou cos.; sw. Ore. June–Aug.

Var. **Congdònii** (S. Stokes) J. T. Howell [*E. ursinum* var. *C.* S. Stokes.] Lvs. revolute, narrowly elliptic or ± oblong; branches of infl. ebracteolate.—At 5000–7000 ft.; Red Fir F.; Trinity and Siskiyou cos. July–Aug.

Subgenus Ganýsma (S. Wats.) Greene.

22. **E. angulòsum** Benth. Annuals, erect, with spreading dichotomous ± angled stems 1–4 (–9) dm. long, whitish-tomentose to glabrate; basal lvs. oblanceolate to oblance-

oblong, the lf.-blades 1–3 cm. long, short-petioled, tomentose below, glabrate above, revolute and crisped on the edges; stem-lvs. well distributed, sessile, 0.5–2 cm. long, lanceolate to oblanceolate; peduncles arising from most axils, slender, 1–2 cm. long, glabrous or sparsely tomentose; invols. open-turbinate, 1.5–2.5 mm. long, ± puberulent, with broad rounded lobes; calyx rose, tipped with white, ca. 1.5 mm. long, minutely glandular-puberulent, the outer calyx-segms. obovate to elliptical, deeply concave, sometimes with an inflated area near the base, the inner segms. narrowly spatulate, longer; stamens 2–3 mm. long, usually well exserted; aks. ca. 1 mm. long, grayish, the body subovoid with a sharply angled triangular beak.—Dry open places, mostly below 2500 ft.; V. Grassland, Foothill Wd., Joshua Tree Wd., Pinyon-Juniper Wd.; S. Coast Ranges from Contra Costa Co. to San Diego Co. (rare in the s.), San Joaquin V. and foothills of the Sierra Nevada to w. Mojave Desert. May–Nov.

23. **E. maculàtum** Heller. [*E. angulosum* vars. *rectipes, pauciflorum, flabellatum,* and *patens* Gand. *E. a.* var. *m.* Jeps. *E. a.* ssp. *m.* S. Stokes.] Annuals with 1–several branches from the caudices, 1–2 (–3) dm. high, tomentose almost throughout; basal lvs. lanceolate to obovate, 1–3 (–4) cm. long, 1–1.5 (–2) cm. wide, narrowing to short petioles, tomentose below, glabrate to sparsely pubescent above, occasionally revolute and crisped on the margins; cauline lvs. sessile, 0.5–2 cm. long, 3–10 mm. wide, lanceolate to oblanceolate, tomentose below, glabrate above, becoming reduced above, subtended by scalelike bracts, 1–3 mm. long; branches widely spreading to give an open subglobose crown; peduncles filiform, (5–) 10–30 mm. long, arising axillary, often glandular-puberulent; invols. campanulate, 1–1.5 (–2) mm. long, 1.5–3 (–3.5) mm. wide, glandular-puberulent externally, glabrous to woolly within, with 5 rounded lobes; calyx white to yellow, pink or red with conspicuous rose-purple spots on the outer inflated segms., 1–2.5 mm. long, glandular-puberulent, calyx-segms. dissimilar, the outer segms. elliptic to roundish or obovate, with an inflated area at the base and middle with the sides of the blades incurved below, the inner segms. obtuse to lanceolate, longer; stamens 1–1.5 (–2) mm. long; aks. 1–1.5 mm. long, grayish, the ovoid bases tapering to long, 3-angled beaks; $n = 20$ (Reveal, 1965).—Dry, often sandy or gravelly places, below 7000 ft.; Creosote Bush Scrub, Joshua Tree Wd., Sagebrush Scrub, Pinyon-Juniper Wd.; deserts, e. Wash. to San Diego Co.; to Utah, Ariz., L. Calif. April–Nov.

24. **E. viridéscens** Heller. [*E. angulosum* var. *v.* Jones. *E. bidentatum* Jeps. *E. a.* sspp. *v.* and *b.* S. Stokes.] Annuals with 1–several stems from the caudex, 1–2 (–3) dm. high, tomentose almost throughout; basal lvs. lanceolate to obovate, 2–4 cm. long, 1.5–2 cm. wide, narrowing to petioles 1–2 (–3) cm. long, tomentose below, glabrate to sparsely pubescent above; cauline lvs. sessile, 0.5–2 cm. long, 3–10 mm. wide, similar to the basal lvs. only more reduced above; branches widely spreading to an open subglobose crown; peduncles filiform, 1–2 cm. long, arising axillary, sparsely finely pubescent with capitate hairs; invols. campanulate, 2–3 mm. long, 2–4 mm. wide, finely pubescent externally, tomentose internally, with 5 rounded lobes; calyx white, pink, or red, often with reddish spots on the outer segms., 1–2.5 mm. long, calyx-segms. dissimilar, the outer segms. broadly expanded above the middle of the segms., obovate or spatulate, the apices truncate, the inner segms. acute to acuminate, longer; stamens included; aks. 1–1.5 mm. long, grayish to brownish, ovoid with long 3-angled beaks.—Dry plains and hills about upper San Joaquin V. from inner Monterey Co. and Merced Co. to w. Mojave Desert. May–Oct.

25. **E. gracíllimum** Wats. [*E. angulosum* var. *g.* Jones. *E. a.* ssp. *g.* S. Stokes. *E. variabile* Heller. *E. a.* var. *v.* Parish. *E. a.* var. *victorense* Jones. *E. a.* ssp. *victorense* S. Stokes.] Annuals, freely branched at or just above the base, 1–4 dm. high, thinly woolly nearly throughout; basal lvs. oblong to oblanceolate, 2–4 cm. long, short-petioled, densely tomentose below, less so above, with revolute, crisped edges; cauline lvs. lance-oblong, well distributed, similar to the basal lvs.; peduncles filiform, 8–25 mm. long, glabrous; invols. subcampanulate, angled, 2 mm. long, glandular-puberulent, shallowly 5-lobed; calyx rose, tipped with white, 2–2.5 mm. long, the segms. similar, oblong to elliptic, frequently crenulate; aks. shining black, ca. 1 mm. long, shortly beaked; $n = 20$ (Reveal, 1968).— Common on sandy plains, below 3500 ft.; Grassland, Foothill Wd., Joshua Tree Wd., Coastal Sage Scrub; inner S. Coast Ranges from Merced and Monterey cos. to w. Mojave Desert and interior s. Calif. April–Sept.

26. **E. gossýpinum** Curran. Diffusely dichotomous, erect, slender-stemmed annuals, 0.5–2 dm. high, tomentose; basal lvs. broadly oblanceolate, 1.5–4 cm. long; stem lvs. lanceolate, somewhat smaller; peduncles 2–15 mm. long; invols. turbinate, 3 mm. long, deeply lobed and filled with dense cottony tomentum; calyx white, 1.5 mm. long, concealed in the tomentum of the invol. so as to appear pubescent, the calyx-segms. similar, linear-oblong; aks. 1 mm. long, brownish; $n = 20$ (Reveal, 1967).—Uncommon, sandy places, below 3000 ft.; V. Grassland; about the head of the San Joaquin V., Kings and Kern cos. to se. San Luis Obispo Co. April–Sept.

This group of five species which centers around *Eriogonum angulosum* has been treated in several ways. All except *E. gossypinum* have been reduced to an infraspecific rank under *E. angulosum* using a variety of names. Several years ago, J. T. Howell (1944) wrote an excellent review of these species which is followed here with only minor changes and additions in the ranges and chromosome numbers of some of the species.

27. **E. spergulìnum** Gray. [*Oxytheca s.* Greene.] Erect, slender-stemmed annuals, forking freely above with widely spreading branches, 1–5 dm. high, the internodes generally with capitate glands; basal lvs. linear, 2–3 cm. long, hispid, short-petioled; cauline lvs. linear, whorled, sessile, becoming bracteate above; peduncles filiform, 5–12 mm. long; invols. solitary, glabrous, 0.5–1 mm. long, deeply 4-lobed; calyx white with rose midribs, glabrous or sparsely pubescent, 2.5–3.5 mm. long, the segms. oblong; stamens usually exserted, the anthers 0.35–0.5 mm. long, oblong to elliptic; aks. brownish, ca. 1.5 mm. long, lanceolate in outline, narrowed gradually into narrow beaks.—Dry gravelly flats and gentle slopes, 5000–10,000 ft.; Montane Coniferous F.; Sierra Nevada from Eldorado Co. to Tulare Co. June–Aug.

Var. **Reddingiànum** (Jones) J. T. Howell. [*Oxytheca R.* Jones.] Internodes generally stipitate-glandular; calyx 1.5–2.5 mm. long; anthers 0.2–0.33 mm. long, roundish.—More common, 4000–11,000 ft.; Montane Coniferous F.; N. Coast Ranges from Lake Co. n., Sierra Nevada s. to Mt. Pinos, Ventura Co.; n. to Ore., Ida., Nev. June–Sept.

Var. **pratén se** (S. Stokes) J. T. Howell. [*E. p.* S. Stokes.] Internodes usually glandless; calyx ± hirsutulous, ca. 2 mm. long.—Similar places, 8000–11,500 ft.; Sierra Nevada in Tulare and Inyo cos. July–Aug.

28. **E. hirtiflòrum** Gray ex Wats. [*Oxytheca h.* Greene.] Annuals, 5–15 cm. high, repeatedly dichotomously branched, glandular-puberulent; lvs. basal and at the lower nodes, obovate to spatulate, 1–2.5 cm. long, ciliate, narrowed into winged petioles; invols. sessile in the forks and along the branches, or short-peduncled, narrow, 2-fld., ca. 1 mm. long; calyx reddish, ca. 1 mm. long, hirsutulous with hooked hairs, the segms. oblong; aks. narrow, ca. 1 mm. long, exceeding the calyx, with broad obtuse angled beaks.—Occasional, dry gravelly places, below 6000 ft.; Chaparral, Foothill Wd., Yellow Pine F.; N. Tujunga Creek, Los Angeles Co.; Council Rock, Ventura Co.; The Pinnacles, San Benito Co.; Greenhorn Range, Kern Co.; N. Coast Ranges and Sierra Nevada. June–Oct.

29. **E. inérme** (Wats.) Jeps. [*Oxytheca i.* Wats. *E. vagans* Wats.] Annuals, dichotomously or trichotomously forked just above or at the base, then repeatedly dichotomous, 5–30 cm. high, sparingly stipitate-glandular; lvs. basal, spatulate, 1–2 cm. long, sessile, ciliate, otherwise glabrous; bracts 3-lobed; invols. on pedicellike peduncles, 4-lobed nearly to the base, subglabrous, 1.5 mm. long; calyx rose, 1.5 mm. long, hispid with hooked hairs, the segms. oblong, the inner segms. retuse and smaller than the outer; aks. scarcely if at all longer than the calyx.—Uncommon, dry barren soils or along moist edges of meadows, below 7000 ft.; Foothill Wd., Chaparral, Yellow Pine F.; Coast Ranges from Lake Co. to Kern Co. June–July.

Var. **hispídulum** Goodm. Invols. hispidulous.—From 3000–6000 ft.; Yellow Pine F.; San Bernardino Mts., Greenhorn Range; Sierra Nevada from Tulare Co. to Tuolumne Co. June–Aug.

30. **E. apiculàtum** Wats. [*E. a.* var. *subvirgatum* S. Stokes.] Erect annuals, usually simple at the base, dichotomously or trichotomously branched above, spreading, 2–9 dm. high, somewhat glandular-pubescent in lower portions of the internodes and peduncles, with ultimately very slender branchlets; lvs. strictly basal, oblanceolate to obovate, the lf.-blades 1.5–4 cm. long, pilose, glandular, the petioles ca. as long; bracts 1–2 mm. long; peduncles in forks and scattered along the branchlets, filiform, 2–35 mm. long, often de-

flexed; invols. 1.5 mm. long, glabrous, 4-lobed about half their length; calyx white, 1.5–2 mm. long, puberulent, the segms. oblong-obovate, notched to apiculate; aks. ca. 1.5 mm. long, not distinctly beaked.—Dry open places in disintegrated granite, 3600–8000 ft.; Joshua Tree Wd., Pinyon-Juniper Wd., Yellow Pine F.; Joshua Tree National Monument, San Jacinto, Santa Rosa, Palomar, and Cuyamaca mts. July–Aug.

31. **E. Paríshii** Wats. Annuals with 1–3 erect stems 1–3 dm. high, diffusely branched so as to form a dense rounded mass of very slender ultimate branchlets, glaucous, glabrous except for short-stipitate glands above the nodes; lvs. basal, spatulate, 2–6 cm. long, hirsute; peduncles capillary but rigid, 4–12 mm. long; invols. solitary, 5-lobed, ca. 0.6 mm. long; calyx pinkish, 1–2 per invol. minutely puberulent, ca. 0.6 mm. long, the outer segms. ovate, the inner segms. oblong-spatulate; aks. ca. 1 mm. long, dark brown, the subglobose base tapering to a stout, somewhat angled, beak; $2n = 40$ (Stokes & Stebbins, 1955), $n = 20$ (Reveal, 1967).—Dry gravelly places, 4000–9000 ft.; Pinyon-Juniper Wd., Yellow Pine F., Lodgepole F.; s. Sierra Nevada, Tulare and Inyo cos., south through the San Gabriel Mts. to n. L. Calif. July–Sept.

32. **E. Órdii** Wats. [*E. tenuissimum* Eastw.] Annuals, diffusely paniculate with many capillary ultimate branches, floccose near the base, glabrous above, 4–7 dm. high; basal lvs. oblong-obovate to oblong-oblanceolate, the lf.-blades 2–8 cm. long, on equally long petioles, floccose-tomentose to ± woolly, especially below; bracts of the lower nodes often in foliaceous whorls and similar to the basal lvs., the upper bracts reduced, subulate; peduncles capillary, 1–2 cm. long; invols. solitary, turbinate, 1 mm. long, 4-toothed; calyx white, tinged with pink or pale yellowish, 1.5 mm. long, densely pubescent, 1–3 fls. per invol., the calyx-segms. oblong-ovate; aks. shining, olive-green, ca. 1.5 mm. long, ovoid, 3-angled on the stout beak.—Dry disturbed and barren places, below 3000 ft.; Foothill Wd.; inner Coast Ranges of Monterey and San Benito cos., n. base of Tehachapi Mts. and near Oildale, Kern Co.; also Creosote Bush Scrub and Pinyon-Juniper Wd., in n. Los Angeles Co., and at Split Mt., Colo. Desert; w. Ariz. March–June.

33. **E. cárneum** (J. T. Howell) Reveal, stat. nov. [*E. glandulosum* var. *c.* J. T. Howell, *Leafl. West. Bot.* 8: 38. 1956.] Annuals with one, rarely more, stems from the caudex, erect, 1–2.5 dm. high, glandular with small tack-shaped glands, numerous on the lower nodes becoming only somewhat less numerous above; lvs. basal, broadly elliptic, 6–12 mm. long, 5–10 mm. wide, pilose-hirsutulous and slightly glandular, on petioles 3–12 mm. long, stiffly hispid; bracts sparsely hirsutulous within and at the acute apices in some, glandular along the upper margins, 1 mm. long; branches numerous, spreading, trichotomous at the first node with 1–several branchlets at this node, dichotomous above with ever gradually shortening branches above; peduncles slender, one or two at each node, straight, deflexed or nearly so, 2–3 mm. long below, gradually becoming subsessile above, glandular nearly the entire length; invols, narrowly turbinate, 0.8–1.2 mm. long, glabrous, 5-lobed, few-fld.; calyx white, maturing pinkish, with red midribs, 1–1.8 mm. long, densely pilose externally with numerous long thin white hairs, the calyxsegms. narrowly lanceolate, 0.3–0.4 mm. wide; stamens included, the fils. white or red, the anthers roundish, red; aks. black, shining, 1–1.3 mm. long, the large globose base abruptly tapering to a short beak less than 0.4 mm. long.—Dry sandy soil, 3500–4500 ft.; Sagebrush Scrub, Pinyon-Juniper Wd.; extreme e. Inyo and ne. San Bernardino cos.; sw. Nev. June–Aug.

Eriogonum glandulosum (Nutt.) Nutt. ex Benth. is an exceedingly rare species known only from seven collections. The type of *E. glandulosum* was collected by Gambel along the Old Spanish Trail in southwestern Utah in 1841. Subsequent collections have essentially come from Lincoln Co. north to Elko Co., Nevada, and the adjacent counties in Utah. When J. T. Howell named the var. *carneum* he based the description on a small series of specimens. Recently, a relatively large collection from near Mercury, Nevada (*Beatley 4997*) closed the geographical distance between the two varieties yet strengthened the morphological differences between them.

The inflorescence of *Eriogonum glandulosum* is somewhat ascending with few branches. The peduncles, which are usually glandular about half their 5–15 mm. long length, are ascending or curving upwards in a fashion similar to *E. collinum*. The involucres are broadly turbinate and 1.5–2 mm. long. The flowers, which are yellow, are wider in fruit than those of *E. carneum*. The flower pubescence of *E. glandulosum* is composed of thick white stiff hairs which are less numerous and shorter than in *E. carneum*.

Eriogonum carneum differs in several ways. The inflorescence tends to be more flat-topped, and with the numerous branches, it is more dense. The peduncles are straight, deflexed, and less than 4 mm. long. The glands cover nearly the entire length of the peduncles. The narrowly turbinate involucres are 0.8–1.2 mm. long. The white flowers are exceedingly narrow in fruit, and when compared with *E. glandulosum*, the pilose hairs are more dense, longer and slender, and somewhat less stiff.

When taking into consideration the above morphological differences and the fact that even in Nevada the two remain perfectly distinct, it seems best to elevate the western population to the specific rank.

34. **E. tríchopes** Torr. [*E. trichopodum* Torr. ex Benth. *E. clavatum* Small. *E. t.* ssp. *c.* S. Stokes. *E. cordatum* Torr. ?, nom. dubium. *E. t.* ssp. *cordatum* S. Stokes.] Annuals with 1–several stems from the base, trichotomous at the first node and dichotomous or trichotomous at the upper nodes, with few to many whorled branchlets at each node especially on the lower nodes, glabrous and glaucous nearly throughout, infrequently inflated at the lower internodes; lvs. in a basal rosette, round to somewhat round-oblong, ± cordate at the base, hirsute, often somewhat crinkled, the lf.-blades 1–2 cm. long, on petioles as long to twice as long; peduncles capillary, 8–15 mm. long; invols. turbinate, scarcely 1 mm. long, glabrous, 2–few-fld., essentially 4-lobed; calyx yellow to green, 1 mm. long in anthesis, 1.5 mm. long in fr., white-strigulose, the segms. ovate; aks. shining, brown, 1.5 mm. long, narrow-ovoid, 3-angled with stout beaks; $n = 16$ (Reveal, 1965).—Common in washes and on mesas, below 5500 ft.; mostly Creosote Bush Scrub, Joshua Tree Wd.; Mojave and Colo. deserts, inner S. Coast Ranges; to Utah and New Mex., Son. and L. Calif. April–Aug.

The oldest name for this species is very likely *E. cordatum*, but as early as 1870, Torrey & Gray reported that the specimens had been lost, and attempts to find any collections in both American and European herbaria have failed. At present, as the description is not adequate enough for definite identification, it seems best to consider the name to be a nomen dubium. One name, long associated with *E. trichopes*, is *E. trichopes* ssp. *minor* (Benth.) S. Stokes, based on a series of specimens collected in New Mexico. These plants do not differ from typical *E. trichopes*, and the name should be considered a synonym.

35. **E. inflàtum** Torr. & Frém. DESERT TRUMPET. Perennials, but flowering the first year, or in the northern part of its overall range, a strict annual, 2–10 dm. high, glabrous and glaucous nearly throughout or somewhat hirsute at the very base, with 1–several stems which are simple below and dichotomous above to form diffuse panicles, the stems usually conspicuously inflated in the upper portion of the lower internodes; lvs. oblong-ovate to rounded or even subreniform, usually cordate or truncate at the base, 1–2.5 (–3) cm. long, short-hirsute, green, somewhat crisped, on petioles 2–5 cm. long; peduncles capillary, in forks and racemosely along the branchlets, 5–20 mm. long; invols. glabrous, 1–1.5 mm. long, turbinate, 5-lobed, the lobes occasionally with stipitate glands, several-fld.; calyx yellow often with red-brown midribs, conspicuously and densely pubescent, 2–2.5 mm. long, the segms. lance-ovate; aks. brown, ca. 2 mm. long, sharply 3-angled, lance-ovoid, narrowed gradually toward the apices; $n = 16$ (Stone & Raven, 1958; Reveal, 1965).—Common in washes and along mesas, below 6000 ft.; Creosote Bush Scrub, Joshua Tree Wd., Sagebrush Scrub, Pinyon-Juniper Wd.; Mojave and Colo. deserts, n. to Mono Co.; to Colo., Ariz., and L. Calif. March–Oct.

Var. **deflàtum** Jtn. [*E. glaucum* Small.] Stems not inflated, plants up to 15 dm. high; $n = 16$ (Reveal, 1967). Largely on the Colo. Desert, also in Death V.; L. Calif.

Eriogonum inflatum is often easily confused with *E. trichopes*, yet this confusion is really not necessary. While both species can be annuals, the lower nodes of *E. trichopes* often bear several small branchlets arranged in whorls and the inflorescences often have more numerous branches so that the plants appear filmy when viewed from a distance. As to *E. inflatum*, its branches are usually stouter and fewer in number, and the lower nodes never have whorls of branchlets. The perennial phase of *E. inflatum* is distinct enough, however, it is the first-year flowering plants and the strict annual plants that present problems. Throughout much of eastern Utah and adjacent western Colorado only the strict annual phase is found, although in the southern parts of these states the perennial phase may occur. The biology of the two phases is rather distinct, as is the morphology to some degree, but how to consistently separate the first-year annuals from the strict annuals has not been determined except by means of their respective geographical distribution. At present, therefore, no new taxa are proposed, and only the problem is presented.

36. **E. esmeraldénse** Wats. Glabrous annuals, 1- to few-branched, then repeatedly branched, 1–3 dm. high, the ultimate branches very slender; lvs. basal, somewhat round-obovate, 6–15 mm. long, pilose-hispid, on petioles ca. as long; peduncles filiform, 5–15 mm. long; invols. narrow-turbinate, 1 mm. long, 5-lobed, few-fld.; calyx white to pink, glabrous, the segms. ± oblong, obtuse or retuse; aks. narrow-ovoid, brown, shining, ca.

1 mm. long, gradually narrowed to a stout beak.—Dry gravelly places, 6000–9800 ft.; Pinyon-Juniper Wd.; foothills and low mts. of Inyo and Mono cos., w. Nev. July–Sept.

37. **E. Thomàsii** Torr. [*E. minutiflorum* Wats.] Annuals, 1–several stemmed at the base, 1–2.5 dm. high, glabrous and glaucous nearly throughout, repeatedly trichotomous; lvs. basal, round to round-reniform, 1–2 cm. wide, often glabrate above, densely white-woolly below, on petioles 2–5 cm. long; peduncles filiform, 5–15 mm. long; invols. ca. 1 mm. long, deeply 5-lobed, several-fld.; calyx at first yellow, later white to rose, ca. 1 mm. long, hispidulous externally, the outer segms. ovate, with a saclike dilation on each side of the cordate base when mature, the inner segms. spatulate; aks. ca. 1 mm. long, dark brown, shining, round-ovoid with 3-angled beaks; $n = 20$ (Raven et al., 1965; Reveal, 1967).— Common in dry sandy places, below 5000 ft.; Creosote Bush Scrub, Joshua Tree Wd.; Mojave and Colo. deserts n. to Inyo Co.; to sw. Utah, Ariz., L. Calif. March–June.

38. **E. Thúrberi** Torr. [*E. cernuum* ssp. *T. S.* Stokes. *E. c.* ssp. *viscosum* S. Stokes. *E. T.* var. *Parishii* Gand.] Annuals, simple or several-stemmed from the base, diffusely and trichotomously branched, 1–3 dm. high, floccose at least in the lower parts; lvs. basal, oblong-ovate, 1–3 cm. long, densely white-woolly below, glabrate above, on petioles 1–3 cm. long; peduncles capillary, 5–25 mm. long, ± glandular-puberulent; invols. broadly turbinate, glandular-puberulent, 2 mm. long, 5-lobed near the middle; calyx rose to whitish, 1–1.5 mm. long, glandular-puberulent near the base, the outer segms. roundish or broadly ovate, abruptly narrowed to a clawlike base, with a tuft of white-cottony tomentum within, the inner segms. narrowly lanceolate; aks. almost black, shining, 0.6–0.8 mm. long, round-ovoid with a short sharp beak.—Sandy places below 5000 ft.; Coastal Sage Scrub, Chaparral; Los Angeles region to San Diego Co.; Creosote Bush Scrub, Joshua Tree Wd., Colo. Desert and occasional on Mojave Desert; Ariz., L. Calif. April–July.

39. **S. pusíllum** T. & G. [*E. reniforme* ssp. *p.* S. Stokes. *E. comosum* var. *playanum* Jones. *E. r.* var. *asarifolium* Gand.] Annuals, erect, simple or branched at the base, trichotomously branched above, with glabrous and glaucous stems 1–3 dm. high; lvs. basal, the lf.-blades rounded to oblong-ovate, 1–3 cm. long, densely white-woolly on both surfaces, somewhat greenish above in some, on petioles ca. as long; peduncles very slender, 1–3 cm. long; invols. broadly turbinate to campanulate, glandular-puberulent, 1.5 mm. long, with 5 broad rounded lobes, several-fld.; calyx 1.5 mm. long, glandular puberulent, yellow, later with reddish midribs, the outer segms. obovate, the inner segms. oblong, both elongating to ca. 3 mm. in fr.; aks. dark, shining, 0.6–0.8 mm. long, round-ovoid, with short stout beaks; $n = 16$ (Reveal, 1965).—Common on plains and mesas, mostly 2500–6500 ft.; Creosote Bush Scrub, Joshua Tree Wd., Pinyon-Juniper Wd.; deserts from Mono Co. s. to Palm Springs region; Nev., Utah. March–July.

40. **E. renifórme** Torr. & Frém. [*E. r.* var. *comosum* Jones. *E. c.* Jones.] Annuals with 1 to several stems, ± floccose below, glabrous above, divergently trichotomously branched, 0.5–2.5 dm. high; lvs. basal, round-reniform or rounded, mostly 1–2 cm. wide, mostly white-woolly on both surfaces, or nearly glabrous above, with somewhat crisped margins; peduncles 4–15 mm. long, capillary; invols. glabrous, subcampanulate, almost 2 mm. long, shallowly and broadly 5-lobed, several fld.; calyx pale yellow, 1–1.5 mm. long, glandular-puberulent, the outer segms. elliptic-ovate, the inner segms. narrower; aks. brown, shining, round-lenticular, scarcely beaked, ca. 1 mm. long; $n = 16$ (Reveal, 1965).—Common in sandy places below 4500 ft.; Creosote Bush Scrub, Joshua Tree Wd.; Mojave and Colo. deserts, Inyo Co., s. Nev., L. Calif. March–June.

41. **E. cérnuum** Nutt. [*E. c.* var. *tenue* T. & G.] Annuals, glabrous and glaucous, diffusely branched from or above the base, 1–3 dm. high, less than 5 cm. high at high elevs.; lvs. basal, rounded, (0.5–) 1–2 cm. long, densely white-woolly below, subglabrate above, the petioles up to 4 cm. long; peduncles capillary, deflexed, straight or curved, 5–25 mm. long; invols. turbinate, 1.5–2 mm. long, 5-lobed; calyx white, often becoming rose tinged, glabrous, 1–1.5 mm. long, attenuate at the base, the segms. oblong-obovate, panduriform, undulate and often emarginate; aks. slender, ca. 1.5 mm. long.—At 7000–10,000 ft.; Panamint and White mts., e. slope of Sierra Nevada; to Ore., Rocky Mts. and Great Plains. June–Sept.

Var. **viminàle** (S. Stokes) Reveal, stat. nov. [*E. c.* ssp. *v.* S. Stokes, *Gen. Eriog.* 41. 1936.] Invols. sessile or peduncled less than 2 mm.—Lassen Co., Great Basin of Nev. and w. Utah.

42. **E. Hoffmánnii** S. Stokes. Annuals; scapes usually one, rarely more, 1–5 dm. high; lvs. basal, 1–4 cm. long, 2–4 cm. wide, suborbicular to subcordate, densely white-tomentose below, less so to glabrous and green above; stems less than 5 cm. long, glabrous; with spreading, glabrous branches; peduncles lacking; invols. erect, turbinate, 1–2 mm. long, 5-lobed; calyx 1.5 mm. long, white with greenish midribs, glabrous, the segms. spatulate; aks. brown, 2 mm. long, the globose bases tapering to roughened 3-angled beaks; n = 20 (Reveal, 1968).—Dry talus slopes, 4000–5000 ft.; Pinyon-Juniper Wd.; Wild Rose Spring and Townes Pass, Panamint Mts., Inyo Co. July–Sept.

Var. robústius S. Stokes. Plants up to 10 dm. high with stems up to 4 dm. long; lvs. basal or sheathing up the stems 1–3 (–5) cm., the lvs. 2–5 cm. long, 3–8 cm. wide, crisped; infl. erect and strict, with long whiplike branches, the secondary branches at right angles to the main branches; peduncles, when present, less than 1 mm. long, erect; calyx white or reddish with reddish midribs, the segms. ovate; aks. not known.—Dry sandy washes, 1000–2000 ft.; Creosote Bush Scrub; Black and Funeral mts., Death V., Inyo Co. Aug.–Nov.

43. **E. defléxum** Torr. Annuals with 1–several stems from the base, glabrous and glaucous nearly throughout, up to 7 dm. high; lvs. basal, cordate, reniform to nearly orbicular, 1–4 cm. long, 2–5 cm. wide, densely white-tomentose below, less so to subglabrous and green above; infl. mostly spreading, open to diffuse; peduncles deflexed, up to 3 mm. long, usually sessile; invols. 1.5–2 mm. long, turbinate, 5-lobed; calyx white to pinkish, 1–2 mm. long, the outer segms. ovate to ovate-elliptic, or oblong, usually cordate at the bases, the inner segms. lanceolate to ovate; aks. reddish-brown to dark brown, 2–3 mm. long, the subglobose bases tapering to stout 3-angled beaks; n = 20 (Reveal, 1964; 1968). —Common in sandy to gravelly washes and slopes, mostly below 6000 ft.; Creosote Bush Scrub to Pinyon-Juniper Wd.; Mojave and Colo. deserts, Inyo Co. to San Diego and Imperial cos.; to Utah, Ariz., L. Calif. May–Oct.

Var. barátum (Elmer) Reveal. [*E. b.* Elmer. *E. Watsonii* of all Calif. references, not *E. W.* Torr. & Gray.] Plants up to 10 dm. high, slender or stout, stems and branches often inflated, forming erect, strict crowns, the branches few, often elongated and whiplike; peduncles mostly 5–15 mm. long; invols. 2.5–3 mm. long, narrowly turbinate; calyx 2–2.5 mm. long; n = 20 (Reveal, 1968).—Common on talus, gravelly slopes of mountains and ridges or passes up to 9500 ft.; Montane Coniferous F.; s. Mono Co. and Inyo Co. s. to Ventura and Los Angeles cos.; w. Nev. June–Oct.

44. **E. Rixfórdii** S. Stokes. [*E. deflexum* ssp. *R.* Munz.] Annuals with several stems 2–4 dm. high; lvs. basal, 1–3 cm. long and wide, cordate to orbicular, margins often crispate, densely white-tomentose below, less so to subglabrous and green above; stems erect, the central main stem stout and 3–20 cm. long, dividing repeatedly at the first node, the outer stems slender and 4–12 cm. long, glabrous; branches widely spreading to nearly horizontal in position, diffuse, the few to many branches of varying lengths, the main center branch the longest, dichotomous, with angles above the second to fourth node near to 90°, intricately and divaricately branched so as to form a nearly globose crown suggesting a pagoda by the varying layers of the secondary flat-topped branches, the internodes of the upper branches short, rarely over 5 mm. long, glabrous; invols. turbinate-campanulate, 1–1.5 mm. long, 1.5–2 mm. wide, 5-lobed, glabrous; calyx white with greenish midribs, 1.5 mm. long, glabrous, the outer segms. oblong-oval, the bases cordate and gibbous at maturity, the inner whorl narrowly lanceolate, longer than the outer segms.; aks. dark brown, 1.5 mm. long, lenticular; n = 20 (Reveal, 1968).—Dry sandy to gravelly soils, below 5000 ft.; Creosote Bush Scrub to Pinyon-Juniper Wd.; Panamint Mts., Death V., Inyo Co. July–Oct.

45. **E. Hoòkeri** Wats. [*E. deflexum* ssp. *H.* S. Stokes.] Annuals with only a single stem, rarely more, from the caudex, 1–4 (–6) dm. high; lvs. basal, 2–5 cm. long, 2–6 cm. wide, cordate to subreniform, margins often upward rolled on the edges, densely white felty-tomentose below, white-tomentose above; stems glabrous, erect; branches spreading, the crown subglobose to flat-topped with the outer edge lower than the center so as to give an "umbrella" appearance, glabrous; peduncles lacking; invols. deflexed, hemispheric, 1–2 mm. long, 1.5–3 mm. wide, 5-lobed; calyx yellow, becoming reddish-yellow at maturity, 1.5–2 mm. long, glabrous, the segms. dissimilar, the outer segms. orbicular, cordate or hastate at the base, the inner segms. oblong-ovate and shorter than the outer, the outer expanding in fr., becoming nearly isodiametric, 2–2.5 mm. long and

wide; aks. light brown, 2–2.5 mm. long, the globose bases tapering to 3-angled beaks; $n = 20$ (Reveal, 1968).—Rare in Pinyon-Juniper Wd., from 5000–6000 ft.; s. Mono Co. and n. Inyo Co.; e. to Colo., Wyo., and n. Ariz. July–Oct.

46. **E. brachypòdum** T. & G. [*E. Parryi* Gray. *E. deflexum* var. *b.* Munz. *E. d.* sspp. *b.* and *P. S.* Stokes.] Annuals with 1–several stems, 5–40 cm. high; lvs. basal, 2–4 cm. long, 2–5 cm. wide, orbicular to cordate, densely white-tomentose below, less so to subglabrous and green above; stems stout, erect, 2–7 cm. long, glandular; branches horizontal in a low flat-topped crown or spreading and forming a subglobose one, trichotomous at the first node, usually dichotomous above, the ultimate branches often with alternating secondary branches which too have alternating branches of varying lengths, becoming shortest in the last of the secondary branches and toward the tips of the main ones, glandular throughout; invols. peduncled up to 15 mm. long, slender to stoutish, deflexed; invols. turbinate to campanulate, 1–2.5 mm. long, 1.5–2.5 mm. wide, 5-lobed; calyx white becoming reddish at maturity, 1–2.5 mm. long, glabrous, the outer segms. ovate to oblong, the base cordate to auriculate, the inner segms. narrower and shorter; aks. brown to nearly black, 1.5–2 mm. long, the subglobose bases tapering to 3-angled beaks; $n = 20$ (Reveal, 1968).—Creosote Bush Scrub to Pinyon-Juniper Wd., below 7500 ft.; Kern and San Bernardino cos., across Inyo Co. to Nev., s. Utah, nw. Ariz. March–Oct.

47. **E. insígne** Wats. [*E. deflexum* var. *i.* Jones. *E. d.* ssp. *i.* S. Stokes.] Annuals with usually only a single stem from the caudex, up to 10 dm. high; lvs. basal, up to 8 cm. long and wide, subcordate to orbicular, the base subcordate, densely white-tomentose below, less so to subglabrous and green above; stems erect, stout, up to 20 cm. long, glabrous; branches erect and strict, dichotomous or trichotomous, often 4–5 times taller than wide, the long whiplike branches with alternating right-angled secondary ones which are also with alternating branches, the tips of the main and secondary branches ending in a raceme of 2–8 invols., glabrous throughout; invols. erect on peduncles up to 3 mm. long; invols. turbinate, 2–2.5 (–3) mm. long, 1.5–2.5 mm. wide, 5-lobed; calyx 1.5–2 mm. long, white, glabrous, the outer segms. oblong, the base cordate, the inner segms. narrower and shorter, rarely over 1 mm. wide; aks. dark brown to grayish-black, 2–2.5 mm. long, the globose base tapering to long 3-angled beaks; $n = 20$ (Reveal, 1968).—Sandy soils mostly below 4000 ft.; Creosote Bush Scrub to Sagebrush Scrub; San Diego Co. n. to s. Inyo Co.; s. Nev., sw. Utah, nw. Ariz. May–Nov.

48. **E. eremícola** Howell & Reveal. Annuals with one or occasionally several stems from the caudex, 8–25 cm. high; lvs. basal, 1–2.5 cm. long and wide, rounded, subcordate at the base, densely white-tomentose below, less so to glabrous above, on petioles up to 3 cm. long; stems slender, 3–10 cm. long, capitate-glandular; branches spreading so as to form a subglobose crown, ± open, trichotomous at the first node, dichotomous or trichotomous above, glandular; peduncles slender, deflexed, sessile or subsessile above, peduncled to 10 mm. below, glandular; invols. turbinate-campanulate, 1.8–2 mm. long, 1–1.5 mm. wide, 5-lobed, sparsely glandular; calyx whitish becoming reddish at maturity, 2–2.5 mm. long, glabrous, the calyx-segms. ovate-oblong, the bases obtuse to subcordate; aks. brown, 2 mm. long, with a stout 3-angled beak.—Sandy to gravelly soils from 7500 to 10,000 ft.; Pinyon-Juniper Wd., Yellow Pine F.; Telescope Peak, Panamint Mts., Inyo Co. June–Sept.

The Panamint Mountains harbour several interesting buckwheats, and *Eriogonum eremicola* is certainly one of these. Since the species was described (*Leafl. West. Bot.* 10: 174. 1965) little additional information has been obtained upon it. It is placed following those species centering around *E. deflexum* only because it does not seem to fit better anywhere else, and it approaches *E. Watsonii* closer than *E. Hoffmannii* to which this plant was associated for several years.

49. **E. collìnum** S. Stokes ex Jones. [*E. nutans* of Calif. authors, not T. & G.] Annuals with 1–several stems from the caudex, up to 7 dm. high, floccose at the base becoming glabrous nearly throughout at maturity; lvs. basal, 1–3 cm. long, 1–3.5 cm. wide, round, cordate, elliptic to obovate, the base subcordate to reniform, sparsely hirsute to densely white-tomentose below, subglabrous to glabrate or glabrous above, on petioles 1–5 cm. long; stems trichotomous at the first node, with rather open and divaricated dichotomous branches; peduncles curving or ascending upwards, mostly slender, 1–3 (–5) cm. long; invols. turbinate, (1.5–) 2–3 mm. long, 1.5–2.5 mm. wide, 5-lobed; calyx white with a yellowish cast, to pinkish-yellow, or yellow, glabrous except for the pustulose or rarely

hirsutulous basal perianth tube, the calyx-segms. ovate, lanceolate to spatulate, crispate in some; aks. brownish, 2–2.5 mm. long, fusiform; $n = 18$ (Reveal, 1966).—Dry sandy to heavy clay soils, mostly below 6000 ft.; Sagebrush Scrub, N. Juniper Wd.; Nevada Co. n. to Lassen Co.; w. Nev., s. Ida. June–Sept.

For several years this species has been confused with *Eriogonum nutans* in California and with *E. reniforme* in Nevada, even though it is related to neither. The recent article by Reveal (*Madroño* 18: 167–173. 1966) has reviewed the species and its relationships.

Subgenus **Oregònium** (S. Wats.) Greene.

50. **E. mohavense** Wats. [*E. delicatulum* Wats.] Erect annuals, diffusely and repeatedly dichotomously or trichotomously branched at or above the base, 1–3 dm. high, glabrous and green throughout except at the nodes and lvs., the ultimate branchlets capillary; lvs. basal, rounded or broadly oblong, closely white-woolly, 0.6–2 cm. long, on petioles up to twice as long; invols. sessile in the forks and often terminal on the branchlets, hence in subcymose infls.; glabrous except at the throat, turbinate, 1.7–2 mm. long; calyx yellow, glabrous, ca. 1 mm. long, the outer segms. oblance-oblong to subelliptic, the inner narrower; aks. dark brown to nearly black, ca. 1 mm. long, the stout beaks 3-angled and muriculate.—Dry sandy and gravelly places, mostly ca. 2000–4000 ft.; Creosote Bush Scrub, Joshua Tree Wd.; Mojave Desert from e. base of the San Bernardino Mts. to Owens V. May–Aug.

51. **E. ampullàceum** J. T. Howell. [*E. mohavense* ssp. *a.* S. Stokes.] Erect annuals 1–3 dm. high, glabrous and glaucous nearly throughout; lvs. basal, rotund to subcordate, 0.5–1.5 cm. long and wide, white- tomentose, on petioles 0.5–4 cm. long; infl. dichotomous or trichotomous, mostly narrow and strict, erect; invols. sessile, turbinate-campanulate, 1.5–2 mm. long and wide, 5-lobed; calyx 1 mm. long, the lobes whitish, obtuse, the perianth tube broadly campanulate; stamens as long as to slightly shorter than the calyx; calyx 1.5 mm. long in fruit; aks. 1 mm. long, with globose bases tapering to long 3-angled sharp beaks.—Dry sandy soil, 6500–7000 ft.; Sagebrush Scrub; Mono Co. July–Sept.

52. **E. argillòsum** J. T. Howell. Erect annuals 1–3 dm. high, with 1–several stems, glabrous to sparingly tomentose; basal lvs. oblong, 1.5–2.5 cm. long, white-woolly below, less so above, slightly revolute, on petioles as long as or longer than the blades; cauline lvs. at first node somewhat smaller, becoming still more reduced above; peduncles filiform; invols. turbinate, 2.5–3 mm. long, obscurely 5-lobed, scarious below the sinuses, glabrous; calyx white or rose with dark midribs, 1.5 mm. long, the outer segms. oblong, somewhat broader than the inner; aks. 2–2.5 mm. long.—Clay and serpentine; Foothill Wd.; inner Coast Ranges, Santa Clara Co. to San Benito and Monterey cos. March–June.

53. **E. temblorénse** Howell & Twisselmann. Erect annuals 1–8 dm. high, with 1–several stems, densely white-tomentose almost throughout; lvs. mostly basal or subbasal, rarely axillary, lvs. elliptical, 2–2.5 cm. long, 1–1.5 cm. wide, white-woolly-tomentose on both surfaces, on petioles about as long; lower stem lvs., when present, similar but gradually reduced upwardly; lower peduncles up to 2 cm. long, erect, becoming sessile above, axillary or racemosely arranged; invols. turbinate, 2–2.5 mm. long, 5-lobed, with narrowly scarious sinuses; calyx white with green midribs, 1.5 mm. long in anthesis, becoming reddish and 2–2.5 mm. long in fr., segms. ± similar, oblong-ovate, rarely smooth, with cells longitudinally striate-lineate, ± alveolate at the base; ovary granular, styles 0.7–1 mm. long; aks. 2–2.8 mm. long with a slender granular or papillose beak; $n = 17$ (Reveal, 1968).—Dry slopes; V. Grassland; inner Coast Ranges; se. Monterey, ne. San Luis Obispo, and w. Kern cos. July–Sept.

54. **E. vestìtum** J. T. Howell. Erect annuals, 1–4 dm. high, simple below, branched above, densely white-tomentose nearly throughout, leafy; basal lvs. elliptic to elliptic-oblong, 1–3 cm. long, tomentose on both surfaces, on petioles ca. as long; lower cauline lvs. similar but gradually reduced above; peduncles 1–6 cm. long or almost lacking, axillary or racemosely arranged; invols. turbinate-campanulate, 2 mm. long, 5-lobed, with narrow scarious sinuses; calyx white with red midribs, the segms. oblong-ovate, 1.5–2 mm. long, papillose; aks. 2.5 mm. long, with slender papillose beaks; $n = 17$ (Reveal,

1967).—Dry slopes, V. Grassland; inner Coast Ranges, San Benito and w. Fresno cos. May–June.

55. E. Eastwoodiànum J. T. Howell. [*E. truncatum* var. *adsurgens* Jeps. *E. Covilleanum* ssp. *a.* Abrams. *E. vimineum* ssp. *a.* S. Stokes.] Erect annuals, branched from the base, 2–5 dm. high, floccose-tomentose nearly throughout; lvs. basal, suborbicular, 1–3 cm. long and wide, woolly below, subglabrate above, on petioles 3–8 cm. long; upper branches forming a cymose infl.; invols. peduncled in the forks, sessile on branchlets or terminal, turbinate, 2 mm. long, distinctly 5-toothed; calyx white, 2 mm. long, glabrous, the outer segms. elliptic or oblong-obovate to obtuse, the inner segms. oblong, smaller; aks. 2 mm. long, brownish; *n* = 17 (Reveal, 1967). Stokes & Stebbins, 1955, reported the taxon *adsurgens* to be 2*n* = 22, but as no vouchers were noted, it is impossible to check this count.—Diatomaceous shale; Foothill Wd.; mts. of w. Fresno and e. Monterey cos. June–July.

The type of var. *adsurgens* deposited in the Jepson Herbarium at the University of California is the same kind of plant later named by J. T. Howell as *Eriogonum Eastwoodianum*, and it is therefore reduced to synonymy.
The series of species, *Eriogonum Eastwoodianum*, *E. vestitum*, and *E. temblorense* all occur in the inner Coast Ranges and they are not easily distinguished. The seasonal variation within each species tends to approach features of other species at different times of the year, so that *E. temblorense* is similar to late season forms of *E. vestitum*, and *E. Eastwoodianum* often resembles young plants of *E. temblorense*. All three have the same chromosome number, *n* = 17, and approach the definition of the subgenus *Ganysma* in several respects. Nevertheless, these species are morphologically and cytologically closer to *E. argillosum*, *E. truncatum*, and *E. Covilleanum*, good members of the subgenus *Oregonium*, rather than to any species in *Ganysma*.

56. E. truncàtum T. & G. Erect annuals, with 1–several stems, 1–3 dm. high, floccose-tomentose nearly throughout; lvs. basal and at the lower nodes, oblong-oblanceolate to obovate, tomentose below, less so and greenish above, 2–5 cm. long, attenuate to petioles ca. as long; infl. open, dichotomously or trichotomously branched, subcymose; invols. subsessile, 1–few in the forks and at the ends of branchlets, tomentose, 2.5–3 mm. long, turbinate, shallowly and broadly 5-toothed, the sinuses almost filled with membranes; calyx light rose-colored, ca. 2 mm. long, glabrous, the outer segms. elliptic-obovate, the inner segms. slightly narrower; aks. dark brown, ca. 2 mm. long, narrow-ovoid, with broad 3-angled beaks.—Dry slopes, 1000–1500 ft.; edge of Chaparral, e. base of Mt. Diablo, Contra Costa Co. April–June.

57. E. Covilleànum Eastw. [*E. vimineum* var. *C.* S. Stokes.] Erect annuals, simple below or branched from the base, glabrous, the slender stems 1–4 dm. long, dichotomously or trichotomously branched above in cymose fashion; lvs. basal, suborbicular, densely white-tomentose below, subglabrous above, 0.5–1.5 cm. long, on longer slender petioles; invols. solitary, ca. 2.5 mm. long, sessile at the forks and nodes or terminal, narrowly turbinate, glabrous without, 5-veined, the margins subentire and ciliate; calyx 2–2.5 mm. long, rose or white with red midveins, the segms. elliptic, puberulent toward the base without; aks. ca. 2 mm. long, ovoid, with prominent muriculate beaks; *n* = 17 (Reveal, 1967).—Shale and serpentine talus, 1200–2000 ft.; Chaparral, Foothill Wd.; inner Coast Ranges, Alameda Co. to the Temblor Range, Kern Co. April–June.

58. E. Nortònii Greene. [*E. vimineum* ssp. *N.* S. Stokes.] Erect annuals, 0.5–2 dm. high, with reddish stems, glabrous nearly throughout; lvs. basal and at the lower nodes, round to reniform, deeply emarginate, densely white-tomentose below, subglabrous to glabrous and green above, 5–15 mm. long, on longer petioles; invols. in the forks and at the tips of short slender branchlets, solitary, broadly turbinate, 3–4 mm. long, with ca. 8 short blunt teeth; calyx white to rose, 1.5 mm. long, the segms. obovate, glabrous; aks. ca. 1 mm. long, ovoid, with stout 3-angled beaks.—Dry rocky slopes, 1500–4000 ft.; Chaparral; The Pinnacles, inner Coast Ranges, Monterey and San Benito cos. May–June.

59. E. canìnum (Greene) Munz. [*E. vimineum* var. *c.* Greene. *E. v.* var. *californicum* Gand.] Widely spreading annuals, with several glabrous and reddish stems from the base, 1.5–3.5 dm. long, repeatedly dichotomously or trichotomously branched; lvs. basal and at the lower nodes oblong-ovate, densely white-tomentose below, subglabrous to glabrous and green above, subcuneate at the base, 0.5–3 cm. long, on petioles 2–3 times longer; invols. glabrous, narrowly turbinate, 5-ribbed and -toothed, 3–4 mm. long; calyx rose-red, 1.5–2.5 mm. long, the segms. obovate, glabrous; aks. lance-ovoid, reddish, tapering gradu-

ally to the 3-angled beaks; $n = 12$ (Reveal, 1968).—Dry rocky slopes on shale and serpentine, 1000–2000 ft.; Coastal Prairie; Marin Co. and the Oakland Hills, Contra Costa Co. June–Sept.

The plant in the N. Coast Ranges and on the western slope of the Sierra Nevada, which resembles this species, seems to be unnamed. This plant is taller, more erect, and with larger involucres and flowers than found in *Eriogonum caninum*. The type of *E. pedunculatum* S. Stokes from Calaveras Co. seems to be this kind of plant, but its relationships with *E. vimineum* must be studied before any nomenclatural changes can be logically made.

60. **E. ròseum** Dur. & Hilg. [*E. virgatum* Benth. *E. v.* var. *r.* T. & G. *E. v.* var. *rubidum* Jeps. ex Bauer. *E. vimineum* ssp. *v.* S. Stokes.] Erect annuals, simple or with few ascending virgate branches, floccose-tomentose nearly throughout, 1–8 dm. high; lvs. at the base and lower nodes, the basal lvs. oblong-oblanceolate, 1–3 cm. long, with equally long petioles; invols. cylindric, 4–5 mm. long, 5-toothed, sessile and rather remote, tomentose; calyx yellow to pink or white, 2 mm. long, the outer segms. narrowly obovate, the inner oblong, glabrous; aks. almost 2 mm. long, narrowly ovoid with broad 3-angled scaberulous beaks; $2n = 18$ (Stokes & Stebbins, 1955), $n = 9$ (Reveal, 1967).—Dry, often sandy or gravelly to rocky places, below 5000 ft.; Chaparral, Foothill Wd., Yellow Pine F., N. Oak Wd., etc.; away from the immediate coast, s. Ore. to n. Ventura and Los Angeles cos., especially in the ranges bordering the Great V. June–Oct.

61. **E. grácile** Benth. [*E. vimineum* ssp. *g.* S. Stokes. *E. acetoselloides* Torr. ex Benth. *E. leucocladon* Benth. *E. roseum* var. *l.* Hoover. *E. verticillatum* Nutt.] Erect annuals, strictly or rather diffusely branched from base, 2–5 dm. high, thinly tomentose to floccose-tomentose throughout, the branchlets slender, ascending; lvs. mostly basal, oblanceolate to oblong, the lf.-blades 1–3 (–4) cm. long, tomentose, especially below, on petioles ca. as long; cauline-lvs. becoming strongly reduced above; invols. 1.8–2 (–3) mm. long, turbinate, subglabrous, the 5 teeth conspicuous, rigid; calyx white, pinkish, or yellowish, 1.5–2 mm. long, the outer segms. broadly obovate, the inner segms. oblong, glabrous; aks. ca. 1 mm. long, ovoid, with prominent 3-angled beaks; $2n = 22$ (Stokes & Stebbins, 1955).—Common in dry cismontane washes, on mesas, etc., below 3500 (5000) ft.; Coastal Sage Scrub, Chaparral, Foothill Wd., S. Oak Wd., etc.; inner Coast Ranges and Great V. from Vaca Mts. s. through s. Calif.; L. Calif. July–Oct.

Var. **citharifórme** (Wats.) Munz. [*E. c.* Wats *E. vimineum* var. *c.* S. Stokes. *E. agninum* Greene.] Lvs. practically all basal, crisped on the margins and with conspicuously winged petioles.—San Luis Obispo, Santa Barbara and Ventura cos. May–Aug.

Var. **polygonoìdes** (S. Stokes) Munz. [*E. vimineum* ssp. *p.* S. Stokes.] Stems glabrous and glaucous; lvs. elliptic to ovate-lanceolate, with narrow petioles.—Grain fields and dry slopes; San Luis Obispo to Santa Ynez, Santa Barbara Co. Sept.–Nov.

This species is exceedingly variable and needs critical study in order to understand the inner relationships of the various taxa. As the species is presented here, it is believed to include all of the forms referrable to it. The type of *E. verticillatum* is a non-flowering, exceedingly immature specimen which is believed to represent *E. gracile*.

62. **E. Davidsònii** Greene. [*E. vimineum* var. *D.* S. Stokes. *E. molestum* of authors, not Wats. *E. m.* var. *D.* Jeps. *E. v.* var. *aviculare* S. Stokes. *E. v.* var. *glabrum* S. Stokes.] Erect annuals, few-branched or usually simple at the base, glabrous and glaucous except on the lvs., 1–5 dm. high; lvs. basal, rounded to reniform, 1–2 (–4) cm. long and wide, densely white-tomentose especially below, crisped or undulate, on longer petioles; invols. cylindric-turbinate, 3–5 mm. long, glabrous, scarious between the ribs, sessile and remote, few on a branch; calyx white or tinged with pink to rose-red, 1.5–2 mm. long, the outer segms. oblong-obovate, the inner segms. slightly narrower, glabrous; fils. pilose basally; aks. brown, narrow-ovoid, shining, ca. 2 mm. long, narrowed slightly to stout muriculate, 3-angled beaks.—Occasional, dry places under pines, 3000–7000 ft.; Chaparral, Pinyon-Juniper Wd., Joshua Tree Wd., Yellow Pine F.; Monterey and Tulare cos. s. to San Diego Co.; Ariz. and L. Calif. June–Sept.

For years this plant has been known as *Eriogonum molestum*. However, with the critical examination of types in the Gray Herbarium, Harvard University, this taxon was found to represent not an annual, but the perennial *E. nudum* var. *pauciflorum* (see no. 95). When Watson proposed the species, he based *E. molestum* on a series of collections. In the Gray Herbarium are all those mentioned, Palmer, Cleveland, Parish Brothers, and Nevin. Of these, all represent *E. nudum* except the Palmer collection

which is *E. Davidsonii.* Nevertheless, as the majority of the collections represent the perennial, and
the entire description is based on the perennial, and in particular the Parish Brothers collection, it is
here selected as the lectotype: San Jacinto Mts., San Diego Co., California, July 1881, *Parish & Parish*
972 GH! Isotypes: MO! PH! US!

With the typification of *Eriogonum molestum,* the name *E. Davidsonii* must now be used. In the
past, *E. Davidsonii* has been recognized as a variety of *E. molestum* based on the length of the involucres. As this separation was due to the fact that there was some confusion with the perennial
E. nudum, no such separation will be made here.

63. **E. vimíneum** Dougl. ex Benth. [*E. luteolum* Greene. *E. v.* var. *l.* S. Stokes. ?*E. pedunculatum* S. Stokes.] Erect annuals, with several stems arising from the base, branched
above, 1–3 dm. high, ± floccose-tomentose below, becoming glabrous above, with slender, ± greenish and glaucous stems; lvs. generally all basal, round to round-ovate, white-
woolly below, glabrate above, 1–2 cm. long, on longer petioles; invols. usually sessile
along the branches, narrow-cylindric, 2–3.5 (–4) mm. long, with short blunt teeth,
glabrous; calyx white to rose or yellowish, 2 mm. long, the outer segms. obovate with
rounded apices, the inner narrower, glabrous; fils. glabrous or pilose basally; aks. 2 mm.
long, red-brown, ovoid with prominent muriculate, 3-angled beaks; $2n = 24$ (Stokes &
Stebbins, 1955).—Common in dry rocky and sandy places, below 6000 ft.; Chaparral,
Foothill Wd., Yellow Pine F., etc.; Coast Ranges and Sierran foothills, Monterey, Santa
Clara and Mariposa cos. n. to Wash., Ida., e. to Utah and Ariz. June–Sept.

64. **E. nidulàrium** Cov. [*E. vimineum* ssp. *n.* S. Stokes. *E. n.* var. *luciense* Jones.] Erect
annuals, repeatedly forked from near the base, 5–15 (–20) cm. high, floccose-tomentose
almost throughout, forming dense masses of numerous branches with short internodes
and in age the tips of the branches becoming curved inward; lvs. basal, rounded, sometimes cordate at the base, 1–2 cm. broad, on much longer petioles; invols. cylindrical-
turbinate, 1 mm. long, sessile in all the forks and along the branches, few-fld.; calyx red,
white, or yellow, 1.5–2 (–3) mm. long, the outer segms. obovate, dilated and truncate
at the apices, fan-shaped, the inner narrower, glabrous; fils. glabrous; aks. ca. 1 mm. long,
narrow-ovoid, with long scaberulous beaks.—Common in dry gravelly and rocky places,
mostly below 7000 ft.; Creosote Bush Scrub, Joshua Tree Wd., Pinyon-Juniper Wd.;
deserts from Mono Co. to San Bernardino Co.; Ore., Nev., w. Utah, and Ariz. April–Oct.

65. **E. Palmeriànum** Reveal, nom. nov. [based on *E. Plumatella* var. *Palmeri* T. & G.,
Proc. Amer. Acad. 8: 180. 1870, not *E. Palmeri* Wats. *E. Baileyi* var. *tomentosum* Wats.]
Densely branched and spreading annuals, 1–3 dm. high, forming broad, often flat-topped
crowns up to 3 dm. across, densely tomentose nearly throughout; lvs. basal, suborbicular
to cordate, 0.5–1.5 cm. long, 0.5–2 cm. wide, densely tomentose below, less so and often
green above, on petioles 1.5–3 cm. long; invols. campanulate, 1–1.5 mm. long, sparsely
tomentose with ciliated margins, sessile at the nodes and along the subvirgate branchlets, few-fld.; calyx white to pink with reddish-brown midribs, 1.5–2 mm. long, the outer
segms. oblong to fan-shaped, somewhat constricted near the middle and flaring above,
the inner segms. narrower; aks. 1.5–1.8 mm. long, the scabrous 3-angled beaks ca. 1 mm.
long.—Dry sandy or gravelly flats mostly below 7000 ft.; Creosote Bush Scrub, Joshua
Tree Wd., Pinyon-Juniper Wd.; e. San Bernardino Co. to n. Inyo Co.; s. Nev. and n.
Ariz. to extreme sw. Colo. June–Oct.

66. **E. Báileyi** Wats. [*E. vimineum* ssp. *B.* S. Stokes. *E. v.* var. *B.* R. J. Davis. *E. v.*
var. *multiradiatum* S. Stokes. *E. gracile* var. *effusum* T. & G. *E. restioides* Gand.] Erect
annuals, diffusely branched from the base, 1–4 dm. high, forming broad round-topped
crowns, glabrous except at the white-woolly base of the stems; lvs. basal, suborbicular,
5–20 mm. wide, densely white-tomentose on both surfaces, on somewhat longer petioles; invols. tubular-campanulate, 1–1.5 mm. long, glabrous except for the ciliated margins, sessile at the nodes of the subvirgate branchlets, several-fld.; calyx white to pink,
ca. 1.5 mm. long, the outer segms. oblong or oblong-obovate, somewhat constricted near
the middle and flaring above, the inner narrower, glabrous or glandular; aks. dark brown,
ca. 1 mm. long, the globose bases gradually narrowing into stout muriculate 3-angled
beaks.—Dry sandy or gravelly flats and banks, mostly 2500–7500 ft.; Creosote Bush Scrub,
Joshua Tree Wd. to Yellow Pine F.; e. end of San Bernardino Mts. across the Mojave
Desert along the e. side of the Sierra Nevada; e. Ore., w. Nev. May–Sept.

Var. **divaricàtum** (Gand.) Reveal, comb. nov. [*E. praebens* Gand. *E. p.* var. *d.* Gand.,
Bull. Soc. Bot. Belg. 42: 196. 1906. *E. commixtum* Greene ex Tidestr. *E. vimineum* var. *c.*

S. Stokes.] Stems sparsely floccose-tomentose; calyx glandular.—Dry sandy soil, mostly 4500–6000 ft.; Pinyon-Juniper Wd.; Carson City, Nev. n. to Placer and Nevada cos.; w. Nev.

For several years the name *Eriogonum Baileyi* var. *tomentosum* has been used as the name for the tomentose form of this species. However, in reviewing the types involved, a large number of problems arose. First, Watson did not select a type for var. *tomentosum*, and a recent investigation at the Gray Herbarium revealed only the Arizona specimen cited (a Palmer collection), but those from the other states mentioned were not found. For this reason, no lectotype is selected. The Palmer collection, however, was named first as *E. Plumatella* var. *Palmeri*. It must be recalled that to Torrey & Gray, the name *E. Plumatella* was the same plant that is now named *E. nidularium*. This plant represents what has been called in Stokes' monograph and in the Arizona Flora by Kearney & Peebles, *E. densum* Greene. Nevertheless, the type of *E. densum* from New Mexico is a grazed form of *E. polycladon* Benth. In field studies in Nevada by N. H. Holmgren and Reveal, it has been possible to study both *E. nidularium* and the plant that has been called *E. densum*, and the two are consistently distinguishable. Therefore, with this in mind, the name *E. Palmerianum* is proposed as a new name. The new name also replaces *E. Baileyi* var. *tomentosum* to a large degree and it makes it necessary to propose a name for the true tomentose form of *E. Baileyi*.
In studying the *E. Baileyi* complex, the tomentose plants have been found only in the western Nevada area from about Carson City north to north of Reno. This form just enters California in extreme eastern Placer and Nevada counties. The earliest varietal name for this plant is *E. praebens* var. *divaricatum*, and thus a new combination is made.

67. **E. brachýanthum** Cov. [*E. Baileyi* var. *b.* Jeps. *E. vimineum* var. *b.* S. Stokes.] Erect annuals, simple or diffusely branched from the base, 1–3 dm. high, forming broad round-topped crowns, glabrous except at the white-woolly base of the stems; lvs. basal, rounded to broadly ovate, 5–20 mm. wide, densely white-tomentose on both surfaces or rarely somewhat glabrate above, on petioles somewhat longer; invols. turbinate, 1 mm. long, glabrous, closely appressed to the branchlets, few-fld.; calyx yellow, 0.6–0.8 mm. long, the outer segms. oblong to oblong-obovate, the inner slightly narrower, glabrous; aks. dark brown, ca. 1 mm. long, the globose bases gradually narrowing into long exserted 3-angled beaks.—Dry sandy to gravelly slopes, mostly 2500–7500 ft.; Creosote Bush Scrub, Joshua Tree Wd., Pinyon-Juniper Wd.; Mojave Desert n. to Mono Co.; w. Nev. May–Aug.

68. **E. elegáns** Greene. [*E. vimineum* var. *e.* Jeps. *E. Baileyi* ssp. *e.* Munz.] Erect annuals, usually simple at the base, 1–4 dm. high, forming an open crown of gray to reddish branches, repeatedly dichotomously branched above, glabrous nearly throughout except for the white-woolly base of the stems; lvs. rounded to subcordate or oblong, basal, 3–15 mm. long and wide, white-woolly on both surfaces, undulate on the margins, on somewhat longer petioles; invols. turbinate, 1–1.5 mm. long, glabrous except for the ciliated margins, sessile at the nodes of the branches, few-fld.; calyx rose to pink with reddish midribs, 1–1.5 mm. long, the segms. oblong-obovate, glandular-puberulent externally; aks. brown, ca. 1 mm. long, the globose bases narrowing to 3-angled beaks.—Dry sandy flats and washes; V. Grassland, Foothill Wd.; S. Coast Ranges, Santa Clara Co. to San Luis Obispo Co. May–Aug.

69. **E. foliòsum** Wats. [*E. Baileyi* var. *tomentosum*, in part.] Spreading annuals with imperfectly dichotomously branched tomentose branches, 1–3 dm. long, these often becoming glabrate toward their tips at maturity; basal lvs. ovate to oblong, 0.5–1 cm. long, 0.3–1 cm. wide, densely white-tomentose below, less so to glabrous above, on tomentose petioles up to 2 cm. long; cauline lvs., when present, in pairs at the nodes, narrowly ovate, sessile or nearly so; invols. turbinate, 0.8–1.2 mm. long, solitary, sessile, 5-lobed; calyx white with pink midribs, becoming pink or rose at maturity, 0.8–1.2 mm. long, the outer segms. broadly hastate at the base when mature, obtuse at the apices, the margins ± crispate, the inner segms. narrower, oblong, slightly longer than the outer; fils. minutely pubescent basally; aks. bronze to brown, 1–1.2 mm. long, with long, sharp, 3-angled beaks.—Rare in sandy to gravelly places below 4000 ft.; Pinyon-Juniper Wd.; San Bernardino Mts., s. to extreme n. L. Calif. March–Aug.

This species has not been included in the California flora as it has been called *Eriogonum Baileyi* var. *tomentosum* in southern California. Although Stokes mentioned its presence in her monograph, her citation has been ignored. Her basis, no doubt, is the same as ours, *Abrams 2894* from Bear Valley, San Bernardino Mts. The type of *E. foliosum* was collected either in extreme southern San Diego Co. or adjacent northern Baja California.
Our plant is var. *foliosum* which has been somewhat confused with the var. hastàtum (Wiggins)

Reveal, stat. & comb. nov. (based on *Eriogonum hastatum* Wiggins, Contr. Dudley Herb. 1: 165, pl. 12, fig. 2A–B. 1933) of northern Baja California. The var. *hastatum* differs from the var. *foliosum* in having longer, spreading to decumbent branches up to 5 dm. long, basal lvs. 1–4 cm. long, invols. 2–3 mm. long which are only shallowly divided by the 5 lobes, a calyx 1.5–2.5 mm. long, and achenes 1.8–2 mm. long.

70. E. dasyánthemum T. & G. [*E. vimineum* var. *eriocladon* Benth. *E. d.* var. *Jepsonii* Greene.] Erect annuals, branched from the base or above, 2–6 dm. high, floccose-tomentose nearly throughout, sometimes glabrate; lvs. basal, roundish, white-woolly below, glabrate above, 1–2 cm. wide, on petioles ca. as long; lower nodes also with some lvs.; invols. subcylindric, ca. 4 mm. long, 5-ribbed and -toothed, sessile, scattered along the branchlets, tomentose between the ribs; calyx white or rose, 2 mm. long, pubescent externally, the segms. oblong-obovate; aks. 1.5–2 mm. long, with scabrellous 3-angled beaks; $2n = 24$ (Stokes & Stebbins, 1955).—Dry slopes; Foothill Wd., Chaparral, V. Grassland; inner Coast Ranges from Lake Co. to Tehama Co. Aug.–Oct.

Subgenus Eucýcla (Nutt.) Kuntze.

71. E. saxátile Wats. [*E. Bloomeri* Parish. *E. Stokesae* Jones. *E. s.* var. *S.* Jones.] Perennial herbs with few-branched caudices clothed with the crowded closely white-felted lvs.; lvs. basal, rounded or broadly obovate, the lf.-blades 1–2.5 cm. long, on petioles ca. as long or longer; flowering stems ascending, rather slender, 1–3 (–4.5) dm. high, closely tomentose or floccose, forking above with ascending or spreading branches; invols. turbinate, 3–4 mm. long, solitary at the nodes, scattered along the branches, tomentulose, many-fld.; calyx white, pinkish, or yellowish, 5–7 mm. long, glabrous, narrowed to a sharply triangular narrow base, the outer segms. oblanceolate, the inner segms. obovate and larger; aks. brownish, glabrous, ca. 2 mm. long, ± winged and 3-angled, narrowly elliptic in outline, not beaked; $n = 20$ (Reveal, 1967).—Dry rocky slopes and ridges, mostly 4000–11,000 ft.; Joshua Tree Wd. to Subalpine F.; San Jacinto and Little San Bernardino mts., w. and n. to San Gabriel, Argus and Panamint mts., s. Sierra Nevada to Fresno Co., Santa Lucia Mts. Nev. May–July.

72. E. crocàtum A. Davids. [*E. saxatile* var. *c.* Munz.] Perennial subshrubs, the caudices loosely branched and clothed with old lvs.; lvs. sheathing up the stems, lf.-blades broadly ovate, 1.5–3.5 cm. long, the petioles shorter to ca. as long; flowering stems terminal, 1–2 (–3) dm. high, 1–2 forked at right angles, forming rather dense cymes 3–8 cm. across; invols. broadly campanulate, 3–4 mm. long, white-woolly; calyx sulphur-yellow, 5–6 mm. long, narrowed into a tubular stipe-like base, the outer calyx-segms. oblance-oblong, the inner segms. wider than the outer segms., glabrous; aks. brownish, lance-ovoid, ca. 3 mm. long, glabrous, somewhat 3-angled; $2n = 40$ (Stokes & Stebbins, 1955). —Rocky slopes, at ca. 500 ft.; Coastal Sage Scrub; Conejo Grade, n. base of Santa Monica Mts., Ventura Co. April–July.

73. E. àpricum J. T. Howell. Compact perennial herbs with short woody branching caudices covered with old persistent lvs.; lvs. basal, round-ovate, 3–5 (–10) mm. long and wide, densely and persistently tomentose below, glabrate above at maturity, the bases cordate or round, the apices obtuse or acutish, on petioles 3–10 (–25) mm. long; stems dying back each year, 8–20 cm. long, erect, slender, glabrous; infl. dichotomous or trichotomous; invols. campanulate, 2–2.5 mm. long, solitary, sessile and terminal, rarely spicate, glabrous without, sparsely pubescent within, 5-lobed; calyx white with reddish midribs, 2–3 mm. long, segms. oblong, glabrous without, sparsely long-pilose below the middle within; aks. 2.5–3 mm. long, the subglobose bases tapering to roughened 3-angled beaks; $n = 20$ (Stebbins, per. comm. to J. T. Howell and to J. L. Reveal).—Clay hills at ca. 300 ft.; Chaparral; near Ione and Buena Vista, Amador Co. June–Sept.

This unusually odd addition to the California buckwheats is not easily explained, and from our present knowledge, not understood. Howell suggested that its affinities might lie with the annual *E. vimineum*, but this now seems unlikely in view of the chromosomal differences. He also suggested that it may have originated from the same ancestral stock that gave rise to *E. Batemanii*, but this species belongs to a species complex that is almost entirely restricted to the Green-Colorado river basin of western Colorado and eastern Utah. The new California species, published in *Leafl West Bot.* (7: 237. 1955), is placed before *E. microthecum* only as a matter of convenience and does not reflect an opinion of its relationship although it is probably closer to this species than to any other group.

74. **E. microthècum** Nutt. Low bushy half-shrubs 1–4 dm. high from freely branched woody bases; lvs. linear to linear-oblanceolate, or narrowly obovate to elliptic, 1–3 cm. long, grayish white-tomentose below, glabrous and greenish above, not revolute, narrowing gradually to short petioles; flowering stems herbaceous, leafy from slightly less to considerably more than half their length, 5–20 cm. long, usually glabrous; infl. freely branching, open, cymose, usually flat-topped, 2–20 cm. long; invols. narrowly turbinate, (2–) 2.5–3 mm. long, sparsely floccose or more commonly glabrous except for the ciliated, rounded 5-lobes, solitary, mostly pedunculate becoming sessile above; calyx yellow, 2–3 mm. long, the outer segms. round-oblong to obovate, with subcordate bases, the inner narrower, elliptic, glabrous; aks. narrow, 1.5–2 mm. long.—Dry places mostly below 7000 ft.; N. Juniper Wd., Yellow Pine F.; Lassen and Modoc cos.; e. Ore., w. Ida., and n. Nev.

It should be noted in the beginning that the treatment of this species complex for California is not complete, and the only reason for this is that Reveal would prefer to publish the new varieties that have been found in a separate paper. To date, there are at least three additional new varieties for the state. One, which will be a new combination, is common in Arizona and just enters the state. Two undescribed varieties have been discovered in the San Bernardino Mts. and the Cuyamaca Mts. A possibly third undescribed variety may occur in the alpine regions of the Sierra Nevada. This entire species complex will be the subject of the sixth paper in the series of *Notes on Eriogonum* by Reveal.

The concept of the var. *microthecum* differs from that presented in California floras in the past, and actually it was not until the *Eriogonum* treatment by Hitchcock in the Pacific Northwest Flora series (1964) that its exact nature was noted. The type which was collected by Nuttall in northeastern Oregon represents that part of the species as outlined above which enters California only in Lassen and Modoc cos. Because of the close relationship of var. *microthecum* to another yellow-flowered variety, it is imperative that the following variety be proposed at this time.

Var. **ambíguum** (Jones) Reveal, comb. nov. [based on *E. aureum* Jones var. *a.* Jones, *Proc. Calif. Acad.* ser. 2, 5: 720. 1895. *E. m.* var. *expansum* S. Stokes.] Lvs. floccose above, usually not revolute; stems usually floccose-tomentose above; invols. turbinate, 2–2.5 mm. long; calyx yellow.—Dry rocky and gravelly places, Pinyon-Juniper Wd., Yellow Pine F., 5000–10,000 ft.; w. slopes of the Sierra Nevada from Inyo Co. n. to Placer Co., and White Mts.; w. Nev. July–Sept.

Var. **laxiflòrum** Hook. [*E. confertiflorum* Benth. *E. m.* var. *c.* T. & G. *E. m.* sspp. *c.* and *l.* S. Stokes. *E. m.* var. *panamintense* S. Stokes. *E. effusum* var. *limbatum* S. Stokes. *E. tenellum* var. *erianthum* Gand.] Plants (0.5–) 2–4 dm. high; lvs. usually revolute, narrow; calyx white.—Dry rocky places, mostly 5000–10,000; Inyo Co. n. to Wash.; Rocky Mts. July–Oct. The common form in California.

It should be noted that the author citation of var. *laxiflorum* differs from that usually presented, but Hooker proposed the name in 1854, while Bentham, who is usually cited, proposed the same name in 1856. A name long associated with the California flora is *E. effusum* var. *rosamarinoides* Benth. In reviewing the types of this complex, it was discovered that the var. *rosamarinoides* is an excellent variety of *E. effusum* which was collected by J. C. Frémont in Kansas, though how it came to be cited by Bentham as coming from California is unknown.

75. **E. Heermánnii** Dur. & Hilg. [*E. H.* ssp. *occidentale* S. Stokes.] Woody and branched shrubs, the stems erect, woody and floccose in lower portions, glabrous and light green above, 3–7 (–15) dm. high; lvs. lance-oblong to oblanceolate, 1–2 (–2.5) cm. long, green above, floccose below, somewhat undulate, short-petioled; infl. a cymose panicle of dichotomously branched rigid branchlets, almost or quite smooth, subterete, the lower internodes 2–4 (–6) cm. long; invols. solitary in the forks or terminal, broadly turbinate, 2 mm. long, rather deeply lobed, glabrous; calyx yellowish-white, 3–4 mm. long, the outer segms. orbicular, subcordate at the bases, the inner oblong, glabrous; aks. narrow, 3-angled, 2–2.5 mm. long.—Dry slopes and ridges, 2000–7000 ft.; Pinyon-Juniper Wd., Foothill Wd., Joshua Tree Wd.; borders of San Joaquin V. (San Benito and Kern cos.) and w. Mojave Desert (Little San Bernardino Mts. to Inyo Co.); w. Nev. July–Sept.

Var. **floccòsum** Munz. Lower internodes of infl. 2–3 cm. long, the branchlets floccose-tomentose; fls. 2–3 mm. long.—Largely in Pinyon-Juniper Wd.; mts. of e. Mojave Desert, San Bernardino Co. Aug.–Oct.

Var. **argénse** (Jones) Munz. [*E. sulcatum* var. *a.* Jones. *E. Howellii* S. Stokes.] Low subshrubs, 1–2 dm. high; stems numerous, slender and rather delicate; infl. very compact and intricate, the lower internodes 0.5–1.2 cm. long, the branchlets glabrous and scabrous under a lens; calyx ca. 2 mm. long—Dry rocky slopes and ridges, 5000–8000 ft.; Pinyon-Juniper Wd.; Inyo and Mono cos.; Nev. July–Oct.

Var. **sulcàtum** (Wats.) Munz & Reveal, comb. nov. [*E. sulcatum* Wats., *Proc. Am. Acad.* 14: 296. 1879. *E. H.* ssp. *s.* Munz.] Intricately branched rounded bushes 1.5–4 dm. high; internodes short, strongly angled and grooved, but not scabrellous; fls. as in the typical form of the sp.—At 6300–6800 ft.; Pinyon-Juniper Wd.; Kingston Mts., e. Mojave Desert; to sw. Utah, nw. Ariz. July–Oct.

76. **E. Plumatélla** Dur. & Hilg. [*E. Palmeri* Wats.] Rather woody shrubs at the base, with several erect stems 3–6 dm. high, leafy on lower portions, white-tomentulose almost throughout, forked above; lvs. oblanceolate to oblong-lanceolate, 8–15 mm. long, revolute, acute, hoary-tomentose, with short slender petioles; invols. borne on mostly horizontal branches which spread in tiers to one side of the main axis and form an intricate mass ending in short-noded branchlets; invols. solitary but close together, glabrous, sessile, turbinate-cylindric, 2.5 mm. long; calyx glabrous, white, 2 mm. long, the outer segms. obovate, the inner narrower; fils. pilose basally; aks. narrow, brown, slightly angled, scaberulous above.—Dry stony places, below 4500 ft.; Creosote Bush Scrub, Joshua Tree Wd., Shadscale Scrub, Pinyon-Juniper Wd.; Kern R. region to Walker Pass, Mojave Desert; apparently to Utah, Ariz. Aug.–Oct.

Var. **Jaègeri** (M. & J.) S. Stokes ex Munz. [*E. nodosum* var. *J.* M. & J.] Infl. green and glabrous.—Mojave Desert; to w. Ariz.

77. **E. desertícola** Wats. Erect shrubs 6–12 (–15) dm. tall, much branched, the ultimate branchlets white-tomentose and leafy when young, becoming glabrous, green, and leafless in age; lvs. oblong-ovate to round-oblong, 5–15 mm. long, sometimes wider, white-woolly, on petioles 5–12 mm. long; invols. solitary, terminal, woolly, 1.5 mm. long, with 4 rounded teeth, short-peduncled; calyx yellow with green or reddish midribs, silkyvillous, the segms. oblong-obovate, 2–3 mm. long; fils. pubescent basally; aks. dark, lance-ovoid, strigose, scabrellous above, 3 mm. long.—Locally common along sandy washes, dunes, etc.; Creosote Bush Scrub; Imperial Co. from the Salton Sink to dunes w. of Yuma. Sept.–Dec.

78. **E. Keárneyi** Tidestr. [*E. nodosum* var. *K.* S. Stokes.] Subshrubs with few to several scraggly, fragile stems arising from a woody taproot, usually densely tomentose nearly throughout, 3–8 (–10) dm. high; lvs. on the lower third of the plant, broadly oblanceolate to elliptic, the lf.-blades 1.5–2.5 (–3) cm. long, 5–10 (–12) mm. wide, densely tomentose on both surfaces, petioles up to 1 cm. long; infl. making up more than half the height of the plant; invols. racemosely disposed, scattered and appressed to the branches, turbinate, 2–2.5 mm. long; calyx white with reddish midribs, glabrous, 1.5–2 mm. long, connate nearly ½ the length and forming a campanulate perianth tube, this maturing reddish, the segms. obovate, nearly similar; calyx ca. 2.5 mm. long in fruit; aks. 2 mm. long, the subglobose bases tapering to 3-angled beaks.—Dry sandy soil, 4500–7000 ft.; Sagebrush Scrub, Pinyon-Juniper Wd.; Mono Lake Basin, Mono Co.; Nev., w. Utah, nw. Ariz. July–Oct.

Var. **monoénse** (S. Stokes) Reveal. [*E. nodosum* of California authors, in part. *E. n.* ssp. *m.* S. Stokes.] Plants 8–15 dm. high; lvs. 2–3 cm. long; invols. 2.5–3 mm. long, clustering at the ends of the branches; calyx 2.5–3 mm. long.—Dry gravelly places, 6000–8500 ft.; Sagebrush Scrub, Pinyon-Juniper Wd.; Mono and Inyo cos. July–Oct.

The var. *Kearneyi* is known in California only from the northeast shore of Mono Lake where it is common and somewhat unusual. Equally scattered in this population are glabrous stemmed forms along with the normal densely tomentose plants. Our plants are disjunct from the other known populations, the closest being in Washoe Co., and from near Tonopah, Nye Co., Nevada. A similar Tonopah-Mono Lake disjunct is *Astragalus pseudiodanthus* Barneby. The var. *monoense*, proposed in *Leafl. West. Bot.* 10: 334. 1966, is distinct from the Mono Lake plants, but somewhat similar to the high desert forms in western Utah.

79. **E. Butterworthiànum** J. T. Howell. Caudex low, branched, woody, plants 1–1.5 dm. high; lvs. linear or narrowly elliptical, ± revolute, (0.5–) 1–2 cm. long, 1–4 mm. wide, tomentose on both surfaces, gradually tapering to short petioles; flowering stems 1–3 cm. long, few, simple or divided 1 or 2 times, densely tomentose; invols. mostly solitary, sessile, tomentose, turbinate, 5–6 mm. long, 5-lobed, the teeth 1–2 mm. long,

deposed racemosely along the stems; calyx ochroleucous with reddish midribs, 4–5 mm. long, glabrous, the segms. obovate; fils. ciliated basally; aks. narrow, ca. 3 mm. long.— Crevices of sandstone, 2200 ft.; Mixed Evergreen F.; Santa Lucia Range, Monterey Co. June–Aug.

This species is closest to *Eriogonum Wrightii*, but how close remains to be determined by cytological studies. Named in 1961 (*Leafl. West. Bot.* 9: 153.), the plant has not been found beyond the type area which is near The Indians in the Santa Lucia Range.

80. **E. Wrìghtii** Torr. ex Benth. Low, highly branched perennial subshrubs from branched woody caudices, 1.5–4 dm. high; lvs. on the lower half of the plants, crowded, oblanceolate to elliptic, 0.5–1.5 cm. long, 2–5 (–7) mm. wide, mostly entire, densely white-tomentose above and below, or rarely subglabrous and green above, the petioles 2–5 mm. long; flowering stems several, tomentose or rarely glabrous, up to 25 cm. long; infl. racemose, 5–30 cm. long, once or twice dichotomous or trichotomous; invols. solitary, turbinate, 2–2.5 mm. long, ± tomentose; calyx whitish or pink, 2.5–3.5 mm. long, glabrous, the outer segms. broadly obovate, the inner less so; flls. ± pilose basally; aks. narrow, 2.5–3 mm. long, 3-angled, somewhat scaberulous above; $2n = 34$ (Stokes & Stebbins, 1955).—Gravelly and rocky places, mostly below 5000 ft.; Pinyon-Juniper Wd.; Mojave and Colo. deserts e. to w. Tex. Aug.–Oct.

Var. **trachygònum** (Torr. ex Benth.) Jeps. [*E. W.* ssp. *t.* S. Stokes. *E. t.* Torr. ex Benth.] Low, woody, subshrubs, 2–4 dm. high; lvs. broadly elliptic to elliptic, 1.5–3 cm. long, (3–) 5–10 mm. wide, densely tomentose below, usually less so above, not revolute; invols. 2–3 mm. long, ± tomentose; calyx white to pink, 3–4 mm. long.—Exposed and open rocky places, mostly below 6000 ft.; Foothill Wd., Yellow Pine F.; inner Coast Ranges and w. base of Sierra Nevada, Shasta Co. to n. Los Angeles Co. Aug.–Oct.

Var. **membranàceum** S. Stokes ex Jeps. [*E. W.* ssp. *m.* S. Stokes.] Woody, branched subshrubs, 2–4 dm. high and up to 6 dm. across; petiole bases dilated into glabrate, brownish sheaths which clasp the stems; lvs. strongly involute, 3–6 (–10) mm. long, 1–3 (–4) mm. wide; invols. 2–3 mm. long, often glabrous; calyx white to pink, 3–4 mm. long.— Dry stony places below 6000 ft.; Chaparral, Joshua Tree Wd., Pinyon-Juniper Wd.; Little San Bernardino and Santa Monica mts. to San Diego Co.; L. Calif. Aug.–Oct.

Var. **nodòsum** (Small) Reveal. [*E. n.* Small.] Woody, branched, densely white-lanate shrubs up to 6 dm. high and 15 dm. across; petiole bases dilated but not extending completely around the stems, lvs. 8–12 mm. long, 2.5–4 mm. wide, tomentose, not revolute; invols. 1.5–2.5 mm. long; calyx white, 3–4 mm. long.—Dry stony places below 3000 ft.; Creosote Bush Scrub, Pinyon-Juniper Wd.; w. edge of Colo. Desert e. to Twentynine Palms; L. Calif. Aug.–Nov. The var. *Prínglei* (Coult. & Fish.) Reveal, a form with more numerous branches, shorter invols. and flls., occurs in southwestern Arizona and may be expected in southeastern California.

Var. **subscapòsum** Wats. [*E. W.* ssp. *s.* S. Stokes. *E. junceum* Greene. *E. curvatum* Small. *E. W.* var. *c.* Munz. *E. Kennedyi* ssp. *pinorum* S. Stokes.] Low and loosely matted, 1–2.5 dm. high; lvs. crowded, 5–12 mm. long, grayish- or brownish-white; flowering stems slender, up to 1.5 dm. long, glabrous to floccose; infl. 5–15 cm. long; invols. 1.5–3 mm. long.—Rocky and gravelly places, 5000–11,000 ft.; Montane Coniferous F.; Sierra Nevada to San Jacinto and San Bernardino mts. July–Oct.

Var. **olanchénse** (J. T. Howell) Reveal, comb. nov. [*E. Kennedyi* var. *o.* J. T. Howell, *Leafl. West. Bot.* 6: 151. 1951.] Low and densely matted cespitose perennials, less than 3 cm. high; lvs. crowded, 1–2.5 mm. long, densely white-tomentose; flowering stems slender, up to 1 cm. long, subglabrous; infl. 1–1.5 cm. long; invols. 0.8–1.3 mm. long.—Dry granitic places, 11,500–11,800 ft.; Olancha Pk., Tulare Co. July–Aug.

The *Eriogonum Wrightii* complex is composed of several morphologically distinct, but closely related and often sympatric varieties that occur in the dry places throughout much of southern California. The species has suffered considerable confusion in the herbarium with *E. Kennedyi*, and it is hoped that the present key will alleviate most of the problems encountered in the past.

81. **E. panaminténse** Morton. [*E. reliquum* S. Stokes. *E. racemosum* var. *desertorum* S. Stokes.] Caudex low and matted, branched, woody, often up to 4 dm. across; lvs. basal and along the lower nodes, not crowded, densely white-tomentose below, less so above, elliptic, ovate or obovate, 15–40 mm. long, 10–25 mm. wide, on tomentose peti-

oles 1–5 cm. long; flowering stems several to many, white-tomentose, 1.5–3 cm. high, 1–3 times dichotomous; cauline lvs. verticillate, ± orbicular, similar to the basal lvs. but reduced, short petioled; invols. solitary, sessile, scattered racemosely along the branches and in the forks, 3–5 mm. long, densely white-tomentose; calyx white to whitish-brown, 3.5–5 mm. long, glabrous, the segms. ± similar, oblanceolate; fils. pilose basally; aks. narrow, 3-angled, ca. 3 mm. long.—Dry rocky slopes, 5000–9000 ft.; Pinyon-Juniper Wd., Yellow Pine F.; Inyo-White to New York and Clark mts.; sw. Nev. May–Oct.

Var. **mensícola** (S. Stokes) Reveal, comb. & stat. nov. [*E. m.* S. Stokes, *Leafl. West. Bot.* 3: 16. 1941.] Lvs. strictly basal, the lf.-blades 1–1.5 cm. long and wide, rotund, densely tomentose on both surfaces; bracts not leafy, lanceolate to lance-ovate, mostly 2–6 mm. long; invols. few, scattered along the stems, 2–4 mm. long; calyx 3–4 mm. long. —Dry rocky slopes, 5000–8000 ft.; Pinyon-Juniper Wd.; Inyo-White and Panamint mts.; Sheep Range, Nev. July–Sept.

The recognition of *Eriogonum panamintense* came after Reveal had spent considerable time studying *E. racemosum, Wrightii,* and *panamintense* in the field and in the herbarium. *Eriogonum panamintense,* for several years, has been associated with *E. racemosum,* a form of which just enters California, although *E. panamintense* is more closely related to *E. Wrightii.* The growth habit of *E. panamintense* and *E. racemosum* is totally different, with the latter having a single, or at most, three stems arising from a short, little branched caudex, while the former has several branches arising from a highly branched, spreading matted woody caudex.

82. **E. racemòsum** Nutt. Caudex woody, few-branched, compact; lvs. basal, oblong to oblong-ovate, the lf.-blades mostly 2.5–3.5 cm. long, glabrate above and closely white-tomentose below, on petioles as long or longer; flowering stems slender, mostly 1.5–3 dm. high, tomentose, trichotomous once or twice, usually not leafy bracted; invols. solitary and arranged racemosely along the upper branches, tubular-campanulate, 3–4 mm. long, tomentose; calyx cream-white, 2.5–3 mm. long, the segms. oblong-oblanceolate; fils. pilose basally; aks. lance-ovoid, brownish, ca. 2 mm. long, 3-angled; $n = 18$ (Reveal, 1968).—At ca. 6000–7000 ft.; Pinyon-Juniper Wd.; White and Cottonwood mts., Inyo Co.; to Colo., New Mex. July–Aug.

The plant simply called *Eriogonum racemosum* in this treatment extends from the White Mountains eastward to the Toquima Range of central Nevada. This part of the species is somewhat similar to the kind of plant found in northern New Mexico and adjacent Colorado, but differs considerably from the kind of plant found in eastern Nevada and most of Utah. The western phase of the species seems to be distinct, but until the entire species is studied in some detail, no new taxa are proposed.

83. **E. elongàtum** Benth. [*E. denudatum* Nutt.] Perennial herbs, mostly loosely branched at the base, whitish-tomentulose nearly throughout, leafy in lower portion, passing into elongate, leafless paniculately forked infls. above, 6–12 (–18) dm. high; lvs. lance-oblong to narrowly ovate, crisped-undulate, somewhat glabrate above, white-tomentose below, 3–5 cm. long, cuneate at base, short-petioled; invols. remotely scattered, oblong-cylindric, 6–7 mm. long, tomentose, truncate, obscurely 5-toothed; calyx white or pinkish, glabrous, 2.5–3 mm. long, the segms. obovate, the inner slightly longer than the outer, somewhat pubescent within; fils. glabrous; aks. dark, narrow, 2–2.5 mm. long, glabrous, somewhat 3-angled; $2n = 34$ (Stokes & Stebbins, 1955).—Dry rocky places, below 6000 ft.; Coastal Sage Scrub, Chaparral, Foothill Wd.; Coast Ranges from Monterey and San Benito cos. to n. L. Calif. Aug.–Nov.

84. **E. ovalifòlium** Nutt. Cespitose perennial with closely branched woody caudices thickly beset with lvs., densely white-tomentose; lvs. basal, round to obovate, the lf.-blades 5–15 (–20) mm. long, short-petioled; flowering stems scapose, slender, white-woolly, 1–2 dm. high; infl. capitate, 1.5–2.5 cm. in diam.; invols. several, white-woolly, commonly 4–5 mm. long, narrowly cylindric; calyx whitish or rarely yellow to ochroleucous, glabrous, 4–5 mm. long, the outer lobes elliptic, subcordate at the base, the inner segms. spatulate, exserted; fils. pilose basally; aks. glabrous, 2–2.5 mm. long, 3-angled; $2n = 40$ (Stokes & Stebbins, 1955), $n = 20$ (Reveal, 1965).—Dry slopes and flats, mostly 5000–7000 ft.; Sagebrush Scrub, N. Juniper Wd., Pinyon-Juniper Wd.; e. slope of Sierra Nevada, n. and e. to Alta., Rocky Mts. May–July.

Var. **multiscàpum** Gand. [*E. orthocaulon* Small. *E. o.* Nutt. var. *o.* C. L. Hitchc. *E. o.* var. *celsum.* A. Nels.] Lf.-blades oblong to obovate, 3–6 cm. long; flowering stems ca. 1–3 dm. high, fls. mostly yellow; $n = 20$ (Reveal, 1965).—Dry slopes and flats, Lassen and Modoc cos., 4500–6000 ft.; Sagebrush Scrub, N. Juniper Wd.; s. Ore., Nev. and Ida. May–June.

Var. **vineùm** (Small) Nels. [*E. v.* Small. *E. o.* ssp. *v.* S. Stokes.] Lf.-blades round-ovate, 7–12 mm. long, white, felty-tomentose; flowering stems ca. 1 dm. high; infl. capitate, up to 4 cm. in diam.; calyx 5–7 mm. long, pale.—Desert slopes, San Bernardino Mts., 5000–8000 ft. May–June.

As presently defined, the var. *vineum* is restricted to the San Bernardino Mts. and is the large flow-ered form of *E. ovalifolium*. The application of this name in the various floras and revisions has been mainly to var. *nivale*.

Var. **nivàle** (Canby) Jones. [*E. n.* Canby. *E. rhodanthum* Nels. & Kenn. *E. eximium* Tidestr. *E. o.* ssp. *e.* S. Stokes.] Lvs. nearly round, mostly less than 1 cm. in diam., white to rusty tomentose; flowering stems less than 1 dm. high; calyx white with reddish mid-ribs to rose, 2–3 mm. long; $n = 20$ (Reveal, 1965).—Dry flats and ridges, 7000–12,000 ft.; Montane Coniferous F., Alpine Fell-fields; Sierra Nevada to Ore., w. Utah. July–Aug.

The var. *nivale* is the high alpine form of the species which occurs in the mountains of California, Nevada, and western Utah, but is gradually replaced in the north by the var. *depressum* Blank. The species, *E. rhodanthum* and *E. eximium*, are essentially the same kind of plant, the first coming from the higher elevations of Mt. Rose, Nevada, and the second from the lower elevations. However, while the population is distinctive, it too blends into adjacent forms of var. *nivale* and for this reason, the two species are reduced to synonyms.

85. **E. Gilmánii** S. Stokes. Low compact perennial from an elongated woody root, the caudex covered with old lvs.; lvs. crowded in a basal rosette, few to ca. 14, suberect, densely white-tomentose, the lf.-blades 2–4 mm. long, elliptic, with petioles margined and ca. as long; scapes solitary, 1–2 cm. high and with 2–3 cymosely arranged invols.; invols. turbinate, 1.5 mm. long; calyx reddish, glabrous, the outer segms. inflated, rounded on the back and orbicular in shape so as to form a globose segm. 3–4 mm. in diam., the inner segms. narrower, longer, slightly exserted; aks. 2.5 mm. long, acutely 3-angled.—At 6200 ft., Pinyon Mesa, Panamint Mts., Inyo Co. Aug.–Sept.

86. **E. strictum** Benth. ssp. **proliferum** (T. & G.) S. Stokes. [*E. ovalifolium* var. *p.* Wats. *E. p.* T. & G. *E. Greenei* Gray. *E. niveum* var. *G.* S. Stokes.] Caudex compactly branched, the plants white-tomentose; lvs. basal, the blades ovate, obtuse, sometimes bicolored, 1–2 cm. long, on slender long petioles; flowering stems erect, naked, slender, floccose, 1.5–2.5 dm. high; infl. cymose-umbellate, the rays divaricate, to 4 cm. long; invols. largely solitary in the forks and terminal, oblong-turbinate, tomentose, 5–6 mm. long, 5-toothed; calyx cream to white, 4–5 mm. long, the outer segms. broadly elliptic with obcordate bases, the inner narrower, obovate, somewhat exserted; fils. pilose basally; aks. glabrous, narrow, 3-angled.—Dry open places, 3500–6000 ft.; Sagebrush Scrub, N. Juniper Wd., Yellow Pine F.; Siskiyou Co. and Plumas Co. n.; to B.C. and Ida. June–Aug.

Var. **anserìnum** (Greene) R. J. Davis. [*E. a.* Greene. *E. strictum* ssp. *a.* S. Stokes. *E. flavissimum* Gand. *E. ovalifolium* ssp. *f.* S. Stokes. *E. proliferum* ssp. *a.* Munz. *E. s.* var. *f.* C. L. Hitchc.] Invols. 1–3 in clusters on rays up to 5 cm. long; calyx yellow.—Similar situations, e. Siskiyou Co., Modoc Co.; adjacent Nev. and Ore. June–July.

The var. *proliferum* and var. *anserinum* have suffered much misunderstanding as the list of synonymy shows. *Eriogonum strictum* occurs to the north, with two forms coming into California, both of which are often mistaken for *E. ovalifolium*, a related, but distinct species. The cymose-umbellate inflores-cences of *E. strictum*, sen. lat., quickly distinguish it from the capitate inflorescences of *E. ovalifolium* even though both may have similar flower color, size of plants, and leaf color and shape.

87. **E. Shóckleyi** Wats. [*E. acaule* of Intermountain authors, not Nutt.] Caudex pul-vinate, branched, low, the plants with a dense brownish-white tomentum; lvs. crowded, oblanceolate to elliptic or spatulate, plane, the lf.-blades 3–8 mm. long, 2–4 mm. wide, with petioles ca. as long or slightly longer, densely tomentose on both surfaces; flowering stems scapelike, lacking to 2 cm. long, slender, tomentose; infl. capitate, with 4–10 invols.; invols. campanulate, ± membranaceous but forming distinct tubes, 2–2.5 mm. long, the 5–7 lobes dividing the tube to near the middle; calyx brownish with tan to rusty midribs, densely pubescent without, slightly so within, 2.5–3 mm. long, the segms. obovate, similar; fils. pilose basally; aks. lance-ovoid, ca. 2.5 mm. long, sparsely pubescent. —Dr. rocky slopes and clay hills, 6000–8000 ft.; Sagebrush Scrub, Pinyon-Juniper Wd.; Last Chance Mts., Inyo Co.; e. to Utah, w. Colo., n. Ariz. May–July.

This previously unreported species for California is to be expected along the slopes of the desert ranges adjacent to Nevada in Inyo and possibly Mono cos. Our plant is var. *Shockleyi.*

88. **E. Breedlóvei** (J. T. Howell) Reveal. [*E. ochrocephalum* var. *B.* J. T. Howell.] Caudex cespitose, branched, low, the plants densely olive-green to whitish tomentose with glandular hairs nearly throughout; lvs. crowded, broadly elliptic, plane or with margins slightly revolute, lf.-blades 2–8 (–10) mm. long, 2–4 (–6) mm. wide, densely tomentose below, less so and green above, petioles up to 1 cm. long, petiole bases broadened, hairy on both surfaces; flowering stems scapelike, erect, 1.5–6 cm. tall, densely glandular-hairy, the 3 triangular bracts ca. 2 mm. long; infl. compactly cymose-umbellate with short rays up to 3 (–5) mm. long, the branches often bracteate; invols. 4–6, turbinate-campanulate, 3.5–4 mm. long and wide, glandular-puberulent, 7–9 lobed, the triangular to acute lobes 1–1.5 mm. long, forming a distinct tube; calyx whitish becoming reddish, 2.5–3.5 (–4) mm. long, the segms. cuneate, somewhat dissimilar, the outer segms. wider than the inner, finely glandular-hairy within and without; fils. ± pilose basally; aks. lance-ovoid, 2–3 mm. long, sparsely and minutely hairy above the middle.— Dry rocky outcrops, 7800–8200 ft.; Red Fir F.; Piute Mts., Kern Co., Baker Point, s. Tulare Co. June–Aug.

Eriogonum Breedlovei is an interesting addition to the California buckwheats, and especially to the section *Capitata* T. & G. It is similar to *E. Cusickii* Jones and *E. exilifolium* Reveal in that the inflorescence is not tightly capitate, but rather a compact cymose-umbellate head. However, this single feature seems to be a parallel characteristic and does not reflect any relationship between these species. The Piute Buckwheat, as stated by Howell when he proposed the variety, is most closely related to what is here called *E. anemophilum.* The variety was proposed in *Leafl. West. Bot.* 10: 14, 1963, but following additional field work, it was raised to the species level in *Leafl. West. Bot.* 10: 335. 1966.

89. **E. ochrocéphalum** Wats. Caudex ± cespitose, branched, forming loosely branching mats, the plants with dense whitish tomentum; lvs. crowded, ovate to obovate, or lanceolate to oblong, mostly 2–3.5 cm. long, equally grayish-tomentose on both surfaces, with petioles nearly twice as long; flowering stems scapelike, 1–2.5 dm. long, slender, glabrous and greenish to floccose; infl. capitate, 10–15 mm. across; invols. several, turbinate-campanulate, tubular and rigid, (3–) 3.5–5 mm. long, with 6–8 teeth; fls. yellowish, glabrous, 2–3 mm. long, the segms. ovate-oblong, essentially alike; fils. pilose basally; aks. lance-ovoid, 1.5–2 mm. long.—Dry loose, often volcanic soil, or gumbo clay hills; 4000–6000 ft.; Pinyon-Juniper Wd.; Nevada Co. n.; Ore., Nev., and Ida. May–June.

90. **E. anemóphilum** Greene. [*E. rosense* Nels. & Kenn. *E. ochrocephalum* var. *agnellum* Jeps. *E. o.* sspp. *a.* and *a.* S. Stokes.] Caudex densely cespitose, branched, low, the plants with dense olive-green to whitish tomentum; lvs. crowded, oblanceolate, 4–15 mm. long, 2.5–5 mm. wide, densely white-tomentose below, greenish-tomentose above, the petioles from shorter to as long as the lvs.; flowering stems scapelike, 1–9 cm. tall, slender, glandular; infl. capitate, 6–15 mm. across; invols. few, turbinate, tubular and rigid, 3–3.5 mm. long, with 6–8 teeth; calyx yellow and becoming reddish, glabrous or more frequently glandular, 2–3 mm. long, the segms. obovate, essentially alike; fils. pilose basally; aks. lance-ovoid, ca. 1.5 mm. long; *n* = 20 (Reveal, 1967).—Dry granitic and volcanic soils, 9000–12,000 ft.; Yellow Pine F., Red Fir F., Alpine Fell-fields; Inyo and Fresno cos. to Placer Co.; Nev. July–Aug.

The introduction of the name *Eriogonum anemophilum* comes as a result of two studies, one in the field and the other in the herbarium. The type of *E. ochrocephalum* came from the clay hills north of Reno, Nevada, and extends from the Reno area northward into southern Oregon where it is largely replaced by the var. *calcareum* (S. Stokes) Peck. In the high mountains of Oregon eastward to the Idaho-Montana state line is a related species, *E. chrysops* Rydb. The relationship between *E. chrysops* and *E. ochrocephalum* is the same as that found between *E. anemophilum* and *E. ochrocephalum.* Both species occur in the high mountains, with *E. chrysops* ranging from 7000 to 11,000 feet elevation and *E. anemophilum* occurring from 9000 feet to 12,000 feet elevation. While the distinction between *E. ochrocephalum* and the alpine species is distinct, the relationship between the two alpine species is in need of critical study.

Reveal has seen only an isotype of *Eriogonum anemophilum,* and the holotypes of *E. rosense* and *E. ochrocephalum* var. *agnellum* compare rather favorably with it. The isotype is slightly larger than either of the other specimens, but this condition falls well within the variation seen in the Sierra Nevada populations, although *E. anemophilum* was collected in the West Humboldt Range of western Nevada. The type of *E. rosense* was taken from the summit of Mt. Rose in extreme western Nevada.

91. **E. chrÿsops** Rydb. [*E. ochrocephalum* ssp. *c.* S. Stokes.] Caudex densely cespitose, branched, low, the plants with dense grayish-white tomentum; lvs. crowded, spatulate

to oblanceolate, 4–6 mm. long, 2–3 mm. wide, densely tomentose on both surfaces, the petioles shorter than the blades; flowering stems scapelike, 2–5 cm. tall, slender, glabrous; infl. capitate, ca. 1 cm. across; invols. 3–7, sessile, campanulate, 2–2.5 mm. long, with 5 lobes, glabrous or nearly so; calyx yellow, glabrous, 2.5–3 mm. long, the segms. oblong to oblong-obovate, essentially alike; fils. pilose basally; aks. lance-ovoid, 2–2.5 mm. long. —Dry volcanic soils, at 5500 ft.; N. Juniper Wd.; Modoc Co. n. se. Ore. to Mont. May– June.

Eriogonum chrysops is included in the California flora based upon *Austin*, without number, and *Balls 14780*, both of which differ in a few minor respects from the typical form in Oregon and Idaho.

92. E. Kénnedyi Porter ex Wats. [*E. K.* var. *austromontanum* of authors, in part.] Caudex branched, woody, forming dense leafy mats with numerous lvs.; lf.-blades elliptic to oblong, grayish- to brownish-white tomentose, 2–4 (–5) mm. long, 0.5–1.5 (–2) mm. wide, ± revolute in some, subsessile; flowering stems scapelike, wiry, glabrous, 4–12 cm. long; infl. capitate, 4–8 mm. across; invols. few, sparsely tomentose to glabrous, turbinate, angled, 1.5–2.5 mm. long; calyx glabrous, white with reddish midribs, 1.5–2.5 mm. long, the segms. broadly elliptical, somewhat rounded at the base; fils. subglabrous; aks. ca. 2 mm. long, papillose-puberulent, lance-ovoid, 3-angled.—Dry stony to gravelly slopes and ridges, 5000–7000 ft.; San Bernardino Mts. and Mt. Pinos. April–June.

The var. *Kennedyi* is totally redefined here as a result of an investigation of the original type collection. In the past, the concept of var. *Kennedyi* has been appplied to what is here called var. *Purpusii*. This misapplication has been the result of the inability to exactly determine the type locality. Originally cited as simply "Kern County" it has been assumed that this meant Inyo Co. However this is not the case. At the suggestion of E. C. Twisselmann who is the author of the Kern County Flora, a careful comparison was made with the type and other collections. The original Kennedy collection was found to compare most favorably with specimens from the lower slopes of Mt. Pinos which is just south of the Kern Co. line.

Var. austromontànum M. & J. [*E. K.* ssp. *a.* S. Stokes.] Loosely matted; lf.-blades oblanceolate, (4–) 6–10 (–12) mm. long, 1–2 mm. wide, the lvs. often sheathing up the stems; stems floccose, 8–15 cm. long; invols. turbinate, tomentose, 2.5–4 mm. long; calyx white with reddish-brown midribs, 2–3 mm. long, oblong-obovate, gradually contracted into a cuneate base; aks. 3.5–4 mm. long.—Dry stony slopes, 6300–6500 ft.; Yellow Pine F.; Bear Valley, San Bernardino Mts. July–Aug.

The var. *austromontanum* has been defined in the past to include what is here called var. *Kennedyi* and var. *austromontanum*. By removing the smaller and more compact, early flowering, var. *Kennedyi*, the var. *austromontanum* becomes a distinct taxon.

Var. alpígenum M. & J. [*E. K.* ssp. *a.* Munz.] Mats very dense and woody; lvs. 2–4 mm. long, 0.7–1.5 mm. wide; stems less than 2 cm. long, densely white-tomentose; infl. capitate, 4–8 mm. wide; invols. turbinate, 1.5–2 mm. long, tomentose; calyx white to reddish with reddish-brown midribs, 1.5–2.5 mm. long; aks. 2 mm. long.—Dry granitic gravel slopes and ridges, 10,000–11,500 ft.; Alpine Fell-fields; San Gorgonio Peak, San Bernardino Mts., somewhat lower to 8750 ft. in the San Gabriel Mts. and on Mt. Pinos. July–Aug.

The var. *alpigenum* as treated here is the same as treated previously, the only changes being in the distribution.

Var. Purpùsii (Bdg.) Reveal, stat. & comb. nov. [*E. P.* Bdg., *Bot. Gaz.* 27: 457. 1899.] Lvs. white-tomentose, oblong, (2.5–) 3–6 mm. long, 1.5–3.5 mm. wide; stems thin and wiry, glabrous or rarely tomentose, 4–10 cm. high; infl. capitate, 8–15 mm. wide; invols. turbinate-campanulate, glabrous to sparsely tomentose, 1.5–2 mm. long; calyx white with greenish midribs, 2–2.5 mm. long; aks. 3 mm. long.—Dry granitic flats and slopes, 5000– 8000 ft.; Sagebrush Scrub, Pinyon-Juniper Wd.; e. slope of Sierra Nevada from Mono Co. s. to Argus and Coso mts., Inyo Co. May–June.

To most California authors, this form of the overall species, *E. Kennedyi*, has been regarded as the typical form of the species. It is interesting to note that in the Stokes monograph, she had correctly determined what part of the species was typical *E. Kennedyi* and had recognized the distinctiveness of var. *Purpusii*. The fact that the taxon *Purpusii* is reduced under *E. Kennedyi* is mainly due to the following variety, and to the near intermediacy of some southern forms of var. *Purpusii* with the Bear Valley populations of var. *Kennedyi*.

Var. **pinícola** Reveal, var. nov. A var. *Purpusii* differt foliis 3–5 mm. longis, 1–4 mm. latis, scapis 5–13 cm. altis; involucris 2.5–3.5 mm. longis, perianthiis albis vel rufis, 2.5–3.5 mm. longis. Lvs. grayish- to rusty-white tomentose, oblong, 3–5 mm. long, 1–4 mm. wide; stems thin and wiry, glabrous, reddish, 5–13 cm. high; infl. capitate, ca. 1 cm. across; invols. turbinate-campanulate, sparsely tomentose, 2.5–3.5 mm. long; calyx white to reddish with green to reddish-brown midribs, 2.5–3.5 mm. long; aks. 3 mm. long.— Dry exposed ridgetops, 4900–5600 ft.; Pinyon Wd., Jeffrey Pine F.; known at present only from Sweetwater Ridge and Pine Tree Canyon, Kern Co. May–June. *Type*: Sweetwater Ridge, south of Cache Peak, Kern Co., California, 9 June 1966, *E. C. Twisselmann 12360*. Holotype at the California Academy of Sciences.

This new variety is most closely related to the var. *Purpusii* which occurs on the east side of the Sierra Nevada, and differs in several technical characteristics. This form is also somewhat similar to var. *austromontanum*.

93. **E. gracílipes** Wats. [*E. Kennedyi* ssp. *g.* S. Stokes. *E. ochrocephalum* var. *g.* J. T. Howell.] Caudex cespitose, branched, low, the plants with a dense whitish tomentum; lvs. crowded, oblanceolate to elliptic, plane, the lf.-blades 1–2 cm. long, with petioles ca. as long, tomentose and glandular below, less so above; flowering stems scapelike, 3–8 cm. long, slender, glandular; infl. capitate, 5–7 invols.; invols. campanulate, membranaceous, not rigid, 2–3 mm. long, flaring at the throat, the 5 lobes deeply divided to near the base; calyx white with reddish midribs becoming rose at maturity, glabrous, 2–3 mm. long, the segms. obovate, similar; fils. pilose basally; aks. lance-ovoid, ca. 2 mm. long.—Dry rocky slopes and ridges, 10,000–13,000 ft.; Bristlecone Pine F.; White Mts., Mono and Inyo cos., w. Nev. July–Sept.

The species in the section *Capitata*, which include numbers 87 through 93 are often narrowly endemic and isolated on high mountain peaks. *Eriogonum gracilipes* is most closely related to *E. Holmgrenii* Reveal of the Snake Range in eastern Nevada, which in turn seems to be close to *E. Kingii* Torr. & Gray of the Ruby Mts., northeastern Nevada. Rarely are the species in this section found growing together, and thus the various forms tend to be closely related yet very distinct.

94. **E. latifòlium** Sm. in Rees. [*E. arachnoideum* H. & A.] Caudex low, woody, densely leafy, often much-branched; lf.-blades persistent, ovate to almost oblong, cordate or rounded at the bases, obtuse or acute, often crisped on the margins, lanate or somewhat glabrous above, densely white-lanate below, 2.5–5 cm. long, the petioles shorter or longer, woolly, expanded at base; flowering stems stout, leafless, tomentulose, 2–6 dm. long, simple or rarely 2–4 forked, the forks simple or rarely forked again; infl. of capitate clusters 1.5–3 cm. across, terminal and also sessile in the forks; invols. tomentose, numerous, 3.5–4 mm. long, shallowly 5-toothed; calyx glabrous or with a few scattered hairs near the base in some, white to rose, 3 mm. long, the segms. obovate, subequal; fils. villous basally; aks. glabrous, brown, lance-ovoid, 3-angled, ca. 4 mm. long; $2n = 40$ (Stokes & Stebbins, 1955), $n = 20$ (Reveal, 1968).—Cliffs and sandy places along the immediate coast, Coastal Strand and N. Coastal Scrub; San Luis Obispo Co. n. to Ore. June–Sept.

95. **E. nùdum** Dougl. ex Benth. [*E. latifolium* ssp. *n.* S. Stokes. *E. oblongifolium* Benth. *E. oblanceolatum* Greene. *E. l.* var. *parvulum* S. Stokes. *E. longulum* Greene.] Caudex short, simple or few-branched, the leaf-bearing area not elongated; lf.-blades oblong to oblanceolate or broadly elliptic-ovate, 1–6 cm. long, rounded at the apex, glabrate above, white-lanate below, ± undulate-crisped, the petioles often much longer; flowering stems commonly 1–few, erect, slender, 3–10 dm. high, glabrous or nearly so, glaucous, usually forking or trichotomous near the middle, then branching again; invols. usually in clusters, subcylindric, 3–5 mm. long, glabrous or slightly woolly; calyx 2–2.5 mm. long, mostly white with some pink, or sometimes yellow, usually glabrous without; fils. pilose basally; aks. 1.5–3 mm. long; $2n = 40$ (Stokes & Stebbins, 1955), $n = 20$ (Reveal, 1968).—Dry, usually rocky places, up to ca. 8000 ft.; many Plant Communities; Coast Ranges from about San Francisco Bay n., Sierra Nevada from Tulare Co. n.; to Wash., Nev. June–Nov.

Exceedingly variable and intergrading with the varieties treated below. Subalpine plants from the Sierra Nevada, 7000–11,000 ft., tend to have several stems from the base, 2–3 dm. high and very slender, with lf.-blades 1–2 cm. long, and with branched infls. with largely solitary invols. which may be known as var. **dedúctum** (Greene) Jeps. [*E. d.* Greene.] The extreme in such reduction, with simple stems 1–2 dm. long and ending in single heads of several invols., occurs at elevations from ca. 10,000–12,000 ft. in s. Sierra Nevada and may be known as var. **scapígerum** (Eastw.) Jeps. [*E. s.* Eastw. *E. latifolium* var. *s.* S. Stokes.]

Key to Varieties of **E. nudum**

A. Invols. and flowering stems ± tomentose; heads usually several to many; lvs. in basal rosettes. Interior of n. Calif. .... var. *oblongifolium*

AA. Invols. and flowering stems mostly glabrous or if tomentose, then lvs. scattered along the woody caudices.
   B. Lvs. scattered along the woody caudices, the lf.-blades very strongly undulate-crisped, 3–7 cm. long. Coast Ranges of cent. Calif.
      C. Stems not strongly inflated. Coast Ranges, Sonoma Co. to Monterey Co. var. *auriculatum*
      CC. Stems strongly inflated. Inner Coast Ranges, Merced Co. to Kern Co. .... var. *indictum*
   BB. Lvs. in basal rosettes, the lf.-blades plane or slightly crisped, mostly 1–5 cm. long.
      C. Invols. 2–6 in a cluster.
         D. Fls. mostly glabrous externally, white to pink, rarely yellow.
            E. Flowering stems branched above. Lower elevations. .... var. *nudum*
            EE. Flowering stems scapose, short, ending in a solitary head. Subalpine.
                                                   var. *scapigerum*
         DD. Fls. pubescent externally, yellow to white. Desert edges and borders of San Joaquin and Salinas valleys. .... var. *pubiflorum*
      CC. Invols. solitary, rarely in pairs. Mostly of pine belt.
         D. Branches several from the base. High Sierra Nevada. .... var. *deductum*
         DD. Branches 1–few from the base. Mts. of s. Calif. .... var. *pauciflorum*

Var. **oblongifòlium** Wats. [*E. sulphureum* Greene. *E. latifolium* ssp. *s.* S. Stokes. *E. nudum* var. *s.* Jeps. *S. Harfordii* Small. *E. capitatum* Heller.] Lvs. basal, the lf.-blades largely oblong-spatulate, 2–4 cm. long; flowering stems 5–10 dm. high, white-tomentose, dichotomously branched; invols. mostly 3–6 in a cluster, tomentose, 3–5 mm. long; calyx white or rose or yellowish, 3–4 mm. long, pubescent without near the base; $n = 20$ (Reveal, 1965).—Dry slopes mostly below 4000 ft.; N. Oak Wd., Yellow Pine F., Foothill Wd.; Napa Co. to Humboldt and Siskiyou cos.; up to 7000 ft. from Nevada Co. to Modoc Co.; adjacent Ore., Nev. May–Aug.

Var. **auriculàtum** (Benth.) Tracy ex Jeps. [*E. a.* Benth. *E. latifolium* ssp. *a.* S. Stokes. *E. l.* ssp. *decurrens* S. Stokes. *E. l.* var. *alternans* S. Stokes.] Stems 2–10 (–20) dm. high, caudexlike at the bases, with lvs. on lower part; lf.-blades oblong to elliptic, obtuse at apex, truncate or subcordate at base, green above, white-tomentose below, 3–7 cm. long; flowering stems glabrous and glaucous, or rarely tomentose, often fistulose; invols. solitary or in pairs, 3–4 mm. long; calyx usually cream to pink, sometimes yellowish, mostly glabrous, in heads ca. 1 cm. across; $2n = 80$ (Stokes & Stebbins, 1955).—Dry, often stony places; Coastal Strand, Chaparral, V. Grassland; Coast Ranges from Sonoma Co. to Monterey Co. July–Sept.

A form with unusually strong inflated flowering stems, very robust, and with fls. yellow to whitish, is var. **indictum** (Jeps.) Reveal, comb. nov. [*E. i.* Jeps., *Fl. Calif.* 2: 421. 1913. *E. latifolium* var. *i.* S. Stokes.] from Merced Co. to Kern Co.; $2n = 80$ (Stokes & Stebbins. 1955).

Var. **pubiflòrum** Benth. [*E. saxicola* Heller. *E. gramineum* S. Stokes. *E. latifolium* ssp. *s.* S. Stokes. *E. l.* ssp. *Westonii* S. Stokes.] Flowering stems glabrous, glaucous, 3–6 dm. high, cymose above; invols. clustered, rarely solitary, subcampanulate; calyx yellow to white, pubescent without; $n = 20$ (Reveal, 1965).—Dry hot places below 6000 ft.; largely Foothill Wd., Joshua Tree Wd., Pinyon-Juniper Wd., Yellow Pine F.; Santa Ana Mts., w. Mojave Desert from San Gabriel Mts. n. to Modoc Co., Siskiyou and Humboldt cos. and along the inner Coast Ranges to Santa Lucia Mts. June–Sept.

Var. **pauciflòrum** Wats. [*E. molestum* Wats. *E. vimineum* ssp. *m.* S. Stokes. *E. latifolium* ssp. *p.* S. Stokes. *E. n.* var. *perturbum* Jones.] Caudex rather simple with lvs. crowded; lf.-blades oblong-ovate, 1.5 cm. long, green or glabrate above, white-woolly below, on petioles as long or longer; flowering stems 3–8 dm. high, slender, glabrous, glaucous, forked several times; invols. 1, rarely 2, at a place, rather few on a branch, 5–7 mm. long; calyx whitish, glabrous, 2 mm. long.—Dry slopes, 5000–9000 ft.; Yellow Pine F., Red Fir F.; Cuyamaca Mts., to Santa Rosa and San Bernardino mts. Aug.–Oct.

96. **E. grànde** Greene. [*E. nudum* var. *g.* Jeps. *E. latifolium* ssp. *g.* S. Stokes.] Caudex woody at the base, few-branched with elongated leaf-bearing areas 2–3 dm. long at the base; lf.-blades oblong-ovate, 3–10 cm. long, greenish above, closely white-woolly below, strongly undulate-crisped, the petioles much longer; flowering stems 8–15 dm. long, glabrous, glaucous, forking above; invols. in clusters of 1–3, turbinate, 5–6 mm. long, sub-

glabrous without; calyx whitish, ca. 3 mm. long, the segms. oblong-obovate, spreading; fils. pilose basally; aks. 2.5–3 mm. long; $2n = 40$ (Stokes & Stebbins, 1955).—Bluffs and cliffs, Coastal Sage Scrub, Chaparral; Santa Cruz, Santa Catalina, Anacapa and San Clemente ids. June–Oct.

A form from San Miguel and the w. end of Santa Cruz ids., is lower and more decumbent with a tendency toward subcapitate cymes with red fls. and may be known as var. **rubéscens** (Greene) Munz. [*E. r.* Greene. *E. latifolium* ssp. *r.* S. Stokes.]

97. **E. elàtum** Dougl. ex Benth. Caudex woody, branched or simple; lvs. basal, erect, the lf.-blades lanceolate to lance-ovate, 4–15 cm. long, acutish, green and glabrate above, somewhat tomentose below but not hoary, the petioles ca. as long, villous; flowering stems 4–8 dm. long, glabrous, glaucous, repeatedly trichotomous above, somewhat inflated in some; invols. in terminal clusters of 2–4, solitary in some, glabrous or somewhat pubescent, turbinate, ca. 4 mm. long, 5-toothed; calyx white or pinkish, 2.5 mm. long, pubescent without, the segms. obovate; fils. glabrous except at very base; aks. brownish, ca. 4 mm. long, subovoid with a rather prominently 3-angled beak; $n = 20$ (Hitchcock, 1964; Reveal, 1967).—Dry rocky slopes, 4000–9500 ft.; Sagebrush Scrub, N. Juniper Wd., Yellow Pine F.; Kern Plateau, Kern Co., Mono and Eldorado cos. to Modoc, Siskiyou and Trinity cos.; to Wash., Ida., Nev. June–Sept.

Var. **villòsum** Jeps. [*E. e.* var. *incurvum* Jeps. *E. e.* ssp. *glabrescens* S. Stokes.] Flowering stems villous-pubescent.—Panamint Mts. to Siskiyou Co.; w. Nev.

98. **E. péndulum** Wats. Base woody, few-branched, ascending or decumbent, 1–2.5 dm. high below the flowering branches; lvs. crowded near tips of basal branches, lf.-blades lance-oblong, (1.5–) 2–4 (–5) cm. long, obtusish, thinly floccose above, densely white-tomentose beneath, short-petioled (less than 5 mm.); flowering stems white-tomentose, 2–5 dm. high, leafy-bracted at nodes; invols. solitary, bractless, sessile or peduncled, the peduncles stout, to 1 dm. long, invols. turbinate-campanulate, white-tomentose, 3.5–5 mm. high, with 6–8 shallow lobes; calyx densely villous, 3–6 mm. long, the segms. narrow-oblong; stamens exserted, the fils. densely pilose; aks. villous, 3–5 mm. long.—Dry slopes below 3000 ft.; Mixed Evergreen F.; Del Norte Co.; adjacent Ore. Aug.–Sept.

99. **E. fascículatum** Benth. [*E. f.* var. *maritimum* Parish. *E. f.* var. *oleifolium* Gand. *E. aspalathoides* Gand. *E. f.* ssp. *a.* S. Stokes. *E. rosmarinifolium* Nutt.] CALIFORNIA BUCKWHEAT. Low spreading shrubs, the stems ± decumbent, 6–12 dm. long, branched, leafy; branchlets loosely pubescent to subglabrous, ending in leafless peduncles 3–10 (–15) cm. long, bearing ± open cymose infl. with many capitate clusters at the tips; lvs. numerous, fascicled, oblong-linear to linear-oblanceolate, green and glabrate above, white-woolly beneath, 6–15 mm. long, strongly revolute; invols. prismatic, 3–4 mm. high, glabrous, with 5 short acute teeth; calyx white or pinkish, ca. 3 mm. long, nearly or quite glabrous without, the outer segms. broadly elliptic, the inner obovate; fils. subglabrous basally; aks. lance-ovoid, light brown, angled, shining, ca. 2 mm. long; $2n = 40$ (Stokes & Stebbins, 1955), $n = 20$ (Reveal, 1967).—Dry slopes and canyons near the immediate coast; Coastal Sage Scrub; Santa Barbara to n. L. Calif.

The definition of var. *fasciculatum* as presented here is that which has been used in floras for many years. When Bentham described *E. fasciculatum*, he based his description on two collections, one by Menzies and one by Douglas. The Douglas specimens (BR, GH, K, MO, NY) which Reveal has seen represent what is here called var. *foliolosum*. The only Menzies collection that he has seen is deposited at Glasgow (GL) and does represent what is here called var. *fasciculatum*; there is no record of this collection at Kew. At present it is not known whether Bentham saw the Glasgow specimen or not, but it seems that in order to retain the definition of this species as understood for the last hundred years it will be necessary to typify the name on the Menzies collection. However, until all the English herbaria are investigated, such a step is not yet taken.

Var. **foliolòsum** (Nutt.) S. Stokes ex Jones. [*E. rosmarinifolium* var. *f.* Nutt. *E. fasciculatum* ssp. *foliolosum* S. Stokes. *E. f.* var. *obtusiflorum* S. Stokes.] Upper surface of lvs., outer surface of calyx, invols., etc. pubescent; peduncles 1–2 dm. long; $2n = 80$ (Stebbins, 1942).—Common on interior cismontane slopes and mesas, below 3000 ft.; Chaparral, Coastal Sage Scrub; Monterey Co. and San Benito Co. to n. L. Calif. Exceedingly variable. March–Oct.

Var. polifòlium (Benth.) T. & G. [*E. f.* ssp. *p.* S. Stokes. *E. p.* Benth.] Plants commonly 2–5 (–8) dm. tall; lvs. densely canescent to hoary above, commonly less revolute; invols. and calyx pubescent; heads solitary or in reduced cymes; $2n = 40$ (Stebbins, 1942).—Common on dry slopes, below 7000 ft.; Sagebrush Scrub to Pinyon-Juniper Wd.; both deserts to San Joaquin V. and Inyo Co. and interior of s. Calif.; to Utah and Ariz., L. Calif. April–Nov.

Var. flavovíride M. & J. [*E. f.* ssp. *f.* S. Stokes.] Low, 2–3 dm. tall; lvs. yellow-green, subglabrous above, strongly revolute; peduncles glabrous; invols. and calyx subglabrous, the latter quite reddish.—Rocky places, below 4000 ft.; Creosote Bush Scrub; Eagle Mts., e. Riverside Co. to Little San Bernardino Mts. and Sheephole Mts., San Bernardino Co. March–May.

100. **E. arboréscens** Greene. Loosely branched shrubs 6–15 (–20) dm. tall, the stems to 1 dm. thick, with shreddy bark; branchlets tomentose when young, later glabrate, purplish and glaucous; lvs. in crowded terminal tufts, linear to oblong, revolute, 2–3 cm. long, densely white-tomentose below, glabrate above; infl. dense terminal leafy-bracted cymes, 5–15 cm. across; invols. tomentose, 3 mm. long, turbinate, with obtuse oval teeth; calyx whitish to pink, 2 mm. long, villous at the base; fils. glabrous; aks. lance-ovoid, shining, angled, ca. 2.5 mm. long; $n = 20$ (Reveal, 1968).—Rocky slopes and canyon walls; Coastal Sage Scrub, Chaparral; Santa Cruz, Santa Rosa and Anacapa ids. April–Sept.

101. **E. gigantèum** Wats. St. Catherine's Lace. Coarse rounded branching shrubs, open, 3–20 (–35) dm. high, the cent. trunk to 1 dm. thick, the younger branches tomentose, then glabrate and dark, with lvs. toward the tips; lf.-blades leathery, oblong-ovate to ovate, 3–7 (–10) cm. long, closely white-tomentose below, cinereous and somewhat glabrate above, on stout petioles 1–3 cm. long; peduncles stout, 1–3 dm. long, tomentose, later glabrate, bearing large 2–3-forked horizontal cymes often several dm. across and with leafy bracts at the forks; invols. crowded, campanulate; 3–4 mm. long, tomentose, with short obtuse teeth, subsessile or on short slender peduncles; calyx white, becoming rusty in age, ca. 2 mm. long, white-hairy, the segms. obovate; fils. hairy; aks. brown, shining, narrow-ovoid, angled above, ca. 2 mm. long; $n = 20$ (Reveal, 1968).—Dry slopes; Chaparral, Coastal Sage Scrub; Santa Catalina Id. May–Aug.

Var. compáctum Dunkle. Lvs. oblong; tomentum on young growth looser; involucral peduncles very stout.—Santa Barbara Id.

Var. formòsum K. Bdg. [*E. f.* K. Bdg. *E. g.* ssp. *f.* Raven.] Lvs. oblong-lanceolate.—San Clemente Id.

102. **E. parvifòlium** Sm. in Rees. [*E. p.* var. *commune* Benth. *E. p.* var. *crassifolium* Benth.] Shrubs with loosely branched decumbent or prostrate stems 3–10 dm. long, thinly floccose, densely leafy to the summit; lvs. fascicled, round-ovate to lance-oblong, thickish, revolute, sometimes cordate at the base, 5–15 mm. long, on shorter petioles, the lf.-blades green and glabrate above, densely white-tomentose below; flowering stems few, mostly 2–5 cm. long, simple or forked, bearing compact heads 1–2 cm. in diam.; invols. glabrate or somewhat woolly, turbinate-campanulate, 3–4 mm. long; calyx white or tinged rose, glabrous, ca. 3 mm. long, the segms. obovate; fils. pilose basally; aks. ovoid-deltoid, shining, brown, 2.5 mm. long; $2n = 40$ (Stokes & Stebbins, 1955).—Common on bluffs and dunes along the coast; Coastal Strand, Coastal Sage Scrub; Monterey Co. to San Diego Co. Mostly summer, but with some fls. throughout the year.

Two ill-defined forms are: (1) with greenish-yellow fls., Point Lobos, Monterey Co., var. lùcidum (J. T. Howell ex S. Stokes) Reveal, stat. nov. [*E. p.* ssp. *lucidum* J. T. Howell ex S. Stokes, Gen. Eriog. 87. 1936.] and (2) diffusely branched, with lanceolate lvs. 15–30 mm. long and white fls. in heads scarcely 1 cm. in diam. and broad infl. 1–2 dm. in diam.; from Santa Paula Canyon, Ventura Co., var. Pàynei (C. B. Wolf ex Munz) Reveal, stat. nov. [*E. p.* ssp. *P.* C. B. Wolf ex Munz, *Aliso* 2: 80. 1949.]

103. **E. cinèreum** Benth. Freely branched shrubs, 6–15 dm. high, tomentulose, leafy below the infl.; lvs. ovate, 1.5–3 cm. long, obtuse, cuneate at the base, greenish-cinereous above, white-tomentulose below, crisped-undulate; short-petioled; flowering stems elongated, dichotomous, with scattered heads; invols. cylindric-turbinate, tomentulose, 3–4 mm. long, somewhat angled, 5-toothed; calyx densely white-villous, ca. 3 mm. long, the segms. narrow-obovate, whitish to pinkish; fils. subglabrous; aks. brown, deltoid-ovoid, sharply angled, somewhat roughened, ca. 2 mm. long; $n = 40$ (Reveal, 1968).—Beaches

and bluffs near the coast; Coastal Strand, Coastal Sage Scrub; Santa Barbara to San Pedro, Santa Rosa Id. June–Dec.

Subgenus Clastomỳelon Cov. & Mort.

104. **E. intrafráctum** Cov. & Mort. Perennial, woody at the base, from distinct taproots; lvs. basaḷ, oblong-ovate, somewhat whitish-pilose, the lf.-blades 2.5–7 cm. long, the petioles somewhat longer; flowering stems usually solitary, simple below, sometimes branched in infl., rather stout, glabrous, glaucous, transversely jointed into hollow ring-like segms., each segm. 3–10 mm. long, becoming easily fractured, 6–12 dm. high; infl. usually of 2–3 virgate branches 2–4 dm. long and sometimes with shorter secondary branches; invols. usually in whorls of 3 at each node, usually 1 in the axil of each of 3 bracts, 5-parted into oblong lobes which become more divided with expanding fls., short-pilose; calyx yellow, tinged with red, pubescent, ca. 2 mm. long, the lobes oblong-lanceolate, subequal; aks. flask-shaped, brownish, almost 2 mm. long, 3-ridged on lower part, then abruptly narrowed into triangular beaks.—Local and rare, limestone crevices, 2000–5000 ft.; Creosote Bush Scrub; Grapevine and Panamint mts., Inyo Co. May–Oct.

p. 355.   RUMEX
          Key AA, B, CC, DD, E, FF, change to:

> G. Valves in fruit deltoid, acute, one valve with a large ovate callosity; panicle branches often ascending.
> 7. *R. salicifolius*
> GG. Valves in fruit ovate to ovate-lanceolate, generally all with prominent callosities; panicle-branches curved-spreading.
> 8. *R. transitorius*

p. 356.   3. **R. paucifòlius** Nutt. ex Wats. Various chromosome counts have been reported: $2n = 28$ (Löve & Sarkar, 1956); $2n = 14, 28$ (B. W. Smith, 1958). In 1967 Löve and Evenson (Taxon 16: 423–425) gave $2n = 14$ for the Rocky Mountain plant and $2n = 28$ for the Sierran. They referred the former to *Acetosa paucifolia* (Nutt.) Löve and the latter to *A. gracilescens* (Rech. f.) Löve & Evenson.
              4. **R. venòsus** Pursh. $2n = 40$ (Sarkar, 1958).
p. 357.   5. **R. califórnicus** Rech. f. $2n = 20$ (Sarkar, 1958).
              R. utahénsis Rech. f. For 1959 printing transpose lines 2 and 3.
              6. **R. cràssus** Rech. f. $2n = 20$ (Sarkar, 1958).
              7. **R. salicifòlius** Weinm. $2n = 20$ (Sarkar, 1958).
              8. **R. transitòrius** Rech. f. $2n = 20$ (Sarkar, 1958).
              10. **R. triangulivàlvis** (Danser) Rech. f. California plants are var. **oreolápathum** Rech. f.
p. 358.   11. **R. hymenosèpalus** Torr. ranges n. to Monterey Co., *Howitt & Howell.* $2n = 40$ (Löve & Patil, 1967).
              12. **R. fenestràtus** Greene. $2n = $ ca. 200 (Löve, 1967).
              13. **R. occidentàlis** Wats. $2n = $ ca. 140 (Wellington, 1957).
p. 359.   19. **R. stenophýllus** Ledeb. $2n = 60$ (Löve, 1967).
              23. **R. fuegìnus** Phil, $2n = 40$ (Löve & Löve, 1967).
              24. **R. persicarioìdes** L. $2n = 40$ (Löve & Löve, 1967).
p. 360.   POLÝGONUM
          In Key to Species, after A, B, C, D, EE, F insert:

> G. Branch-lvs. much smaller than stem-lvs.; perianth divided almost to base; fr. trigonous with 3 concave sides.
> 4. *P. aviculare*
> GG. Branch-lvs. not much smaller than stem-lvs.; perianth divided ca. half its length; fr. with 2 sides convex, 1 concave.
> 4a. *P. arenastrum*

p. 360.   In Key A, B, CC, D, EE, FF, change to:

> GG. Upper lvs. not reduced to bracts; calyx with yellowish margins.

H. Pedicels exserted from the ocreae; fls. clustered at apex of stems; lvs. lacking conspicuous lateral veins.
7. *P. ramosissimum*
HH. Pedicels included within the ocreae; fls. not markedly clustered at apex of stems; lvs. rugulose-veiny when dry. .... 7a. *P. prolificum*

p. 361.   In key in line 2 at top of page, insert "heads or" between "or" and "in."
In Key AA, change BB to:

BB. Infl. of heads or open panicles and the lvs. broad, or the infl. of small axillary clusters and terminal spike with the lvs. cordate-sagittate.
B'. Fls. in dense globular heads on long peduncles; lvs. ovate to elliptic; stems prostrate, rooting. .... 36. *P. capitatum*
B'B'. Fls. in open panicles or in small axillary clusters and terminal spikes.
C. Stems twining; plant annual, etc., as in FLORA.

3. Change **P. Fòwleri** Rob. to **P. marinénse** Martens & Raven with shining aks., whereas they are dull in *P. Fowleri*. **P. marinense** ranges in saline marshes of Marin Co., but *P. Fowleri* is from Puget Sound n. and e.
p. 362.   4a. **P. arenástrum** Bor. Forming dense prostrate mats 1–16 dm. across; lvs. to 20 mm. long, 5 mm. wide; infl. 2–3-fld.; calyx greenish-white or pink; fr. 1.5–2.5 mm. long, brown to black; $2n = 40$. San Clemente Id., *Raven*. From Eu.
6. **P. pátulum** Bieb. $2n = 20$ (Löve & Löve, 1956).
7a. **P. prolíficum** (Small) Rob. [*P. ramosissimum* var. *p.* Small.] Differing from *P. ramosissimum* in its pedicels (included within, rather than exserted from the ocreae) and less shiny frs.; fls. not markedly clustered at apex of stems.—Found at Cutting's Wharf on Napa R., Napa Co., *Howell*; central and e. N. Am.
8. **P. Douglásii** Greene. $2n = 40$ (Löve & Löve, 1956).
Var. **latifòlium** (Engelm.) Greene reported from the Greenhorn Range, Kern Co., *Twisselmann*.
p. 363.   12. **P. Kellóggii** Greene. Add to the synonymy [*P. imbricatum* auth.]
16. **P. califórnicum** Meissn. S. in Sierra Nevada to Fresno Co., *Weiler*.
p. 366.   35. **P. sachalinénse** F. Schmidt ex Maxim. Now reported from Calif. as in Humboldt, Mendocino, and Siskiyou cos., *Fuller*; in Grass V., Nevada Co., and Camiso, El Dorado Co., *Fuller*; Atascadero, San Luis Obispo Co., *Fuller*.
36. **P. capitàtum** Ham. in Don. With many stems or branches creeping from a woody rootstock, leafy, glandular-hirsute; lvs. 1–3 cm. long, elliptical, acute, short-petioled, the petiole 2-auricled at its base; stipules short-cupular; heads 1–3, 6–18 mm. diam.; peduncles glabrous or glandular hipid; calyx pink, 5-cleft, the segms. obtuse.—Garden escape at Pacific Grove, Monterey Co., *Howitt & Howell*.
p. 368.   CHENOPÒDIUM
In Key under A, BB, C, DD, add:

E. Plants annual, prostrate; seeds 0.9–1.1 mm. broad; pericarp gray-striped or mottled. Coastal sand, San Luis Obispo and Santa Barbara cos. .... 3a. *C. carnosulum*
EE. Plants mostly perennial, ascending or erect; seeds 0.7 mm. broad; pericarp thin, deciduous, gland-dotted. Widespread.
3. *C. ambrosioides*

In Key AA, B, CC, DD, E, F, G, delete "18. *C. album*" at end of line and add:

H. Blades at least 1½ times as long as wide; sepals not united to broadest part of fruit, variously keeled.
18. *C. album*
HH. Blades scarcely if at all longer than broad, basal lobes often bipartite; sepals united to or above broadest part of fruit, usually strongly keeled. 18a. *C. opulifolium*

p. 369.   In Key under AA, B, CC, DD, EE:

F. Lf.-blades linear to narrow-lanceolate or narrow-oblong, short-petiolate, the blades mostly 1–3-nerved.
G. Lvs. entire, 1-nerved, mostly 2–3 mm. wide.
11. *C. leptophyllum*

GG. Lvs. narrow-lanceolate or broader, the lower 4–18 mm.
wide. .... 12. *C. desiccatum*
FF. Lf.-blades lance-ovate to ovate or broader, long-petioled, pin-
nately veined.
 G. Main lf.-blades definitely longer than broad.
  H. Pericarp separable; lvs. mostly entire; seed 1 mm.
   broad.
    I. Lvs. oblong or oval, 0.8–2 cm. long, mostly less
     than ⅓ as broad. .... 12. *C. desiccatum*
    II. Lvs. ovate to triangular-oblong, 1.5–3 cm. long,
     mostly more than ⅓ as broad...15. *C. atrovirens*
  HH. Pericarp attached; lvs. sometimes toothed.
    I. Seeds 1–1.5 mm. broad; plants mostly 3–12 dm.
     high, openly branched.
      J. Lvs. thin, ovate-lanceolate or broader; seeds
       1.2–1.5 mm. broad. ... 14. *C. incognitum*
      JJ. Lvs. firm, ovate-lanceolate or narrower;
       seeds 1.0 mm. broad. ...... 12a. *C. hians*
    II. Seeds 0.7–0.8 mm. wide; plants 2–3 dm. high,
     bushy-branched .... 16. *C. nevadense*
GG. Main lf.-blades scarcely if at all, etc. as in the FLORA.

Key under AA, BB, CC, D, change EE to:

 EE. Fls. in large spicate glomerules; calyx fleshy and bright red in fr.
  F. Lvs. truncate to cordate-hastate at base, the margins usually
   strongly toothed; principal glomerules in well developed plants
   usually 6–10 mm. in diam.; stigma 0.3–0.4 mm. long, flexuous.
              6. *C. capitatum*
  FF. Lvs. tapering or truncate-hastate at base, the margins somewhat toothed or entire; glomerules usually smaller; stigmas
   chiefly 0.1–0.2 mm. long, squarrose. .... 6a. *C. Òveri*

p. 370. 3a. **C. carnosùlum** Moq. var. **patagónicum** (Phil.) Wahl. [*C. p.* Phil.] Prostrate annual, the branches 1–3 dm. long; primary lvs. narrow-ovate, to 9 mm.
wide, the base cuneate.—Sand near coast, San Luis Obispo and Santa Barbara
cos.; Chile.
   4. **C. Bòtrys** L. $2n = 18$ (Mulligan, 1961).
   6. **C. capitàtum** (L.). Asch. $2n = 18$ (Mulligan, 1957).
   6a. **C. Òveri** Aellen. [*Blitum hastatum* Rydb., not *C. h.* Phil.] Stem slender,
2–4 dm. tall; lvs. very thin, the blades 3–7 cm. long, ovate to lance-ovate, the
upper smaller, not hastate; fls. in the upper axils and in slender, interrupted,
terminal spikes.—Lassen Co.; to Rocky Mts.
   8. **C. chenopodioìdes** (L.) Aellen, not *C. rubrum* L.
p. 371. 12. **C. desiccàtum**, not *dessicatum*.
   Var. **leptophylloìdes** (J. Murr.) Wahl. Reported from Monterey Co., *Howitt*
and *Howell.*
   12a. **C. hìans** Standl. Ill-scented annual, 4–8 dm. high, sparsely branched,
copiously farinose; petioles stout, up to half as long as the blades; lf.-blades
elliptic-oblong to narrowly lance-oblong, 1.2–3 dm. long, green and glabrate
above, white-farinose beneath; glomerules large, in stout dense erect spikes;
calyx farinose; pericarp closely adherent; seed 0.8–1 mm. broad, nearly smooth.
—Inyo and Mono cos. to Siskiyou Co.; to New Mex. and n.w. U.S. and adjacent
Canada.
   15. **C. atròvirens** Rydb. [*C. Fremontii* var. *a.* Fosberg.]
   17. **C. Vulvària** L. reported as in Monterey Co., *Howitt & Howell.*
p. 372. 18. **C. álbum** L. Wahl has identified a *Howell* specimen from San Bernardino
as **C. missouriénse** Aellen, differing from *C. album* in having seeds 0.9–1.2 mm.
broad, not 1.1–1.5 mm. Native of cent. U.S.
   18a. **C. opulifòlium** Schrad. Near to *C. album* (annual, 3–8 dm. tall, farinose,
glaucous) but with thicker lvs. with basal lobes so that the blade is subtrilobed,
the median lobe is short and the blade as a whole is scarcely longer than wide.
—An Eurasian plant sparsely introd. in this country, exemplified from California
by: King City, Monterey Co., *K. Esau* in 1927 and by 5 miles nw. of College
City, Colusa Co., *J. H. Thomas* in 1960.
   20. **C. Berlandièri** Moq. var. **sinuàtum** (J. Murr.) Wahl. [Add to possible

synonymy *C. B.* var. *californicum* Aellen.] This var. is supposed to have thin membranous lvs. Most Calif. material heretofore referred to *C. album* seems to belong here. It may be distinguished with difficulty from

Var. **Zscháckei** (Murr.) Murr. [*C. Z.* Murr.] Lvs. larger, thin to coriaceous; sepals usually strongly keeled; seeds 1.2–1.5 mm. in diam.—Reported by *Howell* from Marin and Monterey cos., by *Twisselmann* as a widespread summer weed in Kern Co. It seems to occur in alkaline spots from San Bernardino Co. to Lassen Co.

CYCLOLÒMA

1. **C. atriplícifolium** (Spreng.) Coult. n. to Tehama Co., *Howell*.

p. 373.   MONOLÈPIS

1. **M. Nuttalliàna** (Schult.) Greene ascends to 10,000 ft. in White Mts.

p. 374.   ATRIPLÉX

Key, AA, B, delete "32. *A. canescens*" and insert:

    C. Lvs. narrowly spatulate to narrowly oblong, 1.5–5 cm. long; fruiting bracts
        stalked. Common. . . . . 32. *A. canescens*
    CC. Lvs. oblong to subobovate, 1.2–2 cm. long; fruiting bracts hardly stalked.
        Rare weed. . . . . 33. *A. Vesicaria*

p 375.   2. **A. pátula** ssp. **hastàta** (L.) Hall & Clements. $2n = 18$ (Löve, 1964).

3. **A. ròsea** L. $2n = 18$ (Mulligan, 1957).

p. 376.   9. **A. Serenàna** A. Nels. reported from interior Monterey Co., *Howitt & Howell*.

p. 378.   19. **A. semibaccàta** R. Br. Found as far n. as Monterey Co., *Howitt & Howell*.

p. 379.   26. **A. lentifórmis** (Torr.) Wats. ssp. **Breweri** (Wats.) Hall & Clem. Found near Maricopa, Kern Co., *Twisselmann*.

p. 380.   33. **A. Vesicària** Heward in Hook. f. Bushy shrub with a scaly white tomentum; lvs. oblong to subobovate, 12–20 mm. long, short-petioled; ♂ fls. in small clusters forming dense leafless spikes 12–25 mm. long; ♀ fls. few together, in axillary clusters; fr. bracts suborbicular, 6–10 mm. in diam., entire, flat, but each with a membranous inflated appendage on the disk nearly as large as the bract itself.—Weed in the Northridge area, Los Angeles Co., *Fuller*; native of Australia.

p. 381.   KÒCHIA

3. **K. scopària** (L.) Schrad. var. **subvillòsa** Moq. A very hairy form reported from Santa Barbara and San Francisco.

Var. **cúlta** Farwell. With dense ovoid to globular habit, very narrow lvs. mostly with long hairs particularly toward the base, purple-red in autumn. Escape in Fresno, *Fuller*.

p. 383.   SUAÈDA

1. **S. depréssa** (Pursh) Wats. $2n = 36$ (Mulligan, 1965).

p. 384.   SALSÒLA

Dr. T. C. Fuller has sent specimens to two European botanists for study: Dr. P. Aellen of Basel and Dr. V. Botschantzev of Leningrad. Apparently our common sp., introduced from Russia, should be called **S. pestífera** A. Nels. [*S. kali* ssp. *ruthenica* (Ilgin) Soó.] In it the fruiting calyx is 3–6 mm. broad.

A new record for Calif. is **S. Paulsènii** Litv. Plant 1–5 dm. tall, ca. 5–6 dm. across, glabrous or sparsely papillose; lvs. 1.5–3 cm. long, semicylindrical, mucronate, yellow; bracts ovate at base, with a linear spinose apex; bracteoles partly connate with the solitary fls.; perianth with a short tube and small stiffly erect spinose tips to the segms.; wings membranous, veined, the fruiting calyx 8–9 mm. wide.—Common in disturbed ground 2 mi. e. of Barstow, San Bernardino Co., *T. C. Fuller*; and at 6000 ft. in San Bernardino Mts.; native of Russia.

HALOGÈTON

1. **H. glomeràtus** (Bieb.) C. A. Mey. in Led. Reported from e. Mojave Desert (Halloran Summit, etc.), *Fuller*.

p. 385.   AMARANTHÀCEAE

Key to Genera:

A.   Lvs. alternate; anthers 4-celled; plants nearly or quite glabrous. . . . . . 1. *Amaranthus*
AA. Lvs. largely opposite; anthers 2-celled; plants white stellate-woolly or villous.
   B.   Fls. glomerate, with an invol. of upper lvs.
      C.   Stamens perigynous. Mostly deserts. . . . . 2. *Tidestromia*
      CC. Stamens hypogynous. Santa Barbara Co. . . . . 2a. *Brayulinia*
   BB. Fls. in axillary headlike spikes, without invol. Mostly near beaches. 3. *Alternanthera*

AMARÁNTHUS
Key to Species, change to:

A.   Sepals of the ♀ fls. broadened upward, the calyx ± urceolate.
   B.   Fls. dioecious; sepals of ♀ fls. not fimbriate.
      C.   Bracts 2–3 times as long as the pistillate calyx.
         D.   Infl. not leafy; bracts rigid and spinose; plants not viscid-pubescent.
                                                1. *A. Palmeri*
         DD. Infl. leafy at least below; bracts not spinose; plants viscid-pubescent.
                                                2. *A. Watsonii*
      CC. Bracts not longer than pistillate calyx. . . . . 2a. *A. arenicola*
   BB. Fls. monoecious; sepals of ♀ flls. fimbriate. . . . . 3. *A. fimbriatus*

AA. etc. as in the FLORA.
In the Key AA, BB, CC, D substitute:

      E.   Style-branches recurved; lateral branches of infl. few to none.
         F.   Base of style-branches slender, forming shallow saddle; midrib
            of bract very slender, rather long excurrent; sepals obovate to
            spatulate, obtuse or emarginate, recurved; lateral spikes of infl.
            few to none. . . . . 6a. *A. caudatus*
         FF. Bases of style-branches stout, forming cleft at summit of broad
            tower; midrib of bract very thick, excurrent; sepals oblong,
            acute, straight; lateral spikes of infl. long, few, widely spaced.
                                            6. *A. Powellii*
     EE. Style-branches erect; lateral spikes of infl. numerous, crowded.
         F.   Sepals oblong, acute, straight; midrib of bract long, excurrent;
            style-branches with slender bases.
            G.   Lateral spikes of infl. long; sepals very short, 1.5 mm.
               long; bracts to 1.5 times as long as sepals, usually red or
               purple. . . . . 7a. *A. cruentus*
            GG. Lateral spikes of infl. short; sepals moderately long, 1.5–2
               mm.; bracts twice as long as sepals, usually green or pale
               reddish. . . . . 7. *A. hybridus*
         FF. Sepals narrowly obovate, emarginate, recurved; midrib of bracts
            barely excurrent; style-branches with moderately stout bases.
                                         5. *A. retroflexus*

DD. "Infl. wholly of axillary glomerules," etc. as in the FLORA.

p. 386.   1. **A. Pálmeri** Wats. $2n = 45$ (Grant, 1958). In the San Joaquin V., *Twisselmann*.

2a. **A. arenícola** Jtn. Differing from *A. Palmeri* and *A. Watsonii* (both of which have bracts 2–3 times as long as the ♀ calyx) in the bracts not exceeding the ♀ calyx which is 2.5–3 mm. long—Adventive in Monterey and Santa Barbara cos., *Howell*; native Ida. to Colo.

4. **A. defléxus** L. $2n = 34$ (Grant, 1959).

A sp. resembling *A. deflexus*, but with wrinkled seeds is **A. gracilis** Desf. Reported from San Francisco.

5. **A. retrofléxus** L. $2n = 34$ (Grant, 1959).

6. **A. Powéllii** Wats. $2n = 34$ (Grant, 1959).

6a. **A. caudàtus** L. Infl. thick and pendulous, terminal spike extremely long, laterals few and short or absent; bract short or medium, with slender, rather long-excurrent midrib; sepals recurved, broadly obovate or spatulate, obtuse to emarginate, 1.5–2 mm. long.—Widely introd. in N. Am. Native of Cent. and S. Am.

7. **A. hýbridus** L. $2n = 32$ (Grant, 1959).

7a. **A. cruéntus** L. Infl. lax, the terminal spike short, the laterals long, very numerous and crowded; bracts extremely short, not much longer than the sepals, with long-excurrent midrib; sepals straight, 1.5 mm. long, oblong, acute, Widely introd. in N. Am. Native in Cent. and S. Am.

8. Apparently the correct name for this sp. is **A. blitoìdes** Wats. for Am. plants and *A. graecìzans* L. for European. $2n = 32$ (Grant, 1959).

Tucker and Sauer (Madroño 14: 252–261. 1958) in discussing weedy populations of *Amaranthus* from the Sacramento-San Joaquin Delta presented evidence to show that several spp. were involved, which added 6a and 7a as here presented to those already treated in the FLORA.

11. **A. spinòsus** L. $2n = 34$ (Grant, 1959).

p. 387. TIDESTRÒMIA

1. **T. oblongifòlia** (Wats.) Small. Wiggins recognizes ssp. **cryptántha** (Wats.) Wiggins on basis of smaller lvs. (2–10 mm. long); invol. deeper (3–4 mm.) and about the Salton Sea.

2a. Brayulínea Small

Prostrate to decumbent perennial herbs; stems branched at base, often zig-zag. Fls. perfect, subtended by bracts and in axillary clusters. Sepals 5, pubescent. Stamens 5, perigynous; fils. broad; anthers 1-celled. Ovary flattened, 1-celled; style short; stigma notched. Utricle membranous, indehiscent.

1. **B. dénsa** (Willd.) Small. [*Illecebrum d.* Willd.] Prostrate perennial, densely lanate; cauline lvs. wing-petioled, elliptic to broadly oval, 3–15 mm. long; fls. densely glomerate; bracts ovate, scarious, white; calyx 2–2.5 mm. long. —Reported from Lompoc, Santa Barbara Co., *Howell*. Native from Ariz. to Texas and S. Am.

p. 388. ALTERNÁNTHERA

1. *A. rèpens* (L.) Kuntze. Change to **A. pungens** HBK, since the comb. *A. repens* had earlier been made for another sp.

2. **A. philoxeroìdes** (Mart.) Griseb. A bad weed in irrigation canals, as at Visalia, Tulare Co., *Fuller*.

PHYTOLÁCCA

2. **P. heterotépala** H. Walter. In San Francisco, *Howell*. Differs from *P. americana* in having sepals unequal; stamens 13–20, while *P. a.* has sepals equal; stamens 10.

p. 389. In caption under Fig. 40 change "inferior" ovary to "superior."

p. 392. OXÝBAPHUS

4. **O. pùmilus** (Standl.) Standl. Found at Kenworthy, Hemet V., San Jacinto Mts., *Ziegler*.

p. 393. MIRÁBILIS

4. **M. laèvis** (Benth.) Curran. At 6 mi. se. of Friant Dam on San Joaquin R., Fresno Co. and at other spots in Sierran foothills, *Quibell*.

p. 394. ABRONIA
Key, in line 3 from bottom, omit word "annuals."

S. S. Tillett (Brittonia 19: 299–327. 1967) has a study of our maritime spp. and proposes:

A. latifòlia and *A. maritíma* are perennial, with perianth limb reflexed and without central eyespot. *A. grácilis* and *A. umbellàta* are annual, with the perianth limb plane and with evident central white eyespot. He separates *A. gracilis* Benth. from *A. umbellata* Lam. as follows:

Lvs. very thin, oval, deeply crenate to sinuately lobed; open sandy areas of scrub at low to middle elevations. Baja Calif. and possibly Imperial and San Diego cos. . . . *A. gracilis* Benth.
Lvs. thicker, oval to elliptic or rhomboidal, asymmetrical, the margin entire to somewhat irregular; strand and disturbed areas in coastal scrub bordering strand. . . *A. umbellata* Lam.

p. 395. 6. **A. umbellàta** Lam. Tillett keys out 3 sspp. of which 2 occur in Calif.:

Perianth light to dark magenta, displayed in a nearly hemispheric umbel, the tube 9–13 mm. long, the limb 7–16 mm. in diam.; wings of anthocarp very well developed, broadly rounded; Sonoma Co. to Baja Calif. . . . . ssp. *umbellata*
Perianth light magenta, somewhat yellowed, displayed in a poorly opened umbel, the tube

6.5–10 mm. long, the limb 6–8.5 mm. diam.; wings less well developed, angled above; Marin Co. to s. Ore. . . . . ssp. *breviflora*

Tillett finds F_1 hybrids between *A. maritima* and *A. umbellata* generally perennial, the pubescence of the lvs. as in *A. m.* Lf. shape and thickness intermediate. Umbel angle as in *A. u.* Perianth tube short, the throat wide as in *A. m.* The corolla limb like *A. u.* in size, reflexed as in *A. m.* Eyespot present.

A. álba Eastw., *A. insuláris* Standl., *A. neurophylla* Standl., *A. platyphýlla* Standl. and *A. variábilis* Standl. represent plants with introgression between *A. umbellata* and *A. maritima.*

A. mìnor Standl. is based on plants of *A. umbellata* introgressed by *A. latifòlia.* Lvs. broad, perianth somewhat reflexed, throat less constricted, anthocarp wings smaller and not extending above the apex, yellow color on the tube and underside of the perianth limb.

p. 396.   6. **A. umbellata** Lam. ssp. **platyphylla** (Standl.) Ferris, not Munz.

BATIDÀCEAE

For 1959 printing, in line 2 from bottom of page, change "exstipulate" to "stipulate."

p. 398.   STÝRAX

1. **S. officinalis** var. **fulvescens** (Eastw.) Munz & Jtn. $2n = 8$ pairs (Raven, Kyhos & Hill, 1965).

p. 403.   DODECÁTHEON

9. **D. pulchéllum** (Raf.) Merr. In the synonymy *"Eximie"* should be *"Exinia."*

p. 404.   CENTÚNCULUS

The genus is best reduced to synonymy under **Anágallis** and the usable binomial is **Anágallis mínima** (L.) Krause.

p. 406.   PLANTÀGO

2. **P. heteróphylla** group. I. J. Bassett (Can. J. Bot. 44: 467–479. 1966) in a study of the spp. referred in the FLORA to *P. heterophylla* and *P. Bigelovii*, recognizes the following for California; which can be keyed out under A, BB, C as follows:

> D.   Caps. 10–25-seeded; seeds 0.5–0.8 mm. long. . . . . . . 2. *P. heterophylla*
> DD. Caps. 4–9-seeded; seeds 0.75–2.5 mm. long.
>   E.   Corolla lobes mostly erect in age, forming a beak; seeds 4, ca. 0.75–
>   1.8 mm. long. . . . . 2a. *P. pusilla*
>   EE. Corolla lobes spreading or reflexed in age, not forming a beak; seeds
>   4–9, 1.5–2.5 mm. long.
>   F.   Scape and lvs. mostly erect; plants 5–15 cm. high; seeds mostly
>   4–5, roughly or finely rugose-pitted, dark brown, elliptic oblong,
>   1.75–2.5 mm. long. . . . . 3a. *P. elongata*
>   FF. Scape and lvs. mostly decumbent to semierect; plants 1.5–8 cm.
>   high; seeds 4–9, irregularly and coarsely pitted, dark brown to
>   black, slightly angled in outline, 1.5–2 mm. long.
>   3. *P. Bigelovii*

2. **P. heteróphylla** Nutt. Occurs only in the e. U.S.

2a. **P. pusílla** Nutt. Plant pubescent to glabrous, erect or strongly ascending, 2–10 cm. high; lvs. ⅓ to ¾ as high as the scape, all basal; scapes several to many; spikes 1.5–6 cm. long; bracts triangular-ovate, scarious-margined, slightly shorter than to equaling the calyx, 1.5–2 mm. long; sepals obovate; corolla lobes 0.5 mm. long, mostly erect and forming a beak over the caps.; caps. ovoid, circumscissile below the middle, ca. 2 mm. long; seeds 4, dark brown, pitted, ca. ⅓ as wide as long, 0.75–1.25 (–1.8) mm. long; $2n = 12$.—Cited from San Diego; Ore., Wash., e. U.S.

p. 407.   3. **P. Bigelòvii** Gray. Plant ± pubescent, decumbent to semierect, 3–5 cm. high; lvs. entire, linear to subfiliform, 1–7 cm. long; bracts ovate, 2 mm. long; hyaline-margined; sepals broadly obovate, ca. 2 mm. long; corolla lobes spreading to sharply reflexed in fr., 0.5–1 mm. long; caps. oblong-ovoid, 2–3 mm. long, circumscissile just below the middle; seeds mostly 4–5, dark brown to black, oblong, slightly angled, irregularly and coarsely pitted, 1.5–2 mm. long; $2n = 20$.—Well distributed in cismontane Calif., mostly near the coast; to B.C.

Ssp. califórnica (Greene) Bassett. [*P. c.* Greene.] Plants 4–8 cm. tall; lvs. often with a few teeth; seeds mostly 6–9.—Mostly inland; central Calif. to L. Calif., Son.

3a. **P. elongàta** Pursh. Plants appressed-pubescent with septate hairs, mostly erect, 5–15 cm. high; lvs. linear to subfiliform, ⅓–¾ as high as the scape; scapes few to many; spikes mostly lax, 2.5–8 cm. long; bracts ovate, 2–2.5 mm. long, hyaline-margined; sepals ovate, 2–2.5 mm. long; corolla-lobes to 1 mm. long, rarely closing; caps. ovoid, circumscissile just below the middle, 2.5–3.5 mm. long; seeds mostly 4, uniform in size, mostly 4–5 mm. long, dark brown, roughly or finely rugose-pitted, 1.75–2.5 mm. long; $2n = 12$.—Alkaline areas, w. central Calif.; to s. Can. and w. Miss. Valley.

Ssp. pentaspérma Bassett. Lvs. and scapes usually subglabrous; spikes generally dense; seeds mostly 5, irregular in shape, one smaller than the others; $2n = 36, 12$.—Saline and alkaline places; central Calif. to B.C.

4. **P. eríopoda** Torr. $2n = 24$ (Bassett, 1967).

7. **P. virgínica** L. $2n = 24$ (Fujiwara, 1956).

p. 408.   13. **P. Púrshii** R. & S. var. **pícta** (Morris) Pilg. should be changed to var. **oblónga** (Morris) Shinners, *P. picta* Morris being antedated by *P. p.* Colenso.

14. **P. erécta** Morris. $2n = 20$ and ssp. **rigídior** Pilg. $2n = 42$ (Moore, 1962).

15. **P. insulàris** Eastw. $2n = 8$ (Moore, 1962); (Raven, Kyhos & Hill, 1965).

p. 409.   16. **P. índica** L. $2n = 12$ (Fujiwara, 1956).

p. 410.   LIMÒNIUM

In Key at top of page, after line 3 insert 4th line:

Fls. ca. 4 mm. long, white. Rare escape, San Francisco. . . . . 2a. *L. perfoliatum*

2a. **L. perfoliàtum** (Karelin ex Boiss.) Kuntze. [*Statice p.* Karelin.] Perennial, to 6 dm. high; lvs. entire, oblong-spatulate, 3–8 cm. long; fls. white, ca. 4 mm. long.—Escape from cult., salt marsh, Islair Creek, San Francisco; from Caspian Sea.

2. **L. Perèzii** F. T. Hubb. reported from 4 mi. n. of Paso Robles, San Luis Obispo Co., *Twisselmann.*

p. 411.   ERICÀCEAE

Key to Genera, A, B, CC, DD, change to:

DD. Corolla urn-shaped or tubular-campanulate.
 E. Corolla urn-shaped; anthers mucronate; lvs. broad, petioled. Native alpine. . . . . 7. *Leucothoe*
 EE. Corolla tubular-campanulate; anthers with 2 hairy awns at the base. Escape in n. Calif. . . . . 7a. *Erica*

p. 412.   LÈDUM

1. **L. glandulòsum** Nutt. ssp. **columbiànum** (Piper) C. L. Hitchc. occurs in Monterey Co., *Howitt & Howell.*

p. 413.   RHODODÉNDRON

2. **R. occidentàle** (T. & G.) Gray. Found in Gabilan Range, Monterey Co., *Howitt & Howell* and on Fremont Peak, San Benito Co., *Arnaud.*

KÁLMIA

1. Add **K. polifòlia** Wang. [*K. p.* ssp. *occidentalis* (Small) Abrams. *K. o.* Small.] Differing from var. **microphýlla** (Hook.) Hall in usually being 2–4 dm. tall; lvs. mostly 2–4 cm. long, less than half as broad; fls. 12–18 mm. broad.— Siskiyou and Modoc cos. to Can. and ne. U.S.

p. 414.   7a. **Érica** L. HEATH

Large genus of shrubs and subshrubs native in S. Afr. and Medit. region. Lvs. usually in whorls of 3–6, small, needle-like. Fls. 1–many, usually nodding; calyx short, 4-parted; corolla withering-persistent, ± cylindrical, with 4 small lobes; stamens usually 8; ovary 4- or 8-celled, with 2–many ovules in each cell; caps. loculicidal.

1. **E. lusitánica** Rudolph. SPANISH HEATH. Erect, dense shrub, 2–3 m. tall;

young stems with short simple hairs; lvs. irregularly arranged or 3–5 in a whorl, glabrous; fls. very many, along entire length of branches, white or pink, ca. 4 mm. long, tubular-campanulate.—On cleared land near Eureka, Humboldt Co.; native sw. Eu.

p. 415.   GAULTHÈRIA

2. **G. humifùsa** (Grah.) Rydb. In Eldorado Co.

3. **G. ovatifòlia** Gray. In Sierra, Butte and Eldorado cos., *Howell.*

ARBÙTUS

1. **A. Menziesii** Pursh. $2n = 26$ (Stebbins & Major, 1965).

p. 417.   ARCTOSTÁPHYLOS

In Key, A, BB, change C to:

C.   Ovary with short stiff hairs.
D.   Young branchlets bristly hairy; fr. splitting open and falling early. Amador Co. to Calaveras Co. . . . . 2. *A. myrtifolia*
DD. Young branchlets with a fine, quickly deciduous pubescence; fr. not splitting as above. San Mateo Co. . . . . 7a. *A. pacifica*

p. 418.   In Key AA, BB, C, change D to:

D.   Lvs. pale green or gray-green; plants without a basal burl.
E.   Bark rough and shreddy; erect shrub. . . . . 24. *A. morroensis*
EE. Bark smooth; prostrate or decumbent shrub. . . . . . 37a. *A. cruzensis*

p. 419.   In Key, AA, BB, CC, D, EE, FF insert:

GGG. Branchlets gray-tomentulose; bracts canescent. San Luis Obispo and Monterey cos. . . . . 29. *A. obispoensis*

In Key, AA, BB, CC, DD, E, FF, G, HH, change to:

I.   Lvs. cordate or auriculate at base.
J.   Shrub 6–12 dm. high; corolla pinkish-white. Santa Cruz Mts. 30. *A. glutinosa*
JJ. Shrub 20–40 dm. high; corolla white. S. Santa Lucia Mts. . . . . . 35a. *A. Hooveri*

p. 420.   At end of Key change to:

GG. Pubescence on branchlets glandular.
H.   Lvs. oblong-lanceolate to ovate-lanceolate; berries viscid. Marin Co. . . . . 34. *A. virgata*
HH. Lvs. elliptic or ovate to broadly oval; berries hairy, but not viscid. Monterey Co. 33a. *A. montereyensis*

2. **A. myrtifòlia** Parry. Ranges quite widely in Amador and Calaveras cos., *Gankin.*

3. **A. nissenàna** Merriam. Mostly low and sprawling; corolla white to pink, *Knight.* A study by Schmid, Mallory & Tucker (Brittonia 20: 34–43. 1968) indicates that *A. nissenana* and *A. viscida* may hybridize freely.

4. **A. Ùva-úrsi** (L.) Spreng. var. **coáctilis** Fern. & Macbr. at Point Sur, Monterey Co., Sonora Pass and Convict Lake Basin in Sierra Nevada. Wiens & Halleck give $n = 13$ for a collection from Colo.

5. **A. Edmúndsii** J. T. Howell seems likely to be a hybrid. J. B. Roof proposes var. **parvifòlia** with lvs. ca. 7 mm. long; frs. 6 mm. diam.; Little Sur R., Monterey Co.

p. 421.   7a. **A. pacífica** Roof. Near the *A. Hookeri* complex, forming carpets of pastel-green hue, on a sandstone outcrop at ca. 1100 ft., ne. slope of San Bruno Mt., San Mateo Co. Lvs. rounded to lanceolate, 10–18 mm. long, reticulate above and beneath, finely serrulate; infls. few, the bracts and rachises minutely puberulent; pedicels glabrous, to 1.5 mm. long; corolla white, slender, 4 mm. long; mature fr. flattened, 6 mm. broad; nutlets separable.

7b. **A. Hearstiòrum** Hoov. & Roof is proposed as a new sp. near to *A. Hookeri* G. Don from near the Arroyo de la Cruz, Hearst Ranch, nw. San Luis Obispo Co. Resembling *A. Hookeri*, but more prostrate, forming mats; petioles ca. 1 mm. long; lf.-blades 10–18 mm. long; infl. small, mostly 3–6-fld.

p. 422.   13. **A. nevadénsis** Gray. In the Greenhorn Range, Kern Co., *Twisselmann.*

p. 423.   14. **A. púngens** var. **montàna** (Eastw.) Munz. $2n = 52$ (Stebbins & Major, 1965).

17. **A. pátula** Greene. Ascends to 11,000 ft. in the Sierra Nevada.

p. 425.   27. **P. canéscens** Eastw. $2n = 26$ (Stebbins & Major, 1965).

p. 426.   29. **A. obispoénsis** Eastw. Add as synonym *A. luciana* P. V. Wells.

33a. **A. montereyénsis** Hoov. Near to *A. columbiana* Piper. Erect, 1.25 m. tall; branchlets with spreading gland-tipped hairs; lvs. elliptic to oval, 15–34 mm. long, mostly obtuse, sparsely hairy on midrib; panicle glandular-hairy; bracts lanceolate, ca. as long as flowering pedicels; corolla tinged with some pink; fr. sparsely hairy, not viscid.—Sand at s. edge of Monterey Airport, Monterey Co.

p. 427.   35a. **A. Hoòveri** P. V. Wells. Tall, to over 4 m.; branchlets densely short-pubescent and glandular-hispid; lvs. ovate to oblong, 3–5 cm. long, cordate, on petioles 2–10 mm. long, gray-green, glandular-hairy on both surfaces; infl. large, open, leafy-bracted, the bracts to 15 mm. long; pedicels to 10 mm. long; corolla 7–8 mm. long; fr. glandular-viscid; nutlets separable.—Near summit of Nascimiento Pass, Santa Lucia Mts., s. Monterey Co. (Near *A. Andersonii* and *A. glandulosa*.)

p. 427.   Mr. James B. Roof has gone into the matter of *A. imbricata* Eastw. in some detail, proposes a new sp., **A. montaraénsis** Roof, and discusses in general the genus on Montara Mt. and San Bruno Mt. (The Four Seasons 2 (3): 6–16. 1967). He feels that *A. imbricata* is not a variety of *A. Andersonii* Gray, as it is treated in the FLORA, but a definitely distinct species. It consists of 5 separate colonies occupying "clean and otherwise bare sandstone outcroppings" on San Bruno Mt., at 1000–1300 ft. He feels that it is of hybrid origin (*A. montaraensis* × *A. Uva-ursi*).

His *A. montaraensis* is compared with *A. pallida* Eastw. (*A. Andersonii* var. *pallida* in the FLORA). It is erect, 1–5 m. tall, twice as high as *pallida*, which is divaricately spreading; has vivid bright green lvs. 3–5 cm. long (not glaucous); lvs. ciliate on margin when young (not so in *pallida*); heavily ciliate bracts (bracts not ciliate in *pallida*); long-hairy glandular ovary (short-hairy, less glandular in *pallida*). It grows on granitic sand and sandstone, at 500–1500 ft., in w. San Mateo Co., from near Lake Pilarcitos to Scarper Peak and Montara Mt.

p. 428.   37a. **A. cruzénsis** Roof is proposed as near *A. pajaroensis* and *A. pechoensis*. Decumbent, spreading to 3 m. across; lvs. sessile, pale dull green, oblong, 2–3 cm. long; infl. compact, subcapitate, closely fine-pubescent; bracts to 10 mm. long; corolla 6 mm. long; fr. depressed-globose, to 10 mm. wide, finely hirsutulous.—Arroyo de la Cruz Creek, on Highway 1, nw. San Luis Obispo Co.

38. **A. pechoénsis** var. **viridíssima** Eastw. Delete the insular references.

p. 428.   38a. **A. refugióensis** Gankin. (The Four Seasons 2 (2): 13. 1967). Erect, 2.5–4 m. tall, 2–3.5 m. wide; without basal burl; young growth with both short and long gland-tipped setose hairs; lvs. mostly sessile, cordate, clasping, entire to serrulate, imbricate, 2.5–4.5 cm. long, 2–3 cm. wide, with equal numbers of stomates on both surfaces; infl. branched, the rachis fine-pubescent and glandular-setose; bracts foliaceous, 5–10 mm. long; pedicels 6–9 mm. long; calyx-segms. 2 mm. long; corolla white to pinkish; ovary glabrous; fr. globose, 1–1.5 cm. in diam., the nutlets coalesced.—At 2250 feet, Refugio Pass and region, Santa Barbara Co. Near *A. pechoensis*, but fr. not depressed. At Rancho Santa Ana Bot. Gard., the herbarium has 3 sheets from Refugio Pass which do not support the distinctness of the proposed sp.

39. **A. glandulòsa** Eastw. var. **Cushingiàna** (Eastw.) Adams ex McMinn. Reported from Monterey Co., *Howitt and Howell*.

p. 429.   41. **A. crustàcea** Eastw. var. **Ròsei** (Eastw.) McMinn. J. B. Roof (The Four Seasons 1: 1–15. 1964) presents data for recognition of **A. Ròsei** Eastw. as a sp. Burls more irregular and pitted; bark terracotta red, exfoliating in long strips (not purple-black and smooth); lvs. often truncate at the base, brighter green, rarely toothed; new branchlets slightly pubescent (not bristly); fls. largely before March 15 (not on into April). He would extend its range from San Francisco to colonies in Monterey Co. (Ft. Ord region, Garrapata Creek, Rocky Creek, Bixby Creek, and Plaskett Creek).

p. 430.   43. **A. subcordàta** Eastw. On Santa Catalina Id., *Thorne.*

p. 432.   EMPÈTRUM
1. American material passing as *E. nigrum* L. should probably be called **E. hermaphrodìtum** (Lange) Hagerup, being tetraploid, with bisexual fls. and larger pollen grains. [*E. Eamesii* ssp. *h.* D. Löve.]

p. 433.   PÝROLA
1. B. Krisa (Bot. Jahrb. 85: 612–637. 1966) recognizes **Pýrola califórnica** Krisa [*P. asarifolia* Am. auth., *P. a.* var. *incarnata* Fern. & var. *purpurea* (Bunge) Fern.] for plants with lance-ovate bracts, 4.5–7.5 mm. long, usually as long as the pedicels; calyx-lobes 3–3.5 mm. long; anthers 2.5–3 mm. long, short-pointed, and
P. bracteàta Hook. [*P. asarifolia* var. *bracteata* (Hook.) Jeps. *P. rotundifolia* var. *b.* Gray.] Bracts linear-lanceolate, 7.5–8.5 mm. long, usually twice as long as the pedicels; calyx-lobes lanceolate and in upper third prolonged into a long point 3.9–4.4 mm. long.

p. 434.   MONÈSES
1. **M. uniflòra** (L.) Gray ssp. **reticulàta** (Nutt.) Calder & Taylor has been published.

p. 435.   CHIMÁPHILA
1. **C. umbellàta** var. **occidentàlis** (Rydb.) Blake. $2n = 26$ (Raven, Kyhos & Hill, 1965).

ALLÓTROPA
1. **A. virgàta** T. & G. ex Gray. $2n = 26$ (D. E. Anderson, 1965).

p. 436.   PTERÓSPORA
1. **P. andromedèa** Nutt. is said by Bakshi to be parasitic on root fungi.

p. 437.   PITYÒPUS
1. **P. califórnicus** (Eastw.) Copel. f. is reported also as in Lake and Colusa cos.

p. 438.   MICROCÀLA
1. **M. quadrángularis** (Lam.) Griseb. D. M. Post (Madroño 19: 134. 1967) takes up the name *Cicendia quadrangularis* (Lam.) Griseb. "The more familiar generic name *Microcala* is apparently invalid due to its being superfluous when published." $n = 13$ (Post, 1967).

p. 440.   EUSTÒMA
1. **E. exaltàtum** (L.) Salisb. is older as a comb. than (L.) Griseb.

p. 443.   GENTIÀNA
10. **G. tenélla** Rottb. is placed in *Comastoma* as *C. tenellum* Toyokuni.
11. *Gentianópsis simplex* (Gray) Iltis is proposed. Its range can be extended in the Sierra Nevada s. into the Greenhorn Range, Kern Co., *Twisselmann.*
12. *Gentianópsis holopetala* (Gray) Iltis is proposed.

p. 446.   MENYÁNTHES
1. **M. trifoliàta** L. Once reported as in San Francisco Co.; also in Mendocino Co. Wade, 1956, gave $2n = 54$, 108.

p. 447.   FRAXINUS
1. **F. dipétala** H. & A. $2n = 23$ pairs (Raven, Kyhos & Hill, 1965).

p. 452.   ASCLEPIADÀCEAE
In Key to Genera, in line 3, change to:

Fls. borne in umbels or racemes (then add:)
   The fls. not white. Native. .... 2. *Sarcostemma*
   The fls. white. Escape from cult. .... 2a. *Araujia*

CYNÁNCHUM L. not *Cynanchium* as in 1959 printing.

p. 453.   SARCOSTÉMMA
1. **S. cynanchoìdes** Dcne. ssp. **Hartwégii** (Vail) R. Holm. Reported from Ojai V., Ventura Co., *Pollard.*

2. **S. hirtéllum** (Gray) R. Holm. Corolla-lobes subpilose without, glabrous to glabrate within (fide *Bacigalupi*).

2a. Araújia Brot.

Corolla tube inflated at the base; lobes 5, overlapping in the bud; crown with 5 scales attached at or below the middle of the tube; stigma often 2-beaked at apex.

1. **A. sericófera** Brot. BLADDER-FLOWER. Vigorous climber; stem covered with pale down when young; lvs. ovate-oblong, 5–10 cm. long, pale green, minutely pitted beneath; fls. white, salverform, 2–3 cm. across, the tube 12 mm. long; pod grooved, 12 cm. long, 5–7 cm. wide.—Escape from cult., Riverside to Placer cos.; native of S. Am.

p. 454. ASCLÈPIAS

In description of genus, under "Follicles," insert "mostly" before "acuminate."

p. 456. 7. **A. subulàta** Dcne. in A. DC. $2n = 22$ (W. H. Lewis, 1961).

p. 457. 14. **A. curassávica** L. $2n = 22$ (Huynh, 1965).

p. 458. CONVOLVULÀCEAE

In Key to Genera, from last line delete "4. *Convolvulus*," add two lines:

Stigma oblong, ± cylindrical, the stigmatic area and style distinct; ovary with an incomplete septum . . . . **5. *Calystegia***
Stigma linear, the stigmatic area and the style ± continuous; ovary with a complete septum. . . . . **4. *Convolvulus***

DICHÓNDRA

1. Change *D. rèpens* Forst. & Forst. f. to **D. Donnelliàna** Tharp & Johnston.

p. 459. IPOMOÈA

Change Key to Species to:

Sepals ca. 7–12 mm. long
  Corolla 5–6 cm. long . . . . **1. *I. purpurea***
  Corolla 1.5–2 cm. long . . . . **1a. *I. triloba***
Sepals ca. 20–30 mm. long
  Corolla 2–4 cm. long; lvs. not canescent . . . . **2. *I. nil***
  Corolla 6–8 cm. long; lvs. silvery-canescent . . . . **3. *I. mutabilis***

1. **I. purpùrea** (L.) Roth. $n = 15$ (A. Jones, 1964).

1a. **I. trilòba** L. Climbing annual herb; stems glabrous; lvs. cordate, entire or 3-lobed, 3–6 cm. long, 2–5 cm. broad, glabrous, subacuminate; petioles 3–5 cm. long; infl. axillary, peduncled, 1–5-fld., umbellate; calyx 8 mm. long, the sepals ciliate, oblong-acuminate; corolla ca. 15 mm. long.—Escape in Imperial and Riverside cos.; native in trop. Am.

2. **I. hederàcea** (L.) Jacq. A. Jones (Jour. Heredity 55: 216–219. 1964) uses **I. níl** (L.) Roth.

3. **I. mutábilis** Ker.-Gawl. Weedy pubescent perennial; lvs. to 1 dm., ca. equally long and wide, cordate, whitish-tomentose beneath; calyx 2–3 cm. long; corolla vivid ultramarine blue, to ca. 8 cm. across.—Escaping as a weed in waste places, as in Santa Barbara and Ventura cos.; native of Mex.

CONVÓLVULUS

Amend the description as follows:

Pollen ± elongate. Stigmas 2, linear, ± applanate, acutate at apices, the stigmatic area and the style ± continuous; ovary 2-locular, the septum complete. A fairly large genus as amended.

A. Plants annual; corolla ca. 6 mm. long, deeply cleft. . . . . **1. *C. simulans***
AA. Plants perennial; corolla 2–6 cm. long, not cleft.
   B. Corolla purple to rose, 2.5–3 cm. long; stems climbing. . . . . **2. *C. althaeoides***
   BB. Corolla white or with some pink, 1.5–2 cm. long; stems largely prostrate.
                                                    3. *C. arvensis*

1. **C. símulans** L. M. Perry is no. 16 in the FLORA.

2. **C. althaeoìdes** L. is no. 17 in the FLORA.

3. **C. arvénsis** L. is no. 15 in the FLORA. $n = 24$ (Khoshoo & Sachideva, 1961).

5. Calystègia R. Br. MORNING-GLORY

Resembling *Convolvulus*, but with pollen sphaeroidal. Stigmas oblong, ±
cylindrical with blunt apices, the stigmatic area and style distinct. Caps. 1-locu-
lar with an incomplete septum. A fairly large genus, of which the spp. have
largely been referred to *Convolvulus* (Greek, *kalux*, cup, and *stegos*, a covering).

A. Calyx enclosed or closely subtended by a pair of large sepallike bracts.
   B. Corolla purple to rose.
      C. Lvs. reniform, obtuse, fleshy, 2–5 cm. broad; prostrate seaside herbs.
                              1. *C. Soldanella*
      CC. Lvs. ovate-hastate, thin, acute to acuminate, 6–10 cm. long; climbing swamp
         plant. . . . . 2. *C. sepium*
   BB. Corolla white to cream, sometimes pinkish in age.
      C. Stems mostly over 1 m. long, twining or trailing.
         D. Plants of swamps and marshes, the stems entirely herbaceous. 2. *C. sepium*
         DD. Plants of dry places, the stems ± woody at base. . . . . 3. *C. macrostegia*
      CC. Stems mostly 1–5 dm. long, erect to prostrate.
         D. Herbage glabrous; corolla 4–5 cm. long. N. Calif. . . . 4. *C. atriplicifolia*
         DD. Herbage pubescent to tomentose.
            E. Corolla 4–5 cm. long; plant stemless or nearly so. Central Coast
               Ranges.
               F. Plant pilose-pubescent; pedicels much shorter than petioles.
                                 5. *C. subacaulis*
               F. Plant ± tomentose; pedicels ca. as long as pedicels. 6. *C. collina*
            EE. Corolla 2.5–3.5 cm. long; plants usually with stems 1–4 dm. long,
               variously pubescent. . . . . 7. *C. malacophylla*
AA. Calyx subtended by more remote bracts that are not much like sepals.
   B. Bracts hastately lobed, like the upper lvs. Interior Calif. from Shasta Co. to San
      Diego Co. . . . . 8. *C. fulcrata*
   BB. Bracts entire.
      C. Plants puberulent to pubescent.
         D. Stems trailing or erect, 3–6 dm. long; outer sepals rounded at apex.
                                9. *C. polymorpha*
         DD. Stems climbing, taller; outer sepals acuminate. . . . . . 10. *C. occidentalis*
      CC. Plants glabrous.
         D. Bracts broadly oblong to oval, attached near the base of the calyx. Desert
            slopes of the San Gabriel Mts. . . . . 11. *C. Peirsonii*
         DD. Bracts subulate to narrowly lanceolate, usually well below the calyx.
            E. Plants climbing; basal lobes of lvs. usually broad and toothed.
                             12. *C. purpurata*
            EE. Plants not climbing; basal lobes of lvs. linear, entire. 13. *C. longipes*

p. 460.   1. **C. Soldanélla** (L.) R. Br. is *Convolvulus* sp. no. 1 of the FLORA.

     2. **C. sèpium** (L.) R. Br. is *Convolvulus* sp. no. 2 of the FLORA. It is Euro-
pean with the basal lf.-lobes having conspicuous subacute angles. It is questionable whether typical *sepium* is in Calif. $2n = 20$ (Smith, 1965).

     Ssp. **americàna** (Sims) Brummitt. [*Convolvulus s.* var. *a.* Sims.] Lf.-lobes
more sharply angled. Perhaps natur., as about San Bernardino; e. U.S.

     Ssp. **limnóphila** (Greene) Brummitt. [*Convolvulus l.* Greene. *C. s.* var. *repens*
auth.] Plants mostly only 6–9 dm. high, herbage glabrous or very slightly pubescent; lvs. narrow, sagittate, the basal lobes ¼–⅓ the length of the body; bracts
unequal, large, the lower partly enfolding the truncate upper one; corolla large,
pinkish.—Tidal marshes, San Francisco Bay region.

     Ssp. **Binghàmiae** (Greene) Brummitt. [*Convolvulus B.* Greene. *Convolvulus
sepium* var. *dumetorum* Pospichal.] Plant glabrous throughout, 1–2 mm. high;
lvs. mostly obtuse at apex; bracts ca. 8–10 mm. long, ca. half as long as the
sepals.—Coastal marshes, Santa Barbara Co. to Orange Co.

     3. **C. macrostègia** (Greene) Brummitt. [*Convolvulus m.* Greene. *Convolvulus
occidentalis* var. *m.* Munz. *Volvulus m.* Farwell.] Is *Convolvulus* sp. no. 3 in
the FLORA.

A. Bracts largely 2–3 cm. long; corolla 5–6 cm. long. Insular. . . . . *C. macrostegia*
AA. Bracts 1–1.5 cm. long; corolla 2–4.5 cm. long. Mostly mainland.
   B. The bracts mostly subcordate at base, membranous and purplish. Near the coast,
      Monterey Co. s. . . . . Ssp. *cyclostegia*
   BB. The bracts mostly rounded at the base, firm and greenish. Largely away from the
      coast.

C. Lvs. and stems cinereous with dense tomentulose puberulence. Interior s. Calif. . . . . Ssp. *arida*
CC. Lvs. and stems glabrous or nearly so.
  D. Middle lobe of lvs. narrowly to deltoid-lanceolate; corolla 3–3.5 cm. long.
    E. Basal lobes of lvs. less than half as long as middle lobe, not strongly divergent. Ventura Co. to Orange Co. and Catalina Id. Ssp. *intermedia*
    EE. Basal lobes of lvs. at least half as long as middle lobe, strongly divergent. Dry hills about San Diego and to w. Riverside and e. Orange cos. . . . . Ssp. *longiloba*
  DD. Middle lobe of lvs. narrowly linear; corolla 2–2.5 cm. long. W. Riverside to n. L. Calif. . . . . Ssp. *tenuifolia*

p. 461.
  Ssp. cyclostègia (House) Brummitt. [*Convolvulus c.* House.] This is *Convolvulus* sp. no. 4 of the FLORA.
  Ssp. árida (Greene) Brummitt. [*Convolvulus a.* Greene.] This is *Convolvulus* sp. no. 5 of the FLORA.
  Ssp. intermèdia (Abrams) Brummitt. [*Convolvulus aridus* ssp. *i.* Abrams.]
  Ssp. longilòba (Abrams) Brummitt. [*Convolvulus aridus* ssp. *l.* Abrams.]
  Ssp. tenuifòlia (Abrams) Brummitt. [*Convolvulus aridus* ssp. *t.* Abrams.]
  4. C. atriplícifolia Hallier f. [*Convolvulus nyctagineus* Greene.] This is *Convolvulus* sp. no. 6 in the FLORA.
  5. C. subacaùlis H. & A. [*Convolvulus s.* Greene. and var. *dolosus* Jeps. *Convolvulus californicus* Choisy.] This is *Convolvulus* sp. no. 7 of the FLORA.
  6. C. collìna (Greene) Brummitt. [*Convolvulus c.* Greene. *Convolvulus malacophyllus* ssp. *c.* Abrams.]
  Ssp. tridactylòsa (Eastw.) Brummitt. [*Convolvulus t.* Eastw.] Prostrate and trailing, gray-tomentose throughout; lvs. 3-parted, cuneate at base, the divisions widely spreading, the middle from ovate-triangular to narrower, ca. 2 cm. long, 4–10 mm. wide, mucronate, the lateral divisions oblong, obtuse, 1–2 cm. long, 5–10 mm. wide; petioles flexuous, the lowest 5 cm. long; pedicels shorter than petioles; bracts lanceolate, acute, equaling or shorter than the elliptical mucronate sepals, these tomentose; fils. shorter than the style.—Mts. near Covelo, Mendocino Co.
  7. C. malacophýlla (Greene) Munz, comb. nov. [*Convolvulus m.* Greene, Pittonia 3: 326. 1898. *Calystegia fulcrata* ssp. *m.* Brummitt. *Calystegia villosa* Kell., not Raf.] Plants densely gray-tomentose; lf.-blades triangular-hastate; bracts 10–15 mm. long.—Sierra Nevada from Tulare Co. n., to Trinity and Siskiyou cos. This is *Convolvulus* sp. no. 8 of the FLORA.
p. 462.
  Ssp. pedicellàta (Jeps.) Munz, comb. nov. [*Convolvulus villosus* var. *pedicellatus* Jeps., Man. Fl. Pl. Calif., 777. 1925. *Convolvulus malacophyllus* ssp. *p.* Abrams. *Calystegia fulcrata* ssp. *p.* Brummitt.] Lf.-blades narrowly lanceolate; plants densely gray-tomentose; bracts 10–15 mm. long.—Coast Ranges, Alameda Co. to Ventura Co.
  Ssp. tomentélla (Greene) Munz, comb. nov. [*Convolvulus tomentellus* Greene. Pittonia 3: 327. 1898. *Calystegia fulcrata* ssp. *t.* Brummitt.] This is sp. no. 9 under *Convolvulus* in the FLORA.
  Var. deltoìdea (Greene) Munz, comb. nov. [*Convolvulus deltoideus* Greene, Pittonia 3: 331. 1898. *Calystegia fulcrata* ssp. *tomentella* var. *d.* Brummitt.] Lvs. 1.2–1.5 cm. long, deltoid, somewhat broader; herbage short-canescent. At 3000–5000 ft.; Foothill Wd., Yellow Pine F.; Tehachapi Mts., Mt. Pinos.
  8. C. fulcràta (Gray) Brummitt. [*Convolvulus f.* (Gray) Greene.] This is *Convolvulus* sp. no. 10 in the FLORA.
  9. C. polymórpha (Greene) Munz, comb. nov. [*Convolvulus polymorphus* Greene, Pittonia 3: 331. 1898.] This is *Convolvulus* sp. no. 11 in the FLORA.
  10. C. occidentàlis (Gray) Brummitt. [*Convolvulus o.* Gray.] This is sp. no. 12 of *Convolvulus* in the FLORA.
p. 463.
  11. C. Peirsònii (Abrams) Brummitt. [*Convolvulus P.* Abrams.] This is *Convolvulus* sp. no. 13 in the FLORA.
  12. C. purpuràta (Greene) Brummitt. [*Convolvulus luteolus* var. *p.* Greene.] This is *Convolvulus occidentalis* var. *purpuratus* of the FLORA.
  Ssp. solanénsis (Jeps.) Brummitt. [*Convolvulus luteolus* var. *s.* Jeps.] This is

the *Convolvulus occidentalis* var. *solanensis* in the FLORA, with ochroleucous fls. and from Solano Co.

Ssp. saxícola (Eastw.) Brummitt. [*Convolvulus s.* Eastw.] This is the *Convolvulus occidentalis* var. *saxicola* of the FLORA. Lvs. small, round-ovate. S. Sonoma Co. and adjacent Marin Co.

13. C. lóngipes (Wats.) Brummitt. [*Convolvulus l.* Wats.] This is sp. no. 14 under *Convolvulus* in the FLORA.

p. 465. CUSCÙTA

In Key after BB, C, DD, EE, delete "13. *C. salina*" at end of line and add:

> F. Fls. 2–3 mm. long; corolla-lobes ovate-lanceolate; scales attached to the corolla-tube most of their length; anthers oval, the fils. well developed. .... 13. *C. salina*
> FF. Fls. 3–4 mm. long; corolla-lobes lanceolate; scales commonly free; anthers oval-oblong. .... 13a. *C. nevadensis*

p. 466.   10. C. indécora Choisy. $n = 15$ (Raven, Kyhos & Hill, 1965).
p. 467.   11. Change name from *C. subinclusa* Dur. & Hilg. to C. Ceanòthi Behr.

13a. C. nevadénsis Jtn. [*C. Veatchii apoda* Yuncker. *C. salina a.* Yuncker.] Fls. 3–4 mm. long, the lobes of the calyx and corolla more lanceolate than in *C. salina* and also somewhat longer; scales mostly broader and commonly free; anthers oval-oblong, subsessile.—On *Atriplex*, etc., Towne's Pass, Panamint Mts., *Eastwood & Howell*; Nev.

14. C. denticulàta Engelm. $2n = 15$ pairs (Raven, Kyhos & Hill, 1965).

p. 469. POLEMÒNIUM

In Key, last line, for 1959 printing of the FLORA, change 69 to 6.

p. 470.   4. P. pulchérrimum Hook.
Wherry (Aliso 6: 99. 1967) recognizes:

> A. Herbage sparingly pubescent; habit lax; corolla normally violet. From n. Calif. northward. .... var. *pulcherrimum*
>   [*P. Berryi* Eastw., a synonym]
> AA. Herbage copiously pubescent; habit compact; corolla white or nearly so. Mt. Shasta to Mt. Rainier. .... var. *pilosum* (Greenm.) Brand
>   [*P. shastense* Baker ex Eastw.]

p. 475. PHLÓX

In Key, change last FF to:

> FF. Lvs. 3–10 mm. long, often ± arched and spreading; plants pulvinate, densely tomentose throughout.
>   G. Lvs. 5–10 mm. long, plane, subulate, not closely imbricated or concealing the stem. .... 12. *P. Hoodii*
>   GG. Lvs. 3–5 mm. long, concave, oblong-elliptic, imbricated, completely concealing the stem. .... 13. *P. bryoides*

p. 477.   10. P. diffùsa Benth. ssp. subcarinàta Wherry. Reported from Piute Mt., Kern Co., *Twisselmann*.

13. P. bryoìdes Nutt. Very compactly pulvinate, 5–10 cm. broad; lvs. closely imbricated, completely concealing the stem, 3–5 mm. long; 3-ribbed on lower surface; fls. solitary, sessile; calyx ca. 5 mm. long; corolla white to lilac, 7–10 mm. long.—Mt. Lassen Park at 8000 ft.; Ore. to Wyo., Nev.

MICRÓSTERIS

1. M. grácilis (Hook.) Greene. [*Gilia g.* Hook. Omit "Dougl."]

p. 479. GÍLIA

In Key, under AA, B, CC, D, E, FF, drop "23. *G. ophthalmoides*" from end of line and insert on next line:

> H. Corolla 7–12 mm. long, the tube well exserted from the calyx. .... 23. *G. ophthalmoides*
> HH. Corolla 3.5–5 mm. long, the tube included in the calyx. .... 23a. *G. Clokeyi*

In Key, under AA, B, CC, DD, E, F drop "28. *G. brecciarum*" and add:

> G. Corolla with broad throat, white to violet. Deserts and e. of Sierra Nevada. .... 28. *G. brecciarum*

GG. Corolla slender in form, deep violet with purple tube.
Inner S. Coast Range, Kern, Ventura and Santa Barbara
cos. .... 28a. *G. jacens*

In Key, AA, BB, C, insert "mostly" between "glomerules" and "of."

p. 480.   In Key, AA, BB, C, DD, EE, FF, GG, insert "Largely" after "pollen mostly blue."

p. 482.   1. **G. capitàta** ssp. **abrótanifòlia** (Nutt. ex Greene) V. Grant. Reported from Santa Lucia Mts., *Howitt & Howell*.

p. 485.   15. **G. ochroleùca** Jones ssp. **bizonàta** A. & V. Grant. Reported from Monterey Co., *Howitt & Howell*.

p. 486.   17. **G. leptántha** Parish ssp. **vívida** A. & V. Grant transferred to 15. **G. ochroleuca** ssp. vivida A. & V. Grant.

p. 487.   19. **G. tenuiflòra** Benth. is reported from the Temblor Range, Kern Co., *Twisselmann*.

p. 488.   21. Under **G. intèrior** (Mason & Grant) A. Grant is mentioned **G. austrooccidentalis** (A. & V. Grant) A. & V. Grant which can be considered a sp.

23a. **G. Clòkeyi** Mason. Differing from **G. ophthalmoìdes** Brand in having corollas 3.5–5 mm. long, the tube included in the calyx, the throat pale yellow below, white above; *n* = 9.—E. San Bernardino and Inyo cos.; to New Mex.

p. 490.   28a. **G. jàcens** A. & V. Grant. Resembling *G. brecciarum* in habit of branching and fl.-size, *G. tenuiflora* in fl.-shape and color, *G. leptantha* in lf.-dissection. From *G. brecciarum* and *G. leptantha* it differs by the slender form and deep violet to purple corollas; from *G. tenuiflora* by smaller corollas (5–7 mm. long) and the spreading habit of branching. S. Coast Ranges, Kern Co. to n. Santa Barbara and Ventura cos.

p. 493.   IPOMÓPSIS

2. **I. aggregàta** ssp. **Bridgèsii** V. & A. Grant. Reported from Kern Plateau, Kern Co., *Twisselmann*.

3. **I. congésta** (Hook.) V. Grant. [Add *Gilia congesta* ssp. *palmifrons* Brand to synonyms.]

p. 495.   ERIÁSTRUM

1. **E. densifòlium** ssp. **elongàtum** (Benth.) Mason occurs in Monterey Co., *Howitt & Howell*.

3. **E. sapphirìnum** ssp. **dasyánthum** (Brand) Mason reported from Monterey Co., *Howitt & Howell*.

p. 501.   NAVARRÈTIA

4. **N. plieántha** Mason. Loch Lomond, Bennett Mt., Lake Co., *Rubtzoff*.

p. 502.   11. **N. cotulifòlia** (Benth.) H. & A. Outer Coast Ranges, Sonoma Co., *Rubtzoff*.

12. **N. nigellifórmis** Greene. In the Greenhorn Range, Kern Co., *Twisselmann*.

p. 503.   17. **N. mitracárpa** Greene in the Greenhorn Range, Kern Co., *Twisselmann*.

Ssp. **Jaredii** (Eastw.) Mason in Monterey Co., *Howitt & Howell*.

20. **N. divaricàta** (Torr.) Greene in the Greenhorn Mts., *Twisselmann*.

p. 506.   LEPTODÁCTYLON

1. **L. púngens** (Torr.) Rydb. ssp. **Hállii** (Parish) Mason ascends to 10,500 ft., in the White Mts.

p. 509.   LINÁNTHUS

2. **L. pygmaèus** (Brand) J. T. Howell ssp. **continentàlis** Raven is proposed for plants from the mainland, restricting insular plants as *L. pygmaeus*. On Guadalupe and San Clemente ids., the corolla is lavender-blue, 4.5–6 mm. long, hence surpassing the calyx by 1.5–2.2 mm.; on the mainland it is white, 3.8–6 mm. long, therefore 0–1.4 mm. longer than the calyx.

p. 513.   26. **L. nudàtus** Greene. Synonym *Gilia n.* Greene, not Brand.

p. 515.   32. **L. bìcolor** (Nutt.) Greene ranges on the mainland s. to Point Sal, Santa Barbara Co., *C. F. Smith*.

p. 519.   EUCRÝPTA

2. **E. micrántha** (Torr.) Heller. *n* = 6 or 12 (Cave & Constance, 1963).

p. 522.   NEMÓPHILA

7. **N. heterophýlla** F. & M. in the San Emigdio Range, Kern Co., *Twisselmann.*

p. 523.   PHACÈLIA
In Key, change 7 to 57, at end of line 3.

p. 525.   In Key AA, B, CC, D, E, FF, GG, H, I, go to:

J. Plant glandular-hirsute, 20–60 cm. high; corolla whitish, 5–6 mm. long; lvs. entire to dentate-lobed, the petiole ca. as long as the blade; calyx-lobes unequal. San Luis Obispo and Monterey cos. ... 55. *P. grisea*

JJ. Plant glandular-villous, 10–40 cm. tall; corolla lavender to violet, 6–7 mm. long; lvs. entire or with salient teeth, the petioles almost as long as blades; calyx-lobes unequal. W. base of Sierra Nevada and to Modoc Co. 56. *P. Purpusii*

JJJ. Plant glandular-pubescent, 2–12 cm. tall; corolla lavender, 5–7 mm. long; lvs. crenate, the petiole ½ to ⅓ as long as the blade; calyx-lobes subequal. Ventura Co. 55a. *P. Hardhamiae*

p. 527.   In Key AA, BB, CC, DD, EE, change F to:

F. Corolla yellow, 2.5–4 mm. long; stamens 1.5–2 mm. long; fls. 5-merous.
G. Plant finely glandular throughout. Inyo and Mono cos. 86. *P. inyoensis*
GG. Plant not glandular. Mono Co. n. ..... 86a. *P. scopulina*

3. **P. serícea** (Grah.) Gray ssp. **ciliòsa** (Rydb.) Gillett is the name taken up for our plants which range from Modoc Co. to adjacent Ore. and to nw. Ariz. *P. sericea* ssp. *sericea* is ne. of Calif. and has campanulate rather than ± urceolate corollas.

p. 528.   4. **P. Bolánderi** Gray. n = 11 (Cave & Constance, 1963).
5. **P. ramosíssima** Dougl. ex Lehm. is in Monterey Co., *Howitt & Howell.*
Var. **válida** Peck is reported from the Piute Mts., Kern Co., *Twisselmann.*

p. 529.   7. **P. Lyònii** Gray. n = 11 (Cave & Constance, 1963).
8. **P. floribúnda** Greene. n = 11 (Cave & Constance, 1959).
9. After **P. dístans** Benth. insert **P. umbròsa** Greene. Resembling *P. distans,* but with slender weak stems to ca. 3 dm. high; calyx-lobes linear; corolla tubular-campanulate, 3–6 mm. long.—W. edge of Colo. Desert, from Santa Rosa Mts. to L. Calif.

p. 530.   12. **P. cicutària** Greene var. **híspida** (Gray) J. T. Howell is reported as in Monterey Co., *Howitt & Howell.*
13. **P. cryptántha** Greene occurs in King's R. region, Fresno Co., *Howell.*
14. **P. vállis-mórtae** var. **helióphila** J. Voss. n = 11 (Cave & Constance, 1963).

p. 531.   16. **P. Rattánii** Gray is in Ventura Co., *Hardham.*
19. **P. crenulàta** Torr. n = 11 (Cave & Constance, 1963).
20. **P. minutiflòra** J. Voss. n = 11 (Cave & Constance, 1963).

p. 532.   22. **P. pedicellàta** Gray. n = 11 (Cave & Constance, 1963).
25. **P. imbricàta** Greene. Heckard adds **P. oreópola** Heckard which keys out:

Corolla white; stems usually more than 5 dm. long, erect to ascending; Coast Ranges, w. Sierra Nevada and cismontane s. Calif. below 5000 ft. .... *P. imbricata*
Corolla largely lavender to pale pink; stems 2.5–5 dm. long, decumbent to ascending. Above 5000 ft.
   Plants decumbent; corolla narrowly cylindrical with incurved lobes; lobes of rosette lvs. 3–5 pairs. San Gabriel Mts. .... *P. oreopola* Heckard
   Plants ascending; corolla urceolate; lobes of rosette lvs. 1–2 pairs or lvs. entire. San Bernardino Mts. .... *P. oreopola* ssp. *simulans* Heckard

p. 533.   25. **P. imbricàta** ssp. **bernardìna** (Greene) Heckard. n = 11 (Heckard, 1960).
26. **P. califórnica** Cham. Add. *P. Biolettii* Greene as synonym. n = 22 (Heckard, 1960).

27. **P. egèna** (Greene ex Brand) Const. $n = 22$ (Cave & Constance, as *bernardina*). Occurs in Monterey Co., *Howitt & Howell*.

29. **P. heterophýlla** Pursh. Heckard (Univ. Calif. Publ. Bot. 32: 68–76. 1960) has 2 sspp. under *P. heterophylla*: the ssp. **heterophýlla** ranging from Wash. and cent. Ore. to Mont. and Mex. Calif. material is referred to ssp. **virgàta** (Greene) Heckard, a biennial; infl. virgate; lower stem and rosette lvs. lack gland-tipped hairs; infl. and calyx-lobes usually with dull, whitish hairs.— Range Wash. to nw. Wyo., n. Calif., e. Nev. [Synonyms are *P. californica* var. *rubacea* Jeps. and *P. Peirsoniae* Williams.]

p. 534.   30. **P. hastàta** Dougl. ex Lehm. ssp. **compácta** (Greene) Heckard. $n = 22$ (Cave & Constance, 1947, as *frigida*).

31. **P. nemoràlis** Greene. Delete *P. Bioletti* Greene as a synonym. The typical form occurs in cent. Calif.

Ssp. **oregonénsis** Heckard, with stouter stems, 2 or more pairs of lobes on rosette lvs. (instead of 1 pair) and upper surface of lvs. sparsely appressed hispid or strigose instead of spreading hispid.—Nw. Calif. to Wash. $n = 22$ Cave & Constance, 1942 as *nemoralis*).

32. **P. mutábilis** Greene. Dele *P. californica* var. *rubacea* Jeps. $n = 11, 22$ (Cave & Constance, 1942, 1958).

33. **P. corymbòsa** Jeps. $n = 11, 22$ (Cave & Constance, 1958; Kruckeberg, 1956).

34. **P. frígida** Greene. Heckard recognizes 2 sspp.:

Ssp. **frígida.** Lvs. ovate or lance-ovate to lenticular in outline with cuneate to obtuse base; upper lf.-surface smooth-strigose, grayish to whitish; calyx-lobes linear-lanceolate; corolla white, broadly campanulate; $n = 33$ (Heckard, 1960). —Modoc Co. and Mt. Shasta to n. Ore.

Ssp. **dasyphýlla** (Macbr.) Heckard. [*P. d.* Greene.] Lvs. lanceolate or lenticular to narrow-lanceolate with attenuate base; upper lf.-surface shaggy-strigose or with hairs little appressed, green to yellowish-green; calyx-lobes linear or linear-lanceolate; corolla white to lavender, tubular-campanulate; $n = 22, 33$ (Heckard, 1960).—Sierra Nevada and White Mts.

p. 535.   37. **P. Leònis** J. T. Howell. $n = 11$ (Cave & Constance, 1963).

40. **P. orógenes** Brand. $n = 9$ (Cave & Constance, 1959).

p. 536.   43. **P. marcéscens** Eastw. ex Macbr. $n = 8$ (Cave & Constance, 1963).

47. **P. austromontàna** J. T. Howell. $n = 9$ (Cave & Constance, 1959).

p. 537.   52. Howitt & Howell use **P. Davidsònii** Gray instead of *P. curvipes* var. *macrantha* (Parish) Munz and report it for Monterey Co.

p. 538.   53. **P. Douglásii** var. **cryptántha** Brand. $n = 11$ (Cave & Constance, 1959), as *P. stellaris.*

55. **P. grísea** Gray. $n = 9$ (Cave & Constance, 1959). Found near San Marcos Pass, Santa Barbara Co., *Raven.*

55a. **P. Hárdhamiae** Munz. Resembles *P. grisea* and *P. Purpusii* in its small promptly deciduous, pelviform corolla, deeply parted style, glandular pubescence, lax, scorpioid infl., dentate rather than pinnate lvs., but differs from the former in smaller stature, 2–12 cm. tall, more constantly crenate lvs.; longer petioles with reference to blade length (½ to ⅓), more lax, few-fld. cymes, lavender rather than white corollas, subequal rather unequal calyx-lobes, more southern occurrence. From *P. Purpusii* it differs in smaller, more delicate habit, rounder lvs. with more shallow, less pointed teeth, more coastal range. It was found at Rose Lake, Ventura Co., at 3600 ft.

p. 539.   57. **P. perityloìdes** Cov. $n = 11$ (Cave & Constance, 1959).

58. **P. suaveòlens** Greene. In Monterey Co., *Howitt & Howell* and San Luis Obispo Co., *Hardham.*

60. **P. rotundifòlia** Torr. ex Wats. $n = 12$ (Cave & Constance, 1959).

61. **P. mustelìna** Cov. $n = 12$ (Cave & Constance, 1959).

62. **P. Peirsoniàna** J. T. Howell. $n = 12$ (Cave & Constance, 1959).

p. 540.   68. **P. Nashiàna** Jeps. $n = 11$ (Cave & Constance, 1963).

p. 541.   74. **P. pachyphýlla** Gray. $n = 11$ (Cave & Constance, 1959).

p. 542.   75. **P. calthifòlia** Brand. $n = 12$ (Cave & Constance, 1959).

76. **P. neglécta** Jones. $n = 11$ (Cave & Constance, 1959).

77. **P. Ivesiàna** Torr. reported as having $n = 11$, *Cave & Constance*.

77a. **P. pediculoìdes** (J. T. Howell) Const. with $n = 23$. [*P. Ivesiana* var. *p.* J. T. Howell.]

79. **P. affìnis** Gray. $n = 12$ (Cave & Constance, 1959).

p. 544.   86. **P. inyoénsis** (Macbr.) J. T. Howell. $n = 12$ (Cave & Constance, 1959).

86a. **P. scopulìna** (A. Nels.) J. T. Howell. [*Emmenanthe s.* A. Nels. *Miltitzia s.* Rydb.] Diffuse annual, with short spreading hairs, not glandular; corolla yellow, 2.5–4 mm. long at anthesis, ca. equalling the calyx, to 5 mm. in fruit; style 1–2.5 mm. long; longer fils. usually surpassing sinuses; $n = 12$ (Cave & Constance, 1959).—Bridgeport, Mono Co.; to Mont., Wash.

87. **P. tetrámera** J. T. Howell. $2n = 22$ (Cave & Constance, 1963).

p. 545.   NÀMA

In Key, in line leading to *N. aretioides*, change to:

Corolla 7–15 mm. long, 7–12 mm. broad. . . . . *N. aretioides*

1. **N. Rothróckii** Gray. $n = 17$ (Cave & Constance, 1959).

p. 546.   5. **N. aretioìdes** (H. & A.) Brand. Add to synonyms *N. a.* f. *californicum* Brand.

p. 547.   8. **N. pusíllum** Lemmon. $n = 7$ (Cave & Constance, 1959).

9. **N. depréssum** Lemmon ex Gray. $n = 7$ (Cave & Constance, 1959).

p. 548.   ERIODÍCTYON

In Key, change line 1 at top of page to:

Calyx 2–4 mm. long; cyme open; corolla sparsely pubescent.
    Calyx-lobes 3–4 mm. long, sparsely hirsutulous; corolla 5–6 mm. long, with white limb; seeds almost 1 mm. long. E. Mojave Desert. . . . . 1. *E. angustifolium*
    Calyx-lobes 2–3 mm. long, ciliate; corolla 11–15 mm. long, with lavender limb; seeds 0.4 mm. long. San Luis Obispo Co. . . . . 1a. *E. altissimum*

1a. **E. altíssimum** P. V. Wells. Viscid shrub 2–4 m. tall; lvs. linear, 6–9 cm. long, 2–4 mm. wide, revolute; infl. with branches 4–9 cm. long, the fls. secund; calyx-segms. narrow-lanceolate, 2–3 mm. long, ciliate; corollas purplish, 11–15 mm. long, villous without.—At 880 ft., Indian Knob, 4 mi. n. of Pismo, San Luis Obispo Co.

4. **E. trichocàlyx** var. **lanàtum** Jeps. $n = 14$ (Cave & Constance, 1959).

5. **E. tomentòsum** Benth. $n = 14$ (Cave & Constance, 1959). Reported from Temblor Range, Kern Co., *Twisselmann.*

p. 549.   6. **E. Tráskiae** ssp. **Smíthii** Munz. subsp. nov. Shrub 0.5–2 m. tall; lvs. elliptic to ovate, the blades 3–7 cm. wide, to 10 cm. long; calyx 4.5–5 mm. long; corolla 6–7 mm. long. (Folia elliptica vel ovata, laminis 3–7 cm. latis, ad 10 cm. longis; calyx 4.5–5 mm. longus; corolla 6–7 mm. longa.) Type, San Marcos Pass, Santa Barbara Co., *Clifton F. Smith 1621*, July 4, 1950 (Pomona College Herbarium). It is a pleasure to dedicate this subspecies to Clifton Smith of Santa Barbara, who has done so much to make known the flora of his county. The proposed subspecies is found in Chaparral up to 2000 ft., on the mainland from San Luis Obispo Co. to Ventura Co.

In **E. Tráskiae** Eastw. ssp. **Tráskiae** of Catalina Id. the lf.-blades are mostly narrow-elliptic, ca. 1.5–2.5 (–3) cm. wide and to 6 or 7 cm. long; the calyx is 6–6.5 mm. long; corolla 7.5–8 mm. long.

7. **E. crássifolium** Benth. var. **crássifolium.** $n = 14$ (Cave & Constance, 1959). Var. **denudàtum** Abrams. Reported from the San Emigdio Range, Kern Co., *Twisselmann.*

p. 549.   HESPEROCHÌRON

1. **H. pùmilus** (Griseb.) Porter. $n = 8$ (Cave & Constance, 1959).

p. 550.   TRICÁRDIA

1. **T. Watsònii** Torr. ex Wats. $n = 8$ (Cave & Constance, 1959).

p. 552.   AMMOBRÒMA

1. **A. sonòrae** Torr. ex Gray. $2n = 18$ (Moore, 1962).

p. 552.   BORAGINÀCEAE

In Key to Genera, after line 4 from the bottom of the page "Nutlets erect," etc., add:

Corolla rotate; anthers connivent itno a cone. .... 5a. *Borago*
Corolla tubular, funnelform or salverform; anthers not forming a cone.
    Attachment of nutlet surrounded by an annular rim, strongly convex and leaving a pit upon the low receptacle.
    Scales or appendages in throat of corolla linear and acute.
    Scales or appendages broad and blunt. .... 6. *Symphytum*
        Lvs. oblong or lanceolate, obscurely veined. .... 6a. *Anchusa*
        Lvs. ovate, netted-veined. .... 6b. *Pentaglottis*

p. 553.   In Key at top of page after "Nutlets attached ± laterally" etc. and after "The nutlets not armed with conspicuous prickles," insert:

Calyx at maturity conspicuously expanded and net-veined; fls. on short recurved pedicels.
13a. *Asperugo*
Calyx not so expanded.
"Corolla bright blue" etc. as in the FLORA.

p. 554.   HELIOTRÒPIUM
Change Key to:

Plants perennial.
    The plant glabrous, succulent; corolla white or pale. Native. .... 1. *H. curassavicum*
    The plant soft-hairy; corolla purple. Escape from cult. .... 3. *H. amplexicaule*
Plants annual.
    Corolla 8–14 mm. broad. Desert native. .... 2. *H. convolvulaceum*
    Corolla 4 mm. broad. Escape in n. Calif. .... 4. *H. europaeum*

Add 4. **H. europaèum** L. Erect annual, 1.5–8 dm. high, hoary-pubescent; lvs. oval; fls. in scorpioid spikes; corolla white or bluish, to ca. 4 mm. broad; nutlets 4, tuberculate.—Tehama and Butte cos. and Modoc-Siskiyou area, *Howell*; native of Eu.

p. 555.   PECTOCARYA
    1. **P. lineàris** DC. var. **feròcula** Jtn. $2n = 24$ pairs (Raven, Kyhos & Hill, 1965).
    2. **P. recurvàta** Jtn. $n = 12$ (Di Fulvio, 1965).
    3. **P. platycárpa** (M. & J.) M. & J. Add as synonym *P. linearis* var. *platycarpa* Cronq.
p. 556.   4. **P. penicillàta** (H. & A.) A. DC. $2n = 12$ pairs (Raven, Kyhos & Hill, 1965). Add as synonym *P. linearis* var. *penicillata* Jones.
    CYNOGLÓSSUM
p. 557.   3. **C. officinàle** L. Biennial, soft short-hairy, leafy; upper lvs. lanceolate, closely sessile; infl. paniculate, of nearly bractless racemes; corolla red-purple; nutlets flat on the broad upper face, 5–7 mm. long, overtopped by the beaklike style.—Established on hillside 6 mi. s. of McCloud (hence in n. Shasta Co.) and 0.3 mi. s. of McCloud, Siskiyou Co., *T. C. Fuller*. Introd. from Eurasia.

5a. Boràgo L. BORAGE

Erect, strigose-hispid herbs. Lvs. alternate. Fls. blue, in loose leafy cymes and on long pedicels. Calyx with 5 linear segms. Corolla rotate, with 5 acute lobes, the throat with scales or hairy crests. Stigma subentire. Nutlets attached by the base. Old World.

    1. **B. officinàlis** L. Coarse hairy annual, 4–6 dm. high; lvs. oblong or ovate, to 15 cm. long; corolla 2 cm. wide; stamens exserted, forming a cone 6 mm. high; nutlets verrucose.—Escape from cult., San Francisco. From Medit. region.

6a. Anchùsa L. ALKANET. BUGLOSS

Hispid or villous herbs with panicled leafy-bracteate scorpioid cymes or racemes with elongate branches; fls. blue, violet or white; calyx-lobes narrow.

Corolla trumpet-shaped, the throat closed by scales. Nutlets basally attached. Eurasia.

1. **A. prócera** Bess. Stem to 18 dm. high, simple or branched at base; lvs. oblong-lanceolate, the cauline clasping; infl. of crowded branches; bracts broadly triangular; calyx subsessile; fls. blue.—Hayfork, Trinity Co., *Howell.* From Se. Eu.

6b. **Pentaglóttis** Tausch

Like *Anchusa*, but with ovate, netted-veined lvs. and nutlets with a stalked small attachment rather than sessile and broad.

1. **P. sempervìrens** (L.) Tausch. [*Anchusa s.* L.] Hairy, 3–9 dm. tall; lvs. to 3 dm. long; cymes very hispid in long-peduncled subcapitate pairs; fls. subsessile; corolla ca. 10 mm. across, bright blue.—Locally established, San Francisco; from Eu.

p. 558.   MYOSÒTIS

2. **M. láxa** Lehm. At Kernville, etc., Kern Co., *Twisselmann.*

4. **M. latifòlia** Poir., not *M. sylvatica* (cf. Johnston, Wrightia 2: 16–17. 1959).—Occurs in Monterey Co., *Howitt & Howell,* as well as in the range given in the FLORA. $2n = 18$ (Merxmuller & Grau, 1963).

p. 559.   LITHOSPÉRMUM
Change Key to:

A.   Plants annual; nutlets tubercled, dull. . . . . 1. *L. arvense*
AA. Plants perennial; nutlets smooth, shining.
    B.   Upper lvs. crowded, lance-linear, with attenuate apex.
        C.   Corolla pale yellowish, often greenish-tinted, the tube 4–6 mm. long, the limb
            7–13 mm. wide, the lobes entire or nearly so. . . . . 2. *L. ruderale*
        CC. Corolla bright yellow, the tube 12–30 mm. long, the limb 12–20 mm. wide,
            the lobes erose. . . . . 2a. *L. incisum*
    BB. Upper lvs. scattered, lance-ovate, acute to obtuse; fls. golden-yellow.
                                                3. *L. californicum*

2a. **L. incìsum** Lehm. Agreeing with *L. ruderale* in the narrow lvs. with attenuate apex, but with bright yellow corolla having a tube 12–20 mm. long and a limb 7–13 mm. wide and with corolla-lobes erose.—New York Mts., e. San Bernardino Co., *Balls & Everett*; to Mont. and B.C.

p. 560.   ÈCHIUM

Plant herbaceous, ± hispid with stiffish white hairs; infl. a loose panicle of coiled racemes.
                                           1. *E. plantagineum*
Plant shrubby, not at all hispid; infl. cylindric and spikelike, of numerous densely flowered 1-sided spikelets. . . . . 2. *E. fastuosum*

2. **E. fastuòsum** Ait. Shrubby, 1–2 m. high, soft, grayish-hirsute; lvs. lanceolate, acuminate; infl. cylindric, spikelike, ca. 15 cm. long, consisting of many densely-fld., coiled, 1-sided spikelets; fls. purple or dark blue, 12 mm. diam.—Escaping from cult. as in San Francisco and Marin cos.; from the Canary Ids.

p. 563.   HACKÈLIA

12. **H. velùtina** (Piper) Jtn. Extends e. to the Greenhorn Range, Kern Co., *Twisselmann.*

13a. **Asperùgo** L. MADWORT

Annual herb, with much branched stems, spreading or procumbent. Fls. axillary, few, small, blue. Calyx lobed to about the middle. Corolla salverform, the wide tube nearly closed by the appendages. Stigma capitellate. Calyx in fr. greatly enlarged, strongly anastomose-veined. Nutlets flattened, minutely verrucose.

1. **A. procúmbens** L. Three to 7 dm. high, with stout recurved prickles; lvs. oblanceolate, 3–6 cm. long; corolla 2–3 mm. long.—Adventive in Modoc Co., *Heiser*; from Eurasia.

p. 564.   CRYPTÁNTHA
In Key, A, B, delete the *C. circumscissa* at the end of the line and insert:

C. Corolla 1–4 mm. in diam.; pollen grains 7–9 long, oblong. 1. *C. circumscissa*
CC. Corolla 4–6 mm. in diam.; pollen grains 5.5–6.5 long. . . . . 1a. *C. similis*

p. 565. In Key, line 6 from bottom of page, the calyx may be 2–4 mm. in *C. incana.*
p. 567. 1. **C. circumscíssa** (H. & A). Jtn. Corolla 1–4 mm. broad; pollen grains 7–9 μ long; *n* = 12.
Var. **rosulàta** J. T. Howell can now become ssp. **rosulàta** Mathew & Raven.
1a. **C. símilis** Mathew & Raven. Differing from **C. circumscissa** in having the corolla 4–6 mm. broad; pollen grains 5.5–6.5 μ long; *n* = 6. Mojave Desert.
2. **C. micrántha** (Torr.) Jtn. and ssp. **lépida** (Gray) Mathew & Raven. Both have *n* = 12.
p. 568. 7. **C. utahénsis** (Gray) Greene occurs in the Greenhorn Mts., Kern Co., *Twisselmann.*
p. 569. 18. **C. intermèdia** (Gray) Greene. *n* = 12 (Di Fulvio, 1965).
p. 579. PLAGIOBÓTHRYS
2. **P. Jònesii** Gray. In the El Paso Range, Kern Co., *Twisselmann.*
p. 580. 8. **P. infectìvus** Jtn. In the Temblor Range, Kern Co., *Twisselmann.*
p. 582. 14. **P. califórnicus** var. **fulvescens** Jtn. In Monterey Co., *Howitt & Howell.*
p. 583. 22. **P. Austíniae** (Greene) Jtn. Ranges n. to Jackson Co., Ore.
p. 586. 36. **P. hispídulus** (Greene) Jtn. *Allocarya h.* Greene, not Jtn.
p. 587. 39. **P. reticulàtus** var. **Rossianòrum** Jtn. As far s. as Monterey Co., *Howitt & Howell.*
p. 589. AMSÍNCKIA
8. **A. Menzièsii** (Lehm.) Nels & Macbr. Cronquist (Vasc. Pl. Pac. N. W. 4: 181. 1959) keys out the following:

A. Stem spreading-hispid and also evidently puberulent or strigose with shorter and softer, ± retrorse hairs; pubescence of the lvs. tending to be ascending instead of widely spreading; corolla 5–8 mm. long. S. Calif. to B.C., Ida., Utah. . . . . *A. retrorsa* Suksd.
AA. Stem spreading-hispid, nearly or quite without shorter and softer hairs below the infl.; hairs of the lvs. often widely spreading.
B. Corolla 7–10 mm. long, the tube well exserted. . . . . *A. intermedia* F. & M.
BB. Corolla 4–17 mm. long, the tube scarcely exserted.
A. Menziesii (Lehm.) Nels & Macbr.

p. 590. ## 61a. Loganiàceae. LOGANIA FAMILY

Herbs to vines or trees. Lvs. simple, usually opposite, stipulate. Infl. of leafy interrupted spikes to cymose. Fls. regular, usually perfect, 4–5-merous. Calyx-lobes imbricate. Corolla sympetalous, the lobes valvate, imbricate or contorted. Stamens as many as the corolla-lobes, alternate with them. Ovary superior, 2-loculed. Style usually simple; stigma capitate or 2-lobed. Fr. in ours a caps. A family of ca. 600 spp., largely tropical.

Fls. in headlike clusters in an interrupted spike; lvs. densely woolly; plant 2–3 dm. high. E. Mojave Desert. . . . . 1. *Buddleja*
Fls. in paniculate cymes; lvs. glabrous above; plant 4–5 m. tall. Escape from cult.
2. *Chilianthus*

1. Búddleja L.

Shrubs to trees; lvs. simple, entire to dentate. Fls. mostly 4-merous. Calyx campanulate. Corolla salverform or rotate-campanulate, the lobes ovate or rounded. Anthers subsessile on throat or tube of corolla. Fr. a septicidal caps.; valves 2-cleft at apex. Seeds many. Ca. 70 spp. of warm N. & S. Am., Asia, S. Afr.
1. **B. utahénsis** Cov. Much-branched shrub 2–3 dm. high, densely lanate-tomentose; lvs. subsessile, linear, with revolute margins, 1–3 cm. long; axils usually with fascicles of very small lvs.; fls. in glomerules forming 2–4 heads in an interrupted spike, ca. 10–15 mm. thick; corolla creamy-yellow to purple, 4–5 mm. long, the lobes rounded, 1 mm. long, the tube tomentulose.—Dry rocky slopes, 3500–5500 ft., Joshua Tree Wd., Pinyon-Juniper Wd.; Kingston and Panamint mts., San Bernardino and Inyo cos.; to Utah. May–Oct.

2. **B. Davídii** Franchet. SUMMER LILAC. To 5 m. tall, deciduous; lvs. 5–30 cm. long, white-felted beneath; panicles 25–40 cm. long; fls. lilac to purple. Escape from cult., as in San Francisco; native of China.

2. **Chiliánthus** Burchell

Arborescent shrubs. Lvs. entire to toothed or lobed. Fls. in terminal pyramidal or subspherical cymes. Fls. small, 4-merous. Corolla tube short, scarcely exserted. Stamens inserted near the base of the corolla-tube, elongate, exserted. Caps. 2-loculed. Seeds small. A S. Afr. genus of ca. 4 spp.

1. **C. oleàceus** Burchell. [*C. arboreus* Benth.] To 4 or 6 m. tall; stems 4-angled; lvs. lanceolate, 7–10 cm. long, rusty-scurfy beneath, but soon glabrate, ± revolute; fls. fragrant, creamy-white, 2.5 mm. long, many, in panicles to 1 dm. across.—Escaping from cult., Saddle Peak, Santa Monica Mts., Los Angeles Co., *Raven & Thompson.*

p. 590.   SOLANÀCEAE

In Key to Genera, after AA, B, CC, DD delete word *Physalis* at end of line and insert:

> E.   Ovary 2-loculed; fruiting calyx 5-toothed. . . . . 4. *Physalis*
> EE. Ovary 3–5-loculed; fruiting calyx 5-parted. . . . . 4a. *Nicandra*
> BB. Corolla not rotate.
> C.   Fr. a berry.
> D.   Corolla urceolate, white. . . . . 5. *Salpichroa*
> DD. Corolla tubular, red. . . . . 5a. *Cestrum*
> CC. Fr. a caps.; etc. as in FLORA.

p. 592.   LÝCIUM

7. Use **L. bárbarum** L. instead of *L. halimifolium* Mill.

p. 593.   PHÝSALIS

After generic description, insert Waterfall, U.T. Taxonomic study of the genus *Physalis* in N. Am. n. of Mex. Rhodora 60: 106–114, 128–141, 152–173. 1958.

In Key, AA, BB, CC, D, after EE, add:

> EEE. Corolla yellow, broader; lvs. mostly entire; perennial.   11a. *P. subglabrata*

p. 594.   2. Change *P. Fendleri* Gray to **P. hederifòlia** var. **cordifòlia** (Gray) Waterfall.

5. Under **P. crassifòlia** Benth. Waterfall recognizes var. **versícolor** (Rydb.) Waterfall. [*P. v.* Rydb.] Corolla often bluish on drying; flowering calyx 3–4 mm. long (instead of 4–6 mm.), on peduncles 5–10 times as long (not 6–7). Colo. Desert; to Nev., Ariz.

p. 595.   6. Waterfall restricts **P. pubéscens** L. to the se. states for the U.S. and places Calif. material in var. **integrifòlia** (Dunal) Waterfall. [*P. hirsuta* var. i. Dunal.] Lvs. with fewer teeth or entire and mostly flaccid and translucent.

10. Change *P. Wrightii* Gray to **P. acutifòlia** (Miers) Sandwith. [*Saracha acutifolia* Miers.] Kern Co. s. to Imperial Co.; to Tex., Mex.

11. Waterfall reduces *P. lanceifolia* Nees to **P. angulàta** L. var. **lanceifòlia** (Nees) Waterfall. $n = 12$ (Gottschalk, 1954).

11a. **P. subglabràta** Mack. & Bush. [*P. virginiana* Mill. var. *s.* Waterfall.] Plants nearly glabrous; lvs. ovate to lance-ovate, mostly entire, sometimes slightly sinuate-dentate; corolla usually 15–20 mm. long; anthers bluish; fruiting calyces mostly 25–35 mm. long.—In a field near Montague, Siskiyou Co., *Fuller;* native of cent. U.S.

12. **P. ixocárpa** Brot. Howitt & Howell report from Monterey Co.

4a. **Nicándra** Adans.

Annual herbs differing from *Physalis* in the 3–5-loculed ovary and deeply parted calyx.

1. **N. Physalòdes** Gaertn. [*Atropa P.* L.] To 1 m., much branched; lvs. ovate

to oblong, 10–15 mm. long, sinuate-toothed; fls. blue, 2.5–4 cm. long and broad, enclosed in the enlarged green calyx 2.5–4 cm. long. Escape, as at Santa Barbara, *Pollard*; native of Peru.

SALPICHRÒA

1. Change S. *rhomboidea* (Gill. & Hook.) Miers to **S. origanifòlia** (Lam.) Thell.

p. 596.   5a. **Céstrum** L.

Shrubs with alternate entire lvs. Fls. tubular, in axillary or terminal cymes. Corolla with a long tube, 5-lobed. Stamens 5. Fr. a berry. A large genus of warm regions.

1. **C. fascículatum** Miers. Shrub 1–2 m. tall; lvs. ovate-acuminate; cymes capitate; corolla deep rose-red.—Natur. in pasture near Hydesville, Humboldt Co.; native of Mex.

SOLÀNUM

Species no. 1 in the Key should be spelled *sarrachoides*, not as in 1959 printing. In Key the first GG after A, B, etc. should be changed in the 1959 printing to:

> G. Infl. umbelliform; calyx-lobes distinct, reflexed at maturity, etc.

In Key A, BB, CC, DD, E add:

> E′. Low native shrub to ca. 1 m. high; berry whitish. Common in Coast Ranges. . . . . 10. *S. umbelliferum*
> E′E′. Tall climbing introduced shrub; berry greenish yellow.
> 10a. *S. Gayanum*

In Key after A, BB, CC, DD, EE, FF, under G and GG delete distribution.
In Key change AA to "Plants prickly."

p. 597. 1. **S. sarrachoìdes** Sendt. ex. Mart., correct spelling for 1959 printing.

6. **S. triflòrum** Nutt. Reported from Greenhorn Mts., Kern Co., *Twisselmann*.

p. 598. 8. *S. aviculare* Forst. f. should probably be called **S. laciniàtum** Ait. $n = 24$ (Gottschalk, 1954).

10a. **S. Gayànum** (Remy) Phil. f. Vigorous climbing shrub, covered with stellate hairs; lvs. petioled, oval-oblong to elliptic, 5–8 cm. long; fls. terminal, lavender-violet, on branched peduncles; corolla stellate-pubescent without; berries greenish-yellow.—Natur. about San Francisco; native of Chile.

p. 599. 12. **S. Xánti** var. **montànum** Munz. Collected in Riverside Co. at 4800 ft. upper end of Hemet V., San Jacinto Mts., *Ziegler*, and at 6500 ft., Santa Rosa Mts., *Weatherby*. Varying in glandulosity, but on the whole matching well material from the San Bernardino Mts.

14. **S. sisymbriifòlium** Lam. $n = 12$ (Gottschalk, 1954).

15. **S. rostràtum** Dunal. $n = 12$ (De Lisle, 1965).

p. 600. 18. **S. lanceolàtum** Cav. Reported from Contra Costa Co., *Fuller*; Monterey Co., *Howitt & Howell*; and Ventura Co., *Fuller*.

19. **S. marginàtum** L. f. Found 4 mi. e. of Pala, San Diego Co., *Fuller*.

20. **S. carolinénse** L. $n = 12$ (Heiser, 1953). Reported as occurring in El Dorado Co., *Fuller*; Sonoma Co., *Fuller*.

DATURA

1. **D. meteloìdes** A. DC. There is a question as to the proper name for the species that has been so widely called *D. meteloides*. Ewan (Rhodora 40: 317–323. 1944) felt that there are inconsistencies in the drawing on which the name was based in 1852 and the applicability uncertain. He proposed the use of the later name *D. Wrìghtii* Regel (1881). Barclay (Bot. Mus. Leaflets, Harvard Univ. 8: 245–272. 1959) considered *D. meteloides* identical with **D. inóxia** Miller, 1786. The latter was based on material cultivated in England from material from Vera Cruz, Mex. If our common southwestern plant is the same as this more southern one, the name inoxia has long priority.

p. 601. NICOTIÀNA

In Key, Change B to:

B. Lvs. ± auriculate-clasping; fls. open during the day. Perennial or biennial.
C. Calyx campanulate; corolla 18–22 mm. long. Desert native. 2. *N. trigonophylla*
CC. Calyx oblong or subglobose; corolla 65–85 mm. long. Coastal introduction.
2a. *N. sylvestris*

p. 602.   2a. **N. sylvéstris** Spegazzini & Comes. Viscid robust perennial 1–2 m. tall; lvs. 20–50 cm. long, the cauline sessile; flowering calyx 10–18 mm. long; corolla white, 6.5–8.5 cm. long exclusive of the limb; caps. ovoid, 15–18 mm. long.— Natur. Pacific Grove, Monterey Co.; native of S. Am.

p. 603.   SCROPHULARIÀCEAE
In family decription, line 1, change last word "or" to "to." (1959 prtg.)

p. 605.   LINDÉRNIA
2. **L. anagallídea** (Michx.) Penn. occurs in Kern Co., *Twisselmann.*

p. 608.   MÍMULUS
In Key, middle of page, "28. *M. purpureus*" should be "29" in 1959 printing.

p. 610.   1. **M. Lewísii** Pursh. $n = 8$ (Vickery et al., 1958).
3. **M. moschàtus** Dougl. ex Lindl. $n = 16$ (Vickery et al., 1958).

p. 611.   5. **M. primuloìdes** Benth. Occurs in Greenhorn Range, Kern Co., *Twisselmann.*

p. 612.   12. **M. discólor** Grant is in the opinion of Dr. Bacigalupi a synonym of **M. montioìdes** Gray.
13. **M. Pálmeri** Gray. Occurs in Monterey Co., *Hardham.*

p. 613.   15. **M. floribúndus** Dougl. ex Lindl. $n = 16$ (Mukherjee & Vickery, 1961).

p. 614.   21. **M. Paríshii** Greene. Reported from the Piute Mts., Kern Co. and Kern Plateau, Tulare Co., *Twisselmann.*

p. 615.   27. **M. barbàtus** Greene. Kern Plateau, Kern Co., *Twisselmann.*
30. **M. diffùsus** Grant. Apparently occurs in Monterey Co., *Hardham* collections.

p. 616.   34. **M. guttàtus** Fisch. ex DC. Mukherjee & Vickery (Madroño 16: 141–154. 1962) report chromosome counts as follows: *M. guttatus* ssp. *guttatus* $n = 14$; *M. guttatus* ssp. *litoralis*, $n = 14$; *M. guttatus* var. *puberulus*, $n = 14$. In Madroño 17: 156–160. 1964, they report *guttatus* as having 14, 16, 28. Vickery (Evolution 18: 52–70. 1964) recognizes **M. platycàlyx** Penn., which can be separated from *M. guttatus* in having the fruiting calyx as wide as long (not ⅔ as wide); corolla 15–20 mm. long (not 18–45) and plant very slender. It occurs in the Sierra Nevada from Mariposa Co. to Tulare Co.
Twisselmann feels that **M. microphýllus** Benth. is quite distinct in being depauperate and occurring in moist cracks in granite, Kern Co.
M. guttàtus ssp. **arenícola** Penn. Accepted by J. T. Howell as a recognizable ssp. Plant low, 5–20 cm. tall, much branched, the infl. not very pubescent; lf.-blades 1–2 cm. long; corolla 25–35 mm. long. Coastal Strand; Monterey Co.

p. 617.   36. **M. nasùtus** Greene. Delete *M. platycalyx* as a synonym. $n = 14$ or 13 Mukherjee & Vickery, 1962).
37. **M. Tilíngii** Regel. Mukherjee and Vickery in 1962 report $n = 14$ for *M. T.*, but for var. **corallìnus** (Greene) Grant $n = 24$.

p. 618.   46. **M. Whítneyi** Gray can be reported from Kern Co. (Greenhorn Range), *Twisselmann.*
48. **M. Fremóntii** (Benth.) Gray occurs in Monterey Co., *Howitt & Howell,* and in w. Kern Co., *Twisselmann.*
50. **M. víscidus** Congd. In Greenhorn Range, Kern Co., *Twisselmann.*

p. 620.   54. **M. Rattánii** Gray. In Monterey Co., *Howitt & Howell,* and in San Luis Obispo Co., *Hardham.*

p. 621.   57. **M. brévipes** Benth. $n = 8$ (Mukherjee & Vickery, 1962).
58. **M. mohavénsis** Lemmon. $n = 7$ (Carlquist, 1953).
59. **M. pygmaèus** Grant. On flats w. of Lake Almanor, Plumas Co., *Vesta Holt.*
61. **M. Douglásii** (Benth. in DC.) Gray. In Greenhorn Mts., *Twisselmann.*

p. 622. 68. **M. Congdònii** Rob. In the Greenhorn Mts., Kern Co., *Twisselmann.*

p. 624. 73. **M. aurantìacus** Curt. $n = 10$ (Mukherjee & Vickery, 1961).

p. 625. GRATÌOLA

In Key, change B. and BB. to:

> B. Lvs. attenuate; sepals 7–11 mm. long; plants often copiously glandular-puberulent above; corollas with yellowish throat and white limb. . . . . 2. *G. ebracteata*
> BB. Lvs. blunt; sepals 4–6 mm. long, 3 of them fused almost half way; plants essentially glabrous; corolla yellow, only the 3 lower lobes white. . . 3. *G. heterosepala*

p. 626. 2. **G. ebracteàta** Benth. ascends to 6800 ft., Lassen Nat. Park, *Gillett.*

3. **G. heterosèpala** Mason & Bacig. Also in Sacramento & Madera cos., *Bacigalupi.*

LIMOSÉLLA

1. **L. aquática** L. in Monterey Co., *Howitt & Howell.*

p. 627. 3. **L. subulàta** Ives. $2n = 20$ (Löve & Löve, 1958).

VERBÁSCUM

3. **V. virgàtum** Stokes ex With. Delete "s." in last line. Reported from Fresno Co., *Weiler.*

p. 631. PÉNSTEMON

3. **P. oreócharis** Greene. Cronquist (Vasc. Pl. Pac. N.W. 4: 402) reduces to synonymy under **P. Rydbérgii** A. Nels.

p. 633. 12. **P. albomarginàtus** Jones. $2n = 8$ pairs (Raven, Kyhos & Hill, 1965).

p. 637. 38. **P. caèsius** Gray. Greenhorn & San Emigdio ranges, Kern Co., *Twisselmann.*

p. 640. 48. **P. Newbérryi** Gray found on the Kern Plateau, Kern Co., *Twisselmann.*

51. **P. nemoròsus** (Dougl. ex Lindl.) Trautv. is transferred to *Nothochelone* (Gray) Straw as *N. nemorosa* (Dougl. ex Lindl.) Straw. See Brittonia 18: 85. 1966. Seeds winged all around.

pp. 640–642.

52–58. The following were transferred by Straw (Brittonia 18: 87–88. 1966) to the genus *Kéckia* Straw. Later (Brittonia 19: 203–204. 1967) he made the following combinations under *Keckiella* Straw:

52. *K. Rothróckii* (Gray) Straw and subsp. *jacinténsis* (Abrams) Straw.
53. *K. breviflòra* (Lindl.) Straw and ssp. *glabrisèpala* (Keck) Straw.
54. *K. Lemmònii* (Gray) Straw.
55. *K. antirrhinoìdes* (Benth.) Straw and ssp. *microphýlla* (Gray) Straw.
56. *K. cordifòlia* (Benth.) Straw.
57. *K. corymbòsa* (Benth.) Straw.
58. *K. ternàta* (Torr.) Straw and ssp. *septentrionàlis* (Munz & Jtn.) Straw.

p. 642. SCROPHULÀRIA

After the generic description insert: Shaw, R. J. The biosystematics of *Scrophularia* in w. N. Am. Aliso 5: 147–178. 1962.

Change the Key to:

> A. Infl. villous, the hairs tipped with small glands; plants shrubby in age; sterile fil. absent or rudimentary. Catalina and San Clement ids. . . . . 2. *S. villosa*
> AA. Infl. puberulent or short-pubescent; stems herbaceous; sterile fil. well developed.
>> B. Sterile fil. clavate to obovate, sometimes with an acute apex.
>>> C. Corolla dark maroon, the upper half blackish; tube urceolate with a constricted orifice; sterile fil. with an acute apex. Santa Barbara Co. 3. *S. atrata*
>>> CC. Corolla dark maroon or garnet-brown; orifice not constricted.
>>>> D. The corolla distinctly bicolored; lf.-blades cuneate. From the Sierra Nevada to w. Nev. . . . . 1a. *S. desertorum*
>>>> DD. The corolla not distinctly bicolored; lf.-bases truncate to cordate. W. of the Sierra Nevada and s. mts. 1. *S. californica*
>> BB. Sterile fil. flabellate, wider than long. . . . . 4. *S. lanceolata*

1. **S. califórnica** Cham. & Schlecht. and

Ssp. **floribúnda** (Greene) Shaw. [*S. c.* var. *f.* Greene.]

1a. **S. desertòrum** (Munz) Shaw. [*S. californica* var. *d.* Munz.]

p. 643. COLLÍNSIA

In Key, change "14. *C. bartsiaefolia*" to "4. *C. bartsiifolia*," 1959 printing.
Change C. at bottom of page to:

    C.   Calyx-lobes obtuse or obtusish.
        D.   Corolla 7–10 mm. long; upper fls. bearded. Ventura Co. to San Bernardino Co. . . . . 7. *C. Parryi*
        DD. Corolla 6–7 mm. long; fls. glabrous. Monterey Co. . . . . 7a. *C. antonina*

p. 644.   In Key, CC, DD, change "Upper fls. glabrous" to "Upper fls bearded" in the 1959 printing.
        3. Use **C. multicólor** Lindl. & Paxt. and put *C. franciscana* Bioletti in synonymy.

p. 645.   6. **C. tinctòria** Hartw. ex Benth. occurs in the Greenhorn Mts., Kern Co., *Twisselmann.*
        7a. **C. antonìna** Hardham. With few branches, 1–8 (–14) cm. high; petioles and pedicels puberulent and sparsely glandular; lf.-blades pubescent above, glabrous beneath, crenulate, oblong, 4–8 mm. long; fls. 1–3 at each node; pedicels to 1 cm. long in fr.; calyx 5–6 mm. long, puberulent; corolla 6–7 mm. long, white with red spots at base of lobes; $n = 7$.—San Antonio Hills, near Jolon-Bradley road, Monterey Co.
        Ssp. **purpùrea** Hardham. Corolla purple, white at base of upper lobes and with red spots. Same region.

p. 648.   GALVÈZIA
        1. **G. speciòsa** (Nutt.) Gray. $2n = 15$ pairs (Raven, Kyhos & Hill, 1965).

p. 649.   MOHÁVEA
        1. **M. confertiflòra** Heller. $2n = 15$ pairs (Raven, Kyhos & Hill, 1965).
        2. **M. breviflòra** Cov. in El Paso Range, Kern Co., *Twisselmann.*

p. 650.   ANTIRRHÌNUM
        4. **A. multiflòrum** Penn. $2n = 16$ pairs (Raven, Kyhos & Hill, 1965).

p. 651.   7. **A. Nuttaliànum** Benth. in DC. $2n = 16$ pairs (Raven, Kyhos & Hill, 1965).
p. 652.   12. **A. ovàtum** Eastw. in Temblor Range, Kern Co., *Twisselmann.*
p. 653.   LINÀRIA
        2. **L. dalmática** (L.) Mill. Reported from a number of counties: Siskiyou, Modoc, Lassen, Butte, Alpine, Sierra, Monterey, Shasta and Sacramento.
        5. **L. canadénsis** var. **texàna** Penn. $2n = 12$ (W. H. Lewis, 1958).
        7. **L. reticulàta** (SM.) Desf. may be an older name for **L. pinifolia** (Poir.) Thell. Recently reported for Santa Barbara Co., *Fuller.*

p. 654.   KÍCKXIA
        2. **K. Elátine** (L.) Dumort. caused abandonment of ca. 1500 acres of barley stubble sw. of Dayton, Butte Co., *Fuller.*
    DIGITÀLIS
        1. **D. purpùrea** L. Spontaneous in Nevada Co., *Howell & True.*

p. 655.   VERÓNICA
    Key, A, B, change CC to:

    CC. Caps. wider than long, deeply notched; corolla pubescent in the tube.
        D.   Fls. in racemes, the upper lvs. bractlike. Common. . . . 4. *V. serpyllifolia*
        DD. Fls. solitary in the axils of lvs. much like the cauline lvs. Lawns, Golden Gate Park, San Francisco . . . . 4a. *V. filiformis*

    Key A, BB, change to:

    BB. Plant annual; fls. from most axils.
        C.   Corolla 2–2.5 mm. wide.
            C'.   Pedicels 1–2 mm. long; lvs. not coarsely toothed.
                D.   Lvs. linear-oblong to spatulate; corolla white. . . . . . . 5. *V. peregrina*
                DD. Lvs. rounded to oval; corolla bright blue. . . . . 6. *V. arvensis*
           C'C'. Pedicels 6–12 mm. long; lvs. with 2 or 3 large teeth on each side near the base. Sacramento Co. . . . . 6a. *V. hederifolia*

    Key, under AA, B, add:

    CCC. Lvs. triangular-ovate, sessile or very short-petioled, not clasping; corolla ca. 10 mm. across, deep bright blue with white eye. . . . . . . 9a. *V. Chamaedrys*

4a. **V. filifórmis** Sm. Prostrate pubescent perennial, forming mats; lvs. to 6 mm. long, round to ovate, subcordate, short-petioled; fls. to 8 mm. in diam.— Natur. in San Francisco; native of Asia Minor.

p. 656.   6a. **V. hederifòlia** L. Annual, the stems 5–25 cm. long, pubescent; lvs. petioled, cordate, 3–5-lobed; fls. long-pedicelled, solitary in the axils; corolla rotate, 2–2.5 mm. broad, lilac or blue; seeds 2.5–3 mm. broad.—Natur. in Sacramento Co., *Crampton*; from Eu.

9a. **V. Chamaèdrys** L. Near *V. americana* in its lvs. not clasping and fls. to 10 or 12 mm. across; plant erect or nearly so; lvs. sessile, rounded at base, pubescent.—Lawns, San Francisco; native of Eu.

12. **V. comòsa** Richt. Reported from Monterey Co., *Howitt & Howell*.

p. 660.   PEDÍCULARIS

10. **P. racemòsa** Dougl. ex Hook. Corolla pink to purplish.

Ssp. **álba** Penn. Corolla white or ochroleucous; lvs. rather narrow.—E. of the Sierra Nevada and Cascade Mts.

p. 661.   ORTHOCÁRPUS

1. **O. campéstris** Benth. Found at 6600 ft., Mt. Lassen Park, *Gillett*.

p. 662.   6. **O. castillejoìdes** var. **humboldtiénsis** Keck. $2n = 12$ pairs (D. E. Anderson, 1965).

p. 665.   CASTILLÈJA

Key, change AA, B, C and CC to (following Bacigalupi & Heckard, Leafl. W. Bot. 10: 285. 1966):

    C.   Floral bracts oblong to linear-oblong, either entire or with 3 relatively short, very blunt lobes toward their tips; foliage pubescent, the lvs. not involute; axillary shoots well developed; upper surface of galea ± densely and shaggily pubescent.

    D.   Dorsal portion of galea thin, pale orange to yellow; distal portions of the calyx and of the often terminally lobed floral bracts scarlet; lvs. dark green, lance-oblong. . . . . 30 & 31. *C. subinclusa* and *C. franciscana*

    DD. Dorsal portion of galea thicker, dark green; floral bracts mostly entire and usually green and not suffused by any other color; distal portion of calyx rose-pink; lvs. gray-green, mostly linear-oblong. Inner S. Coast Ranges from San Benito Co. to nw. Los Angeles Co. and to Kern River V., also in San Diego Co.; L. Calif. . . . . 31a. *C. Jepsonii*

    CC. Floral bracts cuneate in outline, deeply and digitately 3-cleft or 3-parted, the spreading lobes narrow and acute, green to rose-pink; foliage and stems (except infl. and very base of stem) glabrous and glaucous, the narrowly linear lvs. involute; axillary shoots mostly weakly developed or lacking; dorsal surface of galea glabrate to sparsely and finely pubescent. . . 29. *C. linariifolia*

Key, middle of page, change J. and JJ. to:

    J.   Lvs. lanceolate; lower corolla-lip not exserted. North Coast Ranges and Sierra Nevada. . . . . 17. *C. Applegatei*

    JJ. Lvs. almost linear; lower corolla-lip exserted. Sierra Nevada. . . . . 18. *C. disticha*

Key, CC, D, EE, change to:

    EE. Plant not glandular-pubescent below the infl.

    E′. Plant whitened by an arachnoid-lanose coat of long flexuous hairs; lvs. linear; sepals of each side united to a roundish tip. Channel Ids. . . . . 27. *C. hololeuca*

    E′E′. Plant not grayish-woolly.

    F.   Calyx-lobes mostly less than 2 mm., etc. as in the FLORA.

p. 667.   3. Change to **C. longispìca** A. Nels. and put *C. psittacina* in synonymy.

p. 668.   4. **C. pilòsa** (Wats.) Rydb. $n = 12$ (Heckard, 1958).

5. Add as synonym under **C. nàna** Eastw., *C. rubida* Piper var. *monoensis* (Jeps.) Edwin.

9. **C. brevilobàta** Piper. $n = 12$ (Heckard, 1958).

10. **C. Brèweri** Fern. Occurs in the Piute Mts., Kern Co., *Twisselmann*.

14. **C. Wìghtii** Elmer. $n = 12$ (Gillett, 1954).

14a. **C. inflàta** Penn. $n = 36$ (Heckard, 1958).

14b. **C. litoràlis** Penn. Ownbey, in Pacific N.W. Fl. 4: 312, treats as a sp.

15. **C. Ròseana** Eastw. $n = 12$ (Heckard, 1958).

p. 670.　18. **C. dísticha** Eastw. Found in Piute Mts., Kern Co., *Twisselmann*.

p. 671.　22. **C. affìnis** H. & A. is used by Bacigalupi (Leafl. W. Bot. 10: 286. 1966) for plants with the lvs. having slender hairs, while **C. affìnis** var. **contentiòsa** (J. F. Macbr.) Bacig. [*C. Douglasii* var. *c.* J. F. Macbr.] has vitreous, thick-based, cellular trichomes on the lf.-margins.—Coast Ranges, Monterey Co. to Santa Monica Mts., Anacapa and Santa Rosa ids.

24. **C. chromòsa** A. Nels. $n = 12$ (Heckard, 1958).

25. **C. Gleasònii** Elmer [*C. pruinosa* ssp. *G.* Munz.] treated as a distinct sp., from the San Gabriel Mts. by Bacigalupi.

p. 672.　28. **C. plagiótoma** Gray. Reported from Piute Mts., Kern Co., *Twisselmann* and from San Luis Obispo and Fresno cos., *Eastwood*.

29. **C. linariifòlia** Benth. $n = 12$ (Heckard, 1958).

31a. **C. Jepsònii** Bacig. & Heckard. Pilose and puberulous leafy, gray-green perennial, the usually many strict stems 6–12 dm. tall, striate, with sterile axillary, quite leafy shoots; cauline lvs. mostly linear-oblong, mostly entire, with long and short hairs, the lvs. 3–8 cm. long, 2–6 mm. wide; infl. eventually as long as 4 dm., with some gland-tipped hairs often among the septate pilosity; upper bracts often tridentate and distally rose-pink; calyx narrow, striate, 2.5–3 cm. long; corolla conspicuously exserted and curved outward, 2.5–5 cm. long, the galea ca. 2 cm. long, the upper surface deep green and densely covered with short, thickish, often gland-tipped hairs, its apex obtuse, the narrow pink margins thin and glabrous; lower lip rudimentary, 1–2.5 mm. long, dark red-purple; $n = 12$.—At 1500–7500 ft.; inner South Coast Ranges from ne. San Benito Co. to Los Angeles Co. and Piute Mts., Kern Co., also in se. San Diego Co.; L. Calif.

32. **C. stenántha** Gray. $n = 12$ (Heckard, 1958).

p. 673.　CORDYLÁNTHUS

In Key, Corolla in *C. Nevinii* is not truly glabrous, *Bacigalupi*.

p. 675.　9. **C. Nevínii** Gray. On Piute Mt. and Mt. Pinos, *Twisselmann*.

p. 676.　1. **C. bernardìnus** Munz, collected in the Nelson Range, Inyo Co., near the head of Grapevine Canyon, *Roos*.

13. **C. Ferrisiànus** Penn. Reported from Greenhorn Mts. and Piute Mts., Kern Co., *Twisselmann*.

16. **C. filifòlius** Nutt. ex Benth. in the Santa Lucia Mts., *Hardham*.

p. 677.　17. **C. pilòsus** Gray. Change to "Plants 5–7 dm. tall."

p. 679.　MARTYNIÀCEAE

In description of the family insert after "Caps." and after "endocarp" the word "often," since in *Ibicella* the caps. is not crested but echinate.

PROBOSCÍDEA

Change description to "Coarse viscid-pubescent plants."

p. 681.　PINGUÌCULA

S. J. Casper (Fedde Repert. 66: 1–148. 1962) refers our plants to **P. macróceras** Link with corolla-lobes of lower lip obovate; calyx deeply divided; corolla, including spur, 20–30 mm. long; spur 6–11 mm. long, while in *P. vulgàris* L. the corolla-lobes of the lower lip are more oblong; the calyx is less deeply divided; the corolla, including spur, is 15–22 mm. long; spur 3–6 mm. long. **P. macróceras** is transcontinental and in ne. Asia. *P. vulgàris* ranges from Greenland to cent. Siberia and the Caucasus. Calder & Taylor make the comb. *P. vulgaris* ssp. *macroceras* (Link).

p. 682.　OROBÁNCHE

1. Change name of **O. uniflòra** L. var. **minùta** (Suksd.) Achey to **O. u.** ssp. **occidentàlis** (Greene) Abrams ex Ferris and have as synonyms: [*Aphyllon u.* var. *o.* Gray and *A. minutum* Suksd. and *O. u.* var. *minuta* Achey.]

p. 863.　2. **O. fascículata** Nutt. $2n = 24$ pairs (Raven, Kyhos & Hill, 1965).

p. 684.　5. **O. Grayàna** var. **Feùdgei** Munz. Reported from Temblor Range, Kern Co., *Twisselmann*.

Var. **Nelsonii** Munz. $2n = 24$ pairs (D. E. Anderson, 1963).

6. **O. califórnica** Cham. & Schlecht. var. **corymbosa** (Rydb.) Munz. Add to synonymy *O. corymbosa* Ferris. Reported from Piute Mts., Kern Co., *Twisselmann.*

7. **O. ludoviciana** var. **Coòperi** G. Beck. $2n = 24$ pairs (Raven, Kyhos and Hill, 1965).

p. 685. 10. **O. ramòsa** L. Reported as in Sacramento Co., *Brown* and in San Joaquin Co., *Nichols.*

p. 686. BELOPERÒNE

1. **B. califórnica** Benth. $2n = 28$ (Grant, 1956).

VERBENÀCEAE

Change Key to:

A. Fls. sessile in spikes which are simple or clustered; lvs. simple.
    B. Nutlets 4; fls. in terminal spikes. .... 1. *Verbena*
    BB. Nutlets 2; fls. in dense spikes or heads.
        C. Spikes globose or cylindrical; fr. dry. .... 2. *Lippia*
        CC. Spikes flat-topped; fr. drupaceous. .... 3. *Lantana*
AA. Fls. pedicelled; lvs. palmately compound. .... 4. *Vitex*

VERBÈNA

In Key, insert "mostly" after "Fls." in A.

In Key, A, B, C, change DD to:

    DD. Lvs. short-petioled, not auriculate-clasping.
        E. Infl. lax, elongate; fls. distant; pubescence on rachis, bractlets, and calyx very minute, closely appressed. .... 2. *V. litoralis*
        EE. Infl. dense, contracted; fls. mostly congested; pubescent on rachis, bractlets and calyx spreading. .... 2a. *V. brasiliensis*

p. 687. In Key, add at very end:

    BBB. The ultimate lf.-divisions linear; corolla ca. 10 mm. long. .... 12. *V. tenuisecta*

2. Moldenke (Phytologia 8: 313. 1962) apparently takes up the name **V. brasiliénsis** Vell. for my *V. litoralis,* but **V. litoràlis** HBK is all right for plants from Amador and San Joaquin cos. (Phytologia 10: 67). $2n = 56$ (Huynh, 1965).

p. 687. 2a. **V. brasiliénsis** Vell. Confused with **V. litoràlis** HBK, but the infl. more condensed, the pubescence of rachis, bracts and calyx more spreading.—Cited in Calif. from Amador, Butte, Eldorado, Nevada, Sacramento, San Joaquin, Solano, Stanislaus, Sutter and Yuba cos. Native of S. Am.

3. After **V. hastàta** L. insert:

Var. **scàbra** Moldenke. Lf.-bases more rigid; lvs. conspicuously scabrous on upper surface, often ± conspicuously pubescent beneath.—Cited from Modoc, San Joaquin and Shasta cos.; to B.C., Mont.

6a. **V. Clemensòrum** Moldenke described as possible hybrid between *V. officinalis* and *V. robusta,* from Jackson, Amador Co. Coarse herb with glabrous stems, stiff ovate incised lvs. 2.5–8 cm. long; infl. spicate, compound, ± puberulent, elongate; corolla 2 mm. wide.

7. **V. lasiostàchys** Link. $2n = 7$ pairs (Raven, Kyhos & Hill, 1965).

p. 688. 8. **V. robústa** Greene. Is reported from Mendocino and Amador cos.

9. **V. bracteàta** Lag. & Rodr. [*V. bracteosa* Michx.] Moldenke has described **V. califórnica** from Keystone, Tuolumne Co. which keys out to **V. bracteàta**, but is said to have a fruiting calyx 3.5–4 mm. long; corolla not known.

10. **V. Gooddíngii** Briq. Add:

Var. **nepetifòlia** Tidestr. [*V. bipinnatifida* var. *n.* Jeps.] Lvs. shallowly lobed or usually more coarsely toothed.—Lanfair, e. Mojave Desert; to Ariz., L. Calif., Nuevo Leon.

11. **V. ténera** Spreng. and **V. tenuisécta** Briq. are confused and both are to be looked for in Calif. According to one author, *V. tenera* has the calyx-hairs appressed and *V. tenuisecta* ascending-spreading. The latter is described as having lvs. 2–4 cm. long, segms. mostly ca. 1 mm. wide; corolla-limb ca. 10 mm.

wide.—Reported from Bakersfield region, Kern Co., *Twisselmann*; native of
S. Am. All California material which I have seen seems to be V. *tenuisecta*.

p. 689   3. Lantàna L.

Shrubs or herbs; scabrous-hirsute, pubescent or tomentose. Lvs. opposite,
dentate, often rugose. Fls. small, sessile in the axils of bracts, forming dense
spikes or heads, which are terminal or axillary. Calyx very small. Corolla somewhat irregular, but not bilabiate; tube slender; lobes 4–5. Stamens 4, included.
Ovary 2-loculed, forming a fleshy drupe with 2 bony nutlets. (Old Latin name.)
    1. **L. montevidénsis** Briq. Stems weak, vinelike, ca. 1 m. long; lvs. ovate,
2–5 cm. long; fls. rose-lilac, in heads 2.5–3 cm. across.—Occasionally spontane-
ous, as at Claremont; native of S. Am.

4. Vìtex L.

Trees or shrubs. Lvs. persistent or deciduous, opposite, digitate, mostly with
3–7 lfts. Fls. white, blue or yellow, in few to many-fld. cymes which are often
panicled; calyx campanulate, usually 5-toothed; corolla tubular-funnelform, the
limb slightly 2-lipped; lobes 5. Stamens 4, often exserted. Fr. a small drupe,
with a 4-celled stone. A rather large genus of warmer regions. (Ancient Latin
name.)
    1. **V. Ágnus-cástus** L. Deciduous shrubs to 3 m. high, aromatic, gray-pubes-
cent; lvs. opposite, digitately 5–7-foliolate, the lfts. linear-lanceolate, 5–15 cm.
long, gray-felted beneath; fls. pale violet, in terminal racemes 7–20 cm. long;
corolla tubular, 8–9 mm. long.—S. Eu. Found in alkali sink e. of Weedpatch,
Kern Co., *Twisselmann*.

p. 690.   LABIÀTAE
Key AA, BB, C, DD, E, F, G, HH, II, JJ, KK, change "lvs." to "fls." in 1959
printing.
p. 692.   TRICHOSTÈMA
    1. **T. oblóngum** Benth. s. to Greenhorn Mts., Kern Co., *Twisselmann*.
    3. **T. simulàtum** Jeps. in Alpine Co., *Lewis*.
    4. **T. rubisépalum** Elmer. $n = 7$ (H. Lewis, 1960).
p. 693.   6. **T. micránthum** Gray. $n = 7$ (H. Lewis, 1960).
    SALAZÀRIA
    1. **S. mexicàna** Torr. $2n = 50$ pairs (Raven, Kyhos & Hill, 1965).
p. 694.   SCUTELLÀRIA. .
In last part of Key, S. *antirrhinoides* has definite petioles, while they are quite
lacking in S. *siphocampyloides* and S. *Austiniae*.
    2. **S. tuberòsa** Benth. Reported from near Woody, Kern Co., *Twisselmann*.
Put ssp. *austràlis* Epl. into synonymy under **S. tuberosa**. Add
Var. *símilis* Jeps. Calyx very densely villous. Range of the sp.
    4. **S. Bolánderi** Gray. Found in Greenhorn Mts., *Twisselmann*.
p. 697.   GLECHÒMA instead of *Glecoma* for genus no. 9.
    PRUNÉLLA
    1. **P. vulgàris** L. var. **atropurpùrea** Fern. Bracts often purplish and short-
ciliate; corollas dark purple.—Along the coast, from San Mateo Co. to Sonoma
Co.
Var. **parviflòra** (Poir.) DC. is a lawn plant in Golden Gate Park, San Francisco; introd. from Eu. and has corollas scarcely exceeding the bracts.
    PHLÒMIS
    1. **P. fruticòsa** L. $2n = 20$ (Strid, 1965).
p. 699.   STÀCHYS
    4. **S. Emersònii** Piper should be called **S. mexicàna** *Benth.* . .
p. 700.   8. **S. pycnántha** Benth. is apparently a serpentine plant. The Tehama Co.
reference in the FLORA is a misidentification for S. *rigida* ssp. *rivularis* Epl.
p. 701.   ACANTHOMÍNTHA

2. **A. obováta** Jeps. is reported from Monterey Co., *Howitt & Howell. 2n =* 19 pairs (Raven, Kyhos & Hill, 1965).

p. 702.   SÁLVIA

In Key under A, B, CC, change D to:

> D. Plants introd. perennials.
> E.   Corolla blue, 10–15 mm. long. . . . . 2. *S. verbenacea*
> EE. Corolla purple, ca. 25 mm. long. . . . . 2a. *S. pratensis*

Under A, BB, insert:

> CCC. Calyx tubular; lvs. oval, obtuse, corolla red. Introd. . . . . . . 6a. *S. Grahamii*

Under AA, B, insert:

> CCC. Fls. 30 mm. long, scarlet; lvs. 7–14 cm. long; plant ca. 4 m. tall. Introd.
> 8a. *S. longistyla*

p. 703.   2a. **S. praténsis** L. Perennial, to 7 dm. high, erect, pubescent; lvs. largely basal, oblong-ovate, those of infl. cordate-ovate; racemes glandular, subsimple, the whorls remote, 6-fld.; corolla bright blue, sometimes red or white, 2.5 cm. long.—Found as escape near Yreka, Siskiyou Co., *Fuller*; native of Eu.

3. **S. carduàcea** Benth. *n* = 16 (Epling, Lewis & Raven, 1962).

4. **S. Columbàriae** Benth. var. **Ziègleri** Munz. var. nov. Plants much like the typical form, but persistent until fall or early winter; lvs. rather coarsely subsinuately pinnatifid into broad oblong divisions with low rounded teeth; calyx ca. 7 mm. long, the 2 upper lobes united for ca. 2 mm., then with 2 divergent spines almost 2 mm. long; lower lip 2-lobed, the lobes ca. 0.5 mm. long, each ending in a spine almost 2 mm. long; corolla ca. 8 mm. long, deep blue, in general like that figured by Epling (Ann. Mo. Bot. Gard. 25: pl. 16. 1938), with shorter stamens; these fertile.

Folia crasse subsinuate pinnatifida, lobis oblongis; calyce ca. 2 mm. longo, labio superiore de 2 spinis divergentibus et ca. 2 mm. longis, inferiore de lobis 0.5 mm. longis, spinosis; corolla ca. 8 mm. longa.

TYPE: from disturbed soil along a road about one mile north of Kenworthy Ranger Station, Hemet Valley, San Jacinto Mts., Riverside County, growing at about 5,000 ft. elev., Sept. 8, 1964, *Louis B. Ziegler* (RSA). Another collection from the same region is *L. B. Ziegler* Nov. 10, 1965.

The proposed variety is for a population extending for a mile or more and remaining green and floriferous many months after the general population of *S. Columbariae* has dried up in the late spring. Mr. Ziegler has had it under observation for more than one season, the plants ripening seeds and sending out new branches that go on into flowering. The coarse lvs. and smaller fls. can be matched by specimens from other parts of the range of the sp., but the very robust and long continued growth seem unique. It is a pleasure to dedicate this plant to Mr. Louis B. Ziegler who has made a number of other interesting botanical discoveries in the same area.

5. **S. funèrea** Jones. *n* = c. 32 (Epling, Lewis & Raven, 1960).

6. **S. Greàtae** Bdg. 2*n* = c. 30 (Epling, Lewis & Raven, 1960).

p. 704.   6a. **S. Gràhamii** Benth. Shrub, to ca. 1 m. tall; lvs. oval, obtuse, rounded or cuneate at base, crenate; racemes to more than 3 dm. long; floral whorls 2-fld.; corolla ca. 2.5 cm. long, crimson, purplish in age, the midlobe of the lower lip obcordate, large, with 2 small white spots.—Escape from cult, as in Marin, Sonoma and Santa Barbara cos.; native of Mex. The correct name may be **S. microphýlla** Benth. in H. & B.

8a. **S. longistỳla** Benth. Herb, 4–4.5 m. tall, tomentose-villous; lvs. petioled, broad-ovate, 7–14 cm. long; racemes 5–8 dm. long; corolla scarlet, ca. 3 cm. long, with long-exserted stamens and style.—Escape from cult., Big Sur, Monterey Co., *Howell*; native of Mex.

7. **S. spathàcea** Greene. 2*n* = 30 (Epling, Lewis & Raven, 1960).

8. **S. sonoménsis** Greene. 2*n* = 30 (Epling, Lewis & Raven, 1960).

p. 705. 10. **S. pachyphýlla** Epl. ex Munz. $2n = 30$ (Epling, Lewis & Raven, 1960).
11. **S. mellífera** Greene. $2n = 30$ (Epling, Lewis & Raven, 1960).
12. **S. Múnzii** Epl. $2n = 30$ (Epling, Lewis & Raven, 1960).
13. **S. Brandègei** Munz. $n = 15$ (Epling, Lewis & Raven, 1960).
14. **S. eremostàchya** Jeps. $2n = 30$ (Epling, Lewis & Raven, 1960).
15. **S. mohavénsis** Greene. $n = 15$ (Epling, Lewis & Raven, 1960).
p. 706. 16. **S. Clevelándii** (Gray) Greene. $2n = 30$ (Epling, Lewis & Raven, 1960).
17. **S. leucophýlla** Greene. $2n = 30$ (Epling, Lewis & Raven, 1960). Found in Monterey Co., *Howitt & Howell.*
18. **S. Vàseyi** (Porter) Parish. $n = 15$ (Epling, Lewis & Raven, 1960).
19. **S. apiàna** Jeps. $n = 15$ (Epling, Lewis & Raven, 1960).
p. 707. LEPECHÍNIA
1. **L. calcyìna** (Benth.) Epl. in Munz. $n = 16$ (Epling, 1948); $2n = 17$ pairs (Raven, Kyhos & Hill, 1965).
3. **L. frágrans** (Greene) Epl. $n = 16$ (Epling, 1948).
4. **L. Gánderi** Epl. $n = 16$ (Epling, 1948).
p. 710. POGÓGYNE
4. **P. serpylloìdes** (Torr.) Gray. $2n = 19$ pairs (Raven, Kyhos & Hill, 1965).
5. **P. zizyphoroìdes** Benth. $2n = 19$ pairs (Raven, Kyhos & Hill, 1965).
p. 712. MONARDÉLLA
5. **M. villòsa** Benth. Mrs. Clare Hardham has proposed a number of new spp. in the *M. villosa* complex and the following key is presented in place of the one in the FLORA:

A. Upper parts of the plant and lower surfaces of lvs. pubescent to villous.
  B. Lvs. ovate to roundish, mostly green above.
    C. The lvs. almost glabrous. Near the coast, San Luis Obispo Co. to Marin Co.
                                                                5a. *M. subglabra*
    CC. The lvs. ± villous-pubescent to tomentose beneath.
      D. Outer leafy bracts 3 pairs; lvs. ± woolly-pubescent beneath. Santa Barbara Co. to Marin Co. 5. *M. v.* var. *franciscana*
      DD. Outer leafy bracts 1–2 pairs.
        E. Lvs. densely white-tomentose beneath with branched hairs. W. San Luis Obispo and Monterey cos. . . . . 5. *M. v.* var. *obispoensis*
        EE. Lvs. ± villous-pubescent beneath with simple hairs. San Luis Obispo to Humboldt cos. . . . . 5. *M. villosa*
  BB. Lvs. lanceolate to ovate-lanceolate, grayish above.
    C. The lvs. almost entire, 20–25 mm. long, soft villous-pubescent, especially beneath. Monterey Co. to w. Ore., possibly Sierra Nevada. 5. *M.v.* ssp. *subserrata*
    CC. The lvs. evidently serrate.
      D. Hairs rather long, curved, multicellular; lvs. 7–17 mm. long. Diablo Range, San Benito Co. and e. Monterey Co. . . . . 5b. *M. benitensis*
      DD. Hairs minute and glandular. San Antonio Hills, Santa Lucia Range.
                                                                5c. *M. antonina*
AA. Upper parts of plant and lower lf.-surfaces puberulent at most.
  B. Bracts leaflike, not markedly ciliate and not purplish. Sierra Nevada and Siskiyou Mts. . . . . 5. *M. v.* ssp. *Sheltonii*
  BB. Bracts membranous, ciliate, the inner purple. San Mateo Co. to Sonoma Co.
                                                                5. *M. v.* ssp. *neglecta*

p. 713. **5a. M. subglàbra** (Hoover) Hardham. [*M. villosa* var. *s.* Hoover.] Rhizomatous perennial; stems with short down-curved hairs; lvs. broadly ovate, 7–16 mm. long, 4–9 mm. wide; petioles 2.5–6 mm. long; blades with 6–10 prominent veins, thickened serrate margins, subglabrous except for dense glandular pubescence beneath; bracts in 3 series: *outer* of 1 or 2 pairs, ± remote, petioled or not, leafy at tip, membranous at base; *middle* of 3 pairs with leafy tips and membranous bases; the *inner* of a few pairs of membranous bracts; leafy bracts often reflexed in age; calyx 7–9 mm. long, 13-veined and with sparsely pubescent teeth 1.3 mm. long; $n = 20$.—San Luis Obispo Co. to Marin Co., below 2000 ft., on exposed or woody places.
    5b. M. beniténsis Hardham. Woody at base, somewhat rhizomatous, forming small clumps 3–5 dm. tall; stems many-branched from above the base; lvs. lanceolate to ovate-lanceolate, 7–17 mm. long, 6–10 mm. wide, usually 8-veined; petiole ca. 3 mm. long, margined; lf.-margins remotely serrate, the teeth gland-

tipped; pubescence of lvs., stems and foliar bracts of rather long curved multicellular hairs and of microscopic glandular hairs beneath the longer ones; fl.-head usually with 1 (–2) pairs of leafy bracts; next 3 pairs less leaflike; inner bracts of several pairs, linear, leathery-membranous; calyx 13-nerved, 6.5–8 mm. long; corolla 13–14.5 mm. long; calyx-teeth 1.66 mm. long, long bristly-hairy; $n = 21$.—Serpentine along Clear Creek, Diablo Range, San Benito Co. and possibly Griswold Hills and Priest Valley.

5c. **M. antonìna** Hardham. Perennial, woody at base, from small clumps to large patches; stems often many-branched; lvs. lance-ovate, 10–26 mm. long, 3–15 mm. wide, cuneate at base; petioles 2–8 mm. long; lf.-margins remotely serrate, usually 7–8-veined; pubescence of numerous minute gland-tipped hairs and short down-curved white hairs; leafy bracts 1 pair, ca. 8 mm. long, 3 mm. wide, 7–8-veined; middle bracts of 3–4 pairs, leafy-tipped; inner bracts of a few pairs, narrow, membranous; calyx 6–9 mm. long, ca. 13-nerved, with teeth 1.3 mm. long; corolla bluish purple, 11–16 mm. long; $n = 21$.—On silicious shale, Foothill Wd., San Antonio Hills of Santa Lucia Range, between Bradley and King City, Monterey Co.

p. 714.   9. **M. odoratíssima** Benth. ssp. **parvifòlia** (Greene) Epl. in the Greenhorn Range, Kern Co., *Twisselmann*; White Mts., *Howell*.

10. **M. Robisònii** Epl. in Munz.; Granite Mts. n. of Amboy, San Bernardino Co., *Haller*; $2n = 21$ pairs (Raven, Kyhos & Hill, 1965).

p. 715.   13. **M. undulàta** Benth. $2n = 21$ pairs (Raven, Kyhos & Hill, 1965).

18. **M. éxilis** (Gray) Greene. Ascends to 6200 ft., S. Fork of Kern R., Kern Co., *Griesel*.

p. 716.   LÝCOPUS

After generic description insert: "Henderson, N.C. A taxonomic revision of the genus Lycopus. Am. Midl. Nat. 68: 95–138. 1962."

1. **L. americànus** Muhl. In Kern R. region, Kern Co., *Twisselmann*; Lake, San Francisco and Inyo cos., *Rubtzoff*.

p. 717.   MÉNTHA

In Key add a last line:

Lvs. lanceolate to lance-ovate, 5–12 cm. long, pubescent to tomentose above, white-tomentose beneath. . . . . 7. *M. longifolia*

p. 718.   5. **M. citràta** Ehrh. Fourth word should be "glabrous."

7. **M. longifòlia** Huds. [*M. silvestris* L.] Stoloniferous; stems erect, puberulent to tomentose, 4–12 dm. high; lvs. nearly sessile, lanceolate to lance-ovate, 5–12 cm. long, sharply serrate, pubescent to tomentose above, white-tomentose beneath; spikes thickish, ± dense, especially above; corolla purplish, 3 mm. long. —Escaped, as at Santa Barbara, *C. Smith*; Ojai Valley, Ventura Co., *Pollard*; from Eurasia.

p. 719.   TILLAÈA

Raven and others use *Crassula* instead of *Tillaea*.

2. **T. mucòsa** L. Reported from Calaveras Co., *Gankin*.

p. 720.   PARVISÈDUM

4. **P. Congdònii** (Eastw.) Clausen. In the Greenhorn Range, Kern Co., *Twisselmann*.

p. 721.   DÚDLEYA

In Key, A, B, CC, DD, EE, FF, G, HH, delete "Insular. 7. *D. Greenei*" from II and insert:

      J.   Caudex 2–5 cm. thick; rosette-lvs. 1.5–3 cm. wide. Insular. . . . . 7. *D. Greenei*
      JJ.   Caudex 1–1.8 cm. thick; rosette-lvs. 3–7 mm. wide. Mainland. . . . . 7a. *D. Bettinae*

p. 723.   4a. Delete *Cotyledon Palmeri* Wats. from synonymy under 4. **D. farinosa** and insert **D. Pálmeri** (Wats.) Britton & Rose. Caudex 2–4 cm. thick, to 2 dm. long, loosely branching; rosettes 5–20 cm. in diam.; lvs. 15–25, green or reddish, oblong-lanceolate, acute to acuminate, 5–20 cm. long, 1.5–5 cm. wide; floral stems 2–6 dm. tall, 5–11 mm. thick, with ca. 3 simple or forked branches; cymes circinnate, 5–8 cm. long, 5–14-fld.; pedicels erect, 2–10 mm. long; sepals deltoid-ovate, acute, 3–5 mm. long; petals yellow with red, elliptic, acute, 11–16 mm. long, connate for 1.5–2 mm.; $2n = 68, 85, 119$.—San Luis Obispo and Monterey cos. May–June.

p. 724.   7a. **D. Bettìnae** Hoov. Much like *D. parva*, but branches below the rosettes 10–18 mm. in diam.; lvs. evergreen, terete to semiterete, 2–7 cm. long, 3–7 mm. wide after drying; fl.-stems 1.5–2.5 dm. tall, few-branched to simple; pedicels erect, 1–4 mm. long; calyx-lobes ovate, 3–5 mm. long; petals straw-color, often purplish-tinged toward apex, erect or slightly curved outward at the tips.— Serpentine, 1 mi. s. of Cayucos and 1 mi. w. of Cerro Romauldo, San Luis Obispo Co. Hoover separates this proposed sp. from its 2 associates as follows:

Plants eventually developing a dense cluster of numerous rosettes; lvs. terete to semiterete; petals cream-color or straw-color, often with midrib purple-tinged toward apex.
    Branches of caudex just below the rosettes 4–8 mm. in diam.; lvs. shriveling in summer, in dried specimens less than 2 mm. wide at the middle. . . . . 3. *D. parva*
    Branches of caudex just below the rosettes 10–18 mm. in diam.; lvs. evergreen after drying, 3–7 mm. wide at middle. . . . . 7a. *D. Bettinae*
Plants usually with a single rosette, rarely more than 4 or 5 even when old; lvs. flat, comparatively thin; petals with purple midrib and purple striations on either side.
                                                   8. *D. Abramsii* ssp. *murina*

p. 725.   15a. Delete *Stylophyllum Hassei* Rose from synonymy under 15. **D. virens** and insert **D. Hàssei** (Rose) Moran. [*S. H.* Rose. *Cotyledon H.* Fedde. *Echeveria H.* Berger.] Caudex 1–3 cm. thick, to 3 dm. long, much branched; rosette 6–10 cm. diam.; lvs. 15–30, farinose, linear-lanceolate, obtuse, 3–10 cm. long, 5–15 mm. wide, 2–4 mm. thick; floral stems 1–3 dm. long, with 2–4 simple or forked branches; cymes 2–8 cm. long, 4–14-fld.; pedicels erect, 1–5 mm. long; sepals deltoid-ovate, acute, 2–3 mm. long; petals white, 8–10 mm. long; connate for 1.5–2 mm., spreading from middle; $n = 34$.—Catalina Id.; L. Calif. May–June.

p. 727.   SÈDUM
In Key, change last DD to:

      DD. Fls. white.
          E. Lvs. narrowed toward base; petals ca. 8 mm. long. San Bernardino Mts. . . . . 10. *S. niveum*
          EE. Lvs. not narrowed toward base; petals ca. 4 mm. long. Escape from cult. . . . . 10a. *S. album*

p. 728.   7. **S. Ròsea** (L.) Scop. ssp. **integrifòlium** (Raf.) Hult. $n = 16$ (Wiens & Halleck, 1962).

p. 729.   10a. **S. álbum** L. Glabrous, creeping, evergreen, forming large mats; fl.-stems 7–15 cm. high; lvs. alternate, linear-oblong to obovate or even globular, 3–15 mm. long, terete or flattened above, sessile; fls. ca. 9 mm. in diam.; petals white, obtuse, ca. equaling the stamens; fr. erect, white, streaked red. Fls. in early summer.—Reported as becoming natur., especially near the coast; native Eurasia.

p. 729.   CONGDÒNIA
      1. **C. pinetòrum** (Bdg.) Jeps. R. Moran (Leafl. W. Bot. 6: 62–63. 1950) expressed doubt as to whether this plant originally came from California. The only collection known is the type at the University of California, for which evidence was presented that it may have come from Mexico, not California. Furthermore, the name *Congdonia* was used earlier for a genus of *Rubiaceae*.

p. 730.   COTYLÈDON
      1. **C. orbiculàta** L. Reported as highly poisonous to sheep and goats, *Fuller*.

p. 731.   SAXIFRAGACEAE
In Key, A, BB, CC, DD, EE, FF, GG, HH, II, change J. to:

      J. Ovary 2-celled.
          K. Placentae axile; petals obovate or spatulate. Widespread. . . . . . 4. *Boykinia*
          KK. Placentae parietal; petals filiform. In extreme n. Calif. . . . 11a. *Bensoniella*
      JJ. Ovary 1-celled, etc. as in the FLORA.

p. 734. SAXÍFRAGA

In Key, AA, BB, change C to:

    C. Lower stems with ± horizontal perennial branches densely covered with elongate lvs.

        D. Lvs. entire, linear; petals oblanceolate, 4–5 mm. long. From Tulare Co. n.

                                            5. *S. Tolmiei*

        DD. Lvs. mostly 3-lobed, ± spatulate; petals obovate to oblong-obovate. Marble Mts., Siskiyou Co. .... 5a. *S. caespitosa*

    1. **S. débilis** Engelm. Raven (Leafl. W. Bot. 10: 142) says this sp. grows at 10,000–12,400 ft., Madera, Mono, Fresno, Tulare, Inyo cos.

    3. Change name to **S. odontolòma** Piper, fide Bacigalupi. [*S. arguta* auth, not D. Don.]

p. 735.   4. **S. Mertensiàna** Bong. $2n =$ ca. 48 (Beamish, 1961).

    5. **S. Tólmiei** T. & G. $n =$ 15 (Beamish, 1961).

    5a. S. caespitòsa L. Dense tufted perennial from a woody, often branching rootstock, the stems depressed, 3–6 cm. long; lvs. mostly cuneate with 3 obtuse apical lobes, glandular-puberulent and villous-ciliate, 5–10 mm. long; flowering stems 4–10 cm. high, few-fld., glandular-pubescent; sepals ca. 3 mm. long; petals 4–5 mm. long.—Damp rocky places at 6500 ft., Marble Mts., Siskiyou Co., *Gilbert Muth*. Previously known from Lincoln Co., Ore. n. and e. through the Rocky Mts. to n. Ariz. Identification of the Muth specimen by R. Bacigalupi.

p. 736. LITHOPHRÁGMA

After generic description, insert: (Taylor, R. L. The genus Lithophragma. Univ. Calif. Publ. Bot. 37: 1–122. 1965).

p. 737. Change Key to:

    A. Basal lvs. truly compound, trifoliolate; stems stout, 4–6 dm. high. San Clemente Id.

                                          10. *L. maximum*

    AA. Basal lvs. not truly compound, but merely lobed; stems slender.

        B. The basal lvs. not lobed to near their bases.

            C. Petals entire or shallowly toothed.

                D. Fl.-tube with a ± rounded, not definitely acute base; pedicels 1–3 mm. long; stem-lvs. alternate.

                    E. Base of petal blade not involute or toothed; fl.-tube campanulate with a truncate base. .... 1. *L. heterophyllum*

                    EE. Base of petal blade somewhat involute, minutely toothed or laciniate; fl.-tube obtuse or rounded at base. .... 2. *L. Bolanderi*

                DD. Fl.-tube with an acute base; pedicels 5–10 mm. long; stem lvs. mostly opposite. .... 4. *L. Cymbalaria*

           CC. Petals deeply parted.

                D. Corolla spreading widely; petals not very lacerate on margins.

                    E. Pedicels 1–2 mm. long; petals 4–7 mm. long; fl.-tube truncate at base. .... 1. *L. heterophyllum*

                    EE. Pedicels 2–8 mm. long; petals 6–10 mm. long; fl.-tube obconic at base. .... 5. *L. affine*

                DD. Corolla campanulate, the petals with very lacerate margins. N. Calif.

                                    3. *L. campanulatum*

        BB. The basal lvs. lobed almost to their base.

            C. Petals mostly 3–5 mm. long; fl.-tube ± rounded at base.

                D. Fls. 3–8; fl.-tube scarcely striate.

                    E. Stem lvs. not bearing axillary bulblets; stems 2–3.5 mm. tall.

                                      6. *L. tenellum*

                    EE. Stem lvs. often bearing axillary bulblets which replace the fls.; stems 1–2 dm. tall. .... 7. *L. glabrum*

                DD. Fls. 8–20; fl. tube ± striate; stems 2–5 dm. tall. .... 6. *L. tenellum*

           CC. Petals mostly 6–10 mm. long; fl.-tube ± acute at the base.

                D. Base of fl.-tube acutish, but not obconic. From San Luis Obispo Co. south.

                                  5. *L. affine* ssp. *mixtum*

                DD. Base of fl.-tube obconic. From Kern and San Benito cos. north.

                    E. Fl.-tube 3 times as long as broad; petals with 3 broadly oblong lobes.

                                    8. *L. trifoliatum*

                    EE. Fl.-tube twice as long as broad; petals with 3–7 linear-oblong lobes.

                                  9. *L. parviflorum*

    1. **L. heterophýllum** (H. & A.) T. & G. [*Tellima h.* H. & A. *L. trilobum* Rydb.] Slender perennial 2–4 dm. tall, the flowering stalks 1–several; herbage

glandular-pubescent or ± hirsutulose; basal lvs. round-reniform, 1.5–4 cm. wide, crenately shallowly lobed; cauline lvs. alternate, usually much reduced, mostly deeply 3-cleft; fls. mostly 3–9; pedicels shorter than fl.-tube which is campanulate with a truncate base; corolla widely spreading; petals 5–12 mm. long, usually 3- (sometimes 5- or 7-) lobed; seeds tuberculate; $2n = 14$ (Taylor, 1965).—Mostly in S. Oak and Foothill Wd., below 4500 ft.; Los Angeles Co. to Humboldt Co.

2. **L. Bolánderi** Gray. [*Tellima heterophylla* var. *B.* Jeps. *T. scabrella* Greene. *L. s.* Greene. *L. heterophylla* var. *s.* Jeps. *L. s.* var. *Peirsonii* Jeps.] Flowering stalks 2.5–8.5 dm. tall, several; herbage pubescent; basal lvs. orbicular, 3–5-lobed; cauline lvs. 2–3, much reduced; fls. 3–5–many; pedicels not longer than fl.-tube which is campanulate, obtuse at base; corolla wide-spreading, the petals ovate-elliptic, 4–7 mm. long, mostly entire or with small serrations near base; seeds tuberculate; $2n = 14, 28, 35, 42$ (Taylor).—Foothill Wd., Yellow Pine F., etc.; Los Angeles and Kern cos. n. to Shasta Co., San Francisco Bay to Mendocino Co.

3. **L. campanulàtum** Howell. [*L. laciniata* Eastw. ex Rydb.] Slender to rather robust, 2.5–4.5 dm. tall; herbage moderately pubescent; basal lvs. round, trilobed, the lobes apiculately toothed; cauline lvs. 1–2, trilobed or trifoliate; fls. 2–11, very short-pedicelled; fl.-tube broadly campanulate; corolla campanulate, the white petals ovate-elliptic, 3–7 mm. long, palmately lobed with lacerate margin, ligulate; seeds large, the tubercles in distinct rows.—Semi-open slopes, N. Oak Wd., Yellow Pine F.; below 7500 ft.; Lake and Colusa cos. to sw. Ore.

4. **L. Cymbalària** T. & G. [*Tellima C.* Walp.] Slender, 2–4 dm. tall, sparingly pubescent; basal lvs. reniform, weakly 3-lobed; fls. 2–5 (–8), the pedicels to twice the turbinate fl.-tube; corolla wide-spreading, bowl-shaped, the petals 4–5 mm. long, entire, spatulate; seeds tuberculate; $2n = 14 + 1$ (Taylor).—Shaded woods, etc. below 3000 ft.; Palomar Mts. (San Diego Co.), Ventura and Santa Barbara cos. to Stanislaus Co.; Santa Cruz and Santa Rosa ids.

5. **L. affìne** Gray. Robust, 2–5 dm. tall, variously pubescent; basal lvs. palmately 3–5-lobed, each lobe sub-lobed into cuspidate lobules; cauline lvs. 1–3, more dissected; fls. 5–9 (–15); fl.-tube widely inflated, obconic below, the pedicels shorter than or equalling it; petals 6–13 mm. long, always 3-lobed; seeds not tuberculate; $2n = 14, 21,$ or 28 (Taylor).—Grassy banks below 3500 ft., many Plant Communities; below 7000 ft.; Santa Barbara Co. to Humboldt Co.

Subsp. **míxtum** R. L. Taylor. [*Tellima tripartita* Greene. *L. t.* Greene.] Basal lvs. 3-lobed, each lobe often subdivided into spreading lobules; petals 4–9 mm. long, 3-lobed; $2n = 28, 35$ (Taylor).—Below 6500 ft.; San Luis Obispo Co. to L. Calif.

6. **L. tenéllum** Nutt. in T. & G. [*Tellima t.* Walp. *L. rupicola* Greene. *L. australis* Rydb. *L. breviloba* Rydb.] Stems 1.5–3 dm. tall; herbage light green and sparsely pubescent; basal lvs. round, simple and irregularly 3–5-lobed or digitately compound; cauline lvs. 2, pinnatifid; fls. 3–12; pedicels not longer than fl.-tube which is campanulate or hemispheric; petals mostly pink, 3–7 mm. long, palmately 5-parted; seeds smooth or wrinkled; $2n = 14$ and 35 (Taylor).—Occasional, 2000–7000 ft. or higher; various Communities; San Gabriel and San Bernardino mts., Butte, Plumas and Modoc cos.; to Ida., Rocky Mts.

p. 738.   7. **L. glàbrum** Nutt. in T. & G. [*Tellima g.* Walp. *L. bulbifera* Rydb. *L. g.* var. *b.* Jeps.] Slender, 1–3.5 dm. tall, subglabrous to sparingly pubescent; basal lvs. orbicular, usually trifoliate, the segms. many-cleft or round-lobed; cauline lvs. 2–4, much reduced; often with bulbils in the axils; fls. 1–5–7, the petals often exceeding the fl.-tubes which are campanulate with an acute or hemispheric base; petals pink or rarely white, ovate, 3.5–6.5 mm. long, palmately 5-parted; seeds tuberculate; $2n = 14, 28$ (Taylor).—In Calif., in dry open places, Sagebrush Scrub, Montane Coniferous F., 4500–11,000 ft.; Sierra Nevada to Siskiyou Co.; to B.C., Rocky Mts.

8. **L. trifoliàtum** Eastw. [*L. parviflora* var. *t.* Jeps.] Slender, 2–5 dm. tall, densely pubescent; basal lvs. round, digitately trifoliate, the segms. many-lobed;

cauline lvs. 2–3, deeply lobed; fls. 4–8, the pedicels not exceeding the length of the fl.-tube which is elongate-obconic; petals pink, obovate-rhombic, 9–11 mm. long, always 3-cleft; seeds smooth or wrinkled; $2n = 28$ (Taylor).—Largely Foothill Wd., below 2000 ft.; w. slope of Sierra Nevada from Tehama Co. to Placer Co.

9. **L. parviflòrum** (Hook.) T. & G. [*Tellima p.* Hook. *Pleurendotria p.* Raf. *L. austromontana* Heller.] Slender, 2–5 dm. tall, nearly glabrous to densely pubescent; basal lvs. orbicular, 3-parted or digitately trifoliate; cauline lvs. 2–3, much like the basal; fls. 4–14, the pedicels not longer than the fl.-tubes, which are oblong-obconic; petals white or pink, obovate-rhombic, 7–16 mm. long, always 3-cleft; seeds smooth or wrinkled; $2n = 14, 21, 28, 35$ (Taylor).—Open slopes 2000–6000 ft.; San Diego Co., Tehachapi Mts. to San Benito Co. and N. Coast Ranges, Sierra Nevada to Modoc Co., to B.C. and Rocky Mts.

10. **L. máximum** Bacig. Stout perennial, the basal lvs. truly compound, the 3 lfts. rhombic, cuneate; petioles to 15 cm. long; fl.-stems stout, 4–6 dm. tall; fl.-tube campanulate, ca. 6 mm. long at anthesis, including the sepals, 8 mm. in fruit; petals 4 mm. long, digitately incised.—San Clemente Id.

p. 738. CHRYSOSPLÈNIUM

1. **C. glechomifòlium** Nutt. in T. & G. $2n = 9$ pairs (Anderson in 1965).

p. 739. TIARÉLLA

1. **T. trifoliàta** L. ssp. **unifoliàta** (Hook.) Kern in Madroño 18: 159. 1966.

p. 739. 11a. **Bensoniélla** Morton.

Perennial with slender branching scaly rootstocks and simple scapiform flowering branches. Lvs. basal, cordate, petioled. Fl.-tube campanulate, free from the ovary. Sepals 5, three approximate, the other 2 more distant, all 3-nerved. Petals 5, filiform, entire. Stamens 5, opposite the sepals. Pistil 2-valved at apex. Carpels subcompressed, sharply angled on the back. Ovules many. (G. T. *Benson*, former botanist at Stanford.)

1. **B. oregòna** (Abrams & Bacig.) Morton. [*Bensonia o.* Abrams & Bacig.] Petioles slender, 3–7 cm. long, with elongate brownish hairs; lf.-blades 2.5–4.5 cm. long, crenately 7-lobed; scape 2 dm. high, sparsely pilose; sepals 2 mm. long, stipitate-glandular; petals ca. 3 mm. long.—Between 4000 and 5000 ft., Siskiyou Mts., nw. Calif. and sw. Ore.

TÉLLIMA

1. **T. grandiflòra** (Pursh.) Dougl. ranges s. into Eldorado Co.

p. 742. HEÙCHERA

6. **H. rubéscens** Torr. var. **pachypòda** (Greene) Rosend. Dr. Bacigalupi informs me that a study of the type specimen of var. *alpicola* as used in the FLORA shows that the correct name is **pachypòda**. This ranges s. into the Piute Mts., Kern Co., *Twisselmann*.

Var. **alpícola** Jeps. is the correct name for var. *Rydbergiana* of the FLORA and that name goes into synonymy.

p. 744. PHILADÉLPHUS

The citation of the Hitchcock reference to Madroño in the 1959 printing should be to vol. 7.

2. **P. Lewísii** Pursh ssp. **califórnicus** (Benth.) Munz, if treated as a var., would have as its oldest name *P. L.* var. *parvifòlius* Torr.

p. 745. CARPENTÈRIA

1. **C. califórnica** Torr. $n = 10$ (Ernst, 1964); $2n = 20$ (Raven, Kyhos & Hill, 1965).

p. 747. RÌBES

4. **R. laxiflòrum** Pursh. $2n = 8$ pairs (D. E. Anderson, 1963).

p. 748. 7. **R. viscosíssimum** Pursh. Twisselmann reports from Kern Co. (Sunday Peak).

p. 749. 10. **R. sanguíneum** var. **glutinòsum** Loud. $2n = 8$ pairs (D. E. Anderson, 1963).

11. **R. malvàceum** Sm. occurs in the Tehachapi Mts., Kern Co., *Twisselmann.*

p. 751.   18. **R. quercetòrum** Greene. is reported from 26 mi. n. of Essex, Mojave Desert, San Bernardino Co., at 4400 ft., *Haller.*

19. **R. velutìnum** Greene. In line 3, change "modal" to "nodal."

p. 753.   27. **R. califórnicum** H. & A. is common on the e. side of the Santa Lucia Mts., San Luis Obispo Co., *Hardham*; also in the Temblor Range, Kern Co., *Twisselmann.*

p. 756.   ROSÀCEAE

In Key, in the E and EE just above AA, for the 1959 printing, change to:

> E.   Pistil 1; fls. bisexual; lvs. mostly serrate. . . . . .30. *Prunus*
> EE. Pistils usually 5; fls. unisexual or bisexual; lvs. entire. 31. *Osmaronia*

In the Key, under AA, BB, change CC to:

> CC. Plants evergreen, with persistent lvs.
>   D.   Carpels with leathery walls at maturity; styles 2–3; fls. in large corymbose panicles; lvs. sharply toothed. Native. . . . . 37. *Heteromeles*
>   DD. Carpels bony at maturity with 2-seeded nutlets; lvs. entire or crenate. Introduced.
>   E.   Lvs. entire; shrubs spineless; styles 2–5. . . . . 37a. *Cotoneaster*
>   EE. Lvs. crenate; shrubs thorny; styles 5. . . . . 37b. *Pyracantha*

LYONOTHÁMNUS

1. **L. floribúndus** Gray $2n = $ c. 48 (Stebbins & Major, 1965). Var. *asplenifòlius* (Greene) Bdg. Raven makes the comb. ssp. *a.* (Greene) Raven. $2n = 27$ pairs (Raven, Kyhos and Hill, 1965).

p. 757.   SPIRAÈA

In Key, after the word "Fls." delete "white" and "pink" in the 1959 printing.

p. 758.   ARÚNCUS

1. **A. vulgàris** Raf. $2n = 18$ (Löve, 1964).

p. 759.   HOLODÍSCUS

1. **H. díscolor** (Pursh) Maxim. has been called "Indian Arrow-wood" in Mendocino Co.

p. 761.   HORKÈLIA

In Key, top of page, under FF, change GG to:

> GG. Cymes few-fld.; lfts. 6–12 pairs.
>   H.   Cymes open; lfts. 3.5–5 mm. long. White Mts.
>   11. *H. hispidula*
>   HH. Cymes congested; lfts. smaller. Kern Plateau.
>   11a. *H. tularensis*

p. 761.   3. **H. califórnica** Cham. & Schlecht. Change in line 2 of 1959 printing the word *carmelina* to *carmeliana.* The sp. has been reported from Monterey Co., *Howitt & Howell.*

p. 763.   11a. **H. tularénsis** (J. T. Howell) Munz, comb. nov. [*Potentilla tularensis* J. T. Howell, Leaflets W. Bot. 10: 254–255. 1966.] Odorless compact cespitose or loosely pulvinate herb, with multicipital caudex, pale cinereous with appressed and spreading hairs; stems erect, 3–10 cm. tall; basal lvs. rosulate, 2–4 cm. long, the petioles 0.5–1.5 cm. long; lfts. in 6–10 pairs, the lower ± petiolulate, the upper crowded, 3–5-palmatifid, the segms. oblong to obovate; cyme laxly few-fld.; fls. 4–5 mm. long; fl.-tube cupulate, 1–1.5 mm. high, pilose within; bracteoles 1–2 mm. long; sepals 2–3.5 mm. long; petals white, linear-oblanceolate, 2–3.5 mm. long; fils. 10, subulate-dilate; styles ca. 11; aks. 2.5 mm. long.—At 9430 ft., Bald Mt., Kern Plateau, Tulare Co., *Twisselmann.*

p. 764.   15. **H. tridentàta** Torr.; line 7 from bottom of page, for 1959 printing change "petals" to "sepals."

p. 765.   IVÈSIA

In Key, AA, BB, C, DD, EE, change F to:

> F.   Fl.-tube campanulate or turbinate to saucer-shaped; sepals 3.5–5.5 mm. long; bractlets thin; herbage densely villous or tomentose.

G. The fl.-tube glabrous within, 2–2.5 mm. deep; pistils 4–7;
lfts. 20–35 pairs, 4–15 mm. long. Plumas Co. to Sierra Co.
H. Petals white, much exceeding the sepals.
              11. *I. sericoleuca*
HH. Petals yellow, not exceeding sepals. . . 11a. *I. aperta*
GG. Fl.-tube saucer-shaped; sepals 2.5–3 mm. long; bractlets
thickened; lfts. 25–50 pairs, 2–5 mm. long. Siskiyou to
Trinity Co. .... 12. *I. Pickeringii*

p. 767. 9. **I. purpuráscens** (Wats.) Keck. Reported from Piute Mts., Kern Co., *Twisselmann*.

11a. **I. apérta** (J. T. Howell) Munz, comb. nov. [*Potentilla aperta* J. T. Howell, Leaflets W. Bot. 9: 239, 1962.] Like *I. sericoleuca* (Rydb.) Rydb. in habit and pubescence and like *I. Kingii* Wats. in its open fls. with a saucer-shaped floral tube. If *I. sericoleuca* is restricted to plants with turbinate fl.-tube and white petals and much exceeding the sepals, the name *I. aperta* can be applied to those with yellow petals not exceeding the sepals and with open shallow, starlike fls.—Sierra Valley, Plumas and Sierra cos.

p. 772. POTENTÍLLA
14. **P. saxòsa** Lemmon ex Greene ssp. **siérrae** Munz is reported from Weldon, Kern Co., *Twisselmann*.

p. 773. 17. **P. grácilis** Dougl. ex Hook. ssp. **Nuttállii** (Lehm.) Keck has been collected at elevs. up to 11,000 ft.
21. **P. récta** L. has been found wild in San Francisco.

p. 774. 23. **P. anserìna** L. 2n = 28 (Taylor, 1967).
26. **P. glandulòsa** Lindl. Line 8 of description, the second word "petals" should be changed to "sepals" in the 1959 printing.

p. 775. Ssp. **Hansènii** (Greene) Keck is reported from the Piute Mts., Kern Co., *Twisselmann*.

FRAGÀRIA
As an additional reference for the genus cite "Staudt, G. Taxonomic studies in the genus Fragaria." Canad. J. Bot. 40: 869–886, 1962.

p. 776. 1. Staudt would consider our w. material of **F. chiloénsis** (L.) Duchn. to be ssp. **pacífica** Staudt.
3. **F. califórnica** Cham. & Schlecht. is **F. vésca** L. ssp. **califórnica** Staudt.
4. *F. platypétala* Rydb. is **F. virginiàna** L. ssp. **platypétala** Staudt.

p. 777. SANGUISÓRBA
1. For *S. occidentàlis* Nutt. use **S. ánnua** (Nutt. ex Hook.) T. & G. according to Nordborg (Opera Bot. 11: 64, 1966).
2. **S. mìnor** Scop. 2n = 28, 56 (Nordborg, 1958).
3. **S. microcéphala** Presl. Add to synonymy *S. officinalis* ssp. *m.* Calder & Taylor.

p. 778. ACAÈNA
2. **A. anserinifòlia** (J. R. & G. Forst.) Druce. [*A. Sanguisorba* Vahl.] Prostrate, creeping, much-branched undershrub with short leafy erect stems 2–15 cm. high; lfts. 3–4 pairs, oblong, crenate-serrate; fls. in globose heads, purplish. —Growing with *Pinus radiata*, *Ceanothus griseus* and *Heteromeles* on Peter Pan road, just off Highway 1, s. of Wild Cat Creek, Carmel Highlands, Monterey Co., *E. K. Balls*. Native of Australia, New Zealand.

AGRIMÒNIA
1. **A. gryposèpala** Wallr. Reported from Eldorado Co., *Fuller*.

ADENÓSTOMA
1. **A. fasciculàtum** H. & A. 2n = 9 pairs (Raven, Kyhos & Hill, 1965).
2. **A. sparsifòlium** Torr. 2n = 9 pairs (Raven, Kyhos & Hill, 1965).

p. 779. GÈUM
1. **G. macrophýllum** Willd. Occurs in the Piute Mts., Kern Co., *Twisselmann*.

p. 780. PÚRSHIA
1. **P. tridentàta** (Pursh) DC. 2n = 18 (Cave, 1956). South to Kern Plateau, Kern Co., *Twisselmann*.

p. 781. CHAMAEBÀTIA
1. **C. foliolòsa** Benth. Found in the Greenhorn Mts., Kern Co., *Twisselmann*.

p. 782.   CERCOCÁRPUS

C. betuloìdes var. *Tráskiae* (Eastw.) Dunkle. Dr. Thorne has recently found several individuals in an arroyo in the Salta Verde on Catalina Id. The very heavy coriaceous large lvs., impressed veins, felty tomentum, thick pedicels, etc. suggest species rank, C. Tráskiae Eastw.

3. **C. ledifòlius** Nutt. reported as on St. John Mt., sw. Glenn Co., and in nw. Tehama Co., *Tucker*.

4. **C. intricàtus** Wats. is common in the King's River region.

p. 783.   RÙBUS

In Key, change A to:

A.   Plants ± herbaceous, creeping; stipules broad, almost or quite free.
  B.   Stems not prickly; sepals 6–7 mm. long; petals white. Humboldt and Siskiyou cos.
          1. *R. lasiococcus*
  BB.   Stems with curved prickles; sepals 7–9 mm. long; petals dull purple. Del Norte Co.
          1a. *R. nivalis*

In Key, AA, BB, C, DD, change and insert:

  D.   Fls. borne in long terminal racemes or large panicles; prickles stout, broad-based or none. Escapes from cult.
    E.   Infl. long, racemose or corymbose.
      F.   Lvs. of primocanes non-glandular and velvety above; infl. 7–12-fld. .... 8a. *R. pensilvanicus*
      FF.   Lvs. of primocanes glandular and pubescent above; infl. with few to many fls. in a long cluster. ...... 8b. *R. alleghaniensis*
    EE.   Infl. a large panicle.
      F.   Lfts. deeply cut or dissected, not whitish-tomentose or canescent beneath. .... 6. *R. laciniatus*
      FF.   Lfts. not deeply cut, whitish-tomentose or gray-canescent beneath.
        G.   Canes and infl. quite unarmed; lf.-margins finely serrate.
                7. *R. ulmifolius*
        GG. Canes and infl. armed; lf.-margins coarsely unequally serrate or toothed. .... 8. *R. procerus*

1a. **R. nivàlis** Dougl. Creeping stems 3–12 dm. long, sparingly armed; lvs. simple to ± distinctly 3-lobed; fls. usually 1; sepals 7–9 mm. long; petals dull purple.—At 4100 ft., upper East Fork of Illinois River, Del Norte Co., *Hobart*; to B.C., Ida.

p. 785.   8a. **R. pensilvánicus** Poir. in Lam. Upright but usually diffuse bramble; lvs. soft-pubescent beneath; floral lvs. and lfts. narrow and acuminate; pedicels nearly or quite unarmed; infl. ± corymbiform.—Reported as natur. in Humboldt Co., *Pollard*; Butte Co., *Howell*; Monterey Co., *Howitt & Howell*; native of e. N. Am.

8b. **R. alleghaniénsis** Porter ex Bailey. Large prickly highbush blackberry; lfts. narrow-acuminate, mostly pubescent and glandular; pedicels glandular; infl. long-racemiform.—Plumas Co.; native of e. N. Am.

10. **R. glaucifòlius** Kell. S. to Piute Mts., Kern Co., *Twisselmann*.

p. 786.   RÒSA

In Key AA, BB, change the rest of the Key to:

  C.   Sepals glandular-hispid on back.
    D.   Lvs. simply serrate, without gland-tipped teeth; fls. mostly corymbose.
            3. *R. pisocarpa*
    DD.   Lvs. doubly serrate with gland-tipped teeth; fls. mostly solitary.
            7. *R. pinetorum*
  CC.   Sepals not glandular-hispid on back.
    D.   The sepals and styles deciduous in fr.; pistils few; pedicels 1–3 cm. long, ± reflexed in fr.; fr. 4–8 mm. thick in maturity. .... 9. *R. gymnocarpa*
    DD.   The sepals and styles persistent in fr.; pedicels usually less than 2 cm. long, not reflexed in fr.; fr. more than 7 mm. thick at maturity.
      E.   Stems armed with stout flattened recurved prickles; pedicels villous; fl.-tube often externally pilose when young; sepals ± pubescent on backs. .... 6. *R. californica*
      EE.   Stems armed with straight or ascending weak, slender prickles; pedicels not villous; fl.-tube glabrous; sepals not pubescent.   8. *R. Woodsii*

p. 787.   7. **R. pinetòrum** Heller in Greenhorn Mts., Kern Co., *Twisselmann.*
p. 788.   8. **R. Woòdsii** Lindl. var. **ultramontàna** (Wats.) Jeps. In Kern Co. (Kernville and Mt. Pinos region), *Twisselmann.*
p. 789.   PRÙNUS
    2. **P. subcordàta** Benth. in Monterey Co., *Howitt & Howell.*

p. 795.   38. Cotoneáster Medic.

Shrubs, sometimes arborescent, evergreen or deciduous, not thorny. Lvs. numerous, alternate, short-petioled, simple and entire, stipulate. Fls. white or pink, small but many, solitary or in cymose clusters terminating lateral spurs, appearing after the lvs. are out; fl.-tube adnate to ovary. Sepals 5, small, persistent. Petals 5. Stamens ca. 20. Pistil 1; ovary 2–5-celled; styles 2–5, distinct. Fr. a red or dark pome. Ca. 50 spp. of the Old World. (Latin, *quince-like,* from the lvs. of some spp.)
    1. **C. pannòsa** Franch. Arching evergreen shrub to 3 m. tall; lvs. elliptic- to ovate-oblong, ± glabrous above, white-tomentose beneath, 1.5–4 cm. long; infl. corymbose; petals white, spreading, roundish; calyx tomentose; fr. red, globose-ovoid, 8 mm. in diam.—Escape from cult., in Marin Co., Ventura Co., etc. From China.
    2. **C. Franchétii** Boiss. Fls. pinkish; lvs. yellowish-tomentose beneath, to 3 cm. long.—Occasional escape from cult., as in San Francisco region. Native to China.

                              39. Pyracántha Roem. FIRETHORN

Near to *Cotoneaster,* but with heavy thorns; lvs. usually crenate or serrate; fls. in corymbs; pistil 1 (actually of 5 pistils ventrally connate or coherent along basal half and 5-celled basally, separating at maturity); fr. with 5 nutlets. Ca. half a dozen spp. of Medit. region and Asia. (Greek, *fire* and *thorn,* from red frs. and thorns.)
    1. **P. angustifòlia** (Franch.) Schneid. [*Cotoneaster a.* Franch.] Evergreen shrub to 3 or 4 m. tall; lvs. narrow-oblong, roundish at ends, 2.5–5 cm. long, gray-tomentose beneath; infl. corymbose, few-fld.; calyx tomentose; petals white; fr. orange-yellow, 6–8 mm. in diam. flattish-globose.—Occasional escape from cult. as in Marin Co., *Howell;* native of China.
p. 795.   CROSSOSÒMA
    1. **C. califórnicum** Nutt. 2n = 12 (Raven, Kyhos & Hill, 1965).
p. 798.   ALBÍZIA
    1. **A. distàchya** (Vent.) Macbr. 2n = 26 (Frahm-Leliveld, 1957).
    PROSÒPIS
    Add as reference: Johnston, M. C. The N. Am. mesquites. Prosopis sect. Algarobia. Brittonia 14: 72–90. 1962.
    1. **P. glandulòsa** Torr. var. **Torreyàna** (L. Benson) M. C. Jtn. is used for our common Mesquite, while **P. juliflòra** (Sw.) DC., which name has also been applied to Calif. plants, is restricted to the area s. of the U.S. If our plants are to be considered a distinct sp., apparently they should be called **P. odoràta** Torr. & Frém. The reference to "Grantland" School under var. **velutina** should read "Grantville" School, *Norland.*
    2. **P. velùtina** Woot., which can be separated from **P. glandulosa** by having lfts. less than 5 times as long as broad, is native e. of Calif. and becomes natur. occasionally in the state; San Diego Co., Orange Co., Santa Barbara Co., Mariposa Co.
p. 799.   CÉRCIS
    1. **C. occidentàlis** Torr. ex Gray. 2n = 14 (Taylor, 1967). Found at Onyx, Kern Co., *Twisselmann.*
p. 800.   CÁSSIA
    1. **C. armàta** Wats. 2n = 14 pairs (Raven, Kyhos & Hill, 1965).

114   *Cassia*

3. C. tomentòsa L. f. Shrub 3–4 m. high; twigs and lower surface of lvs.
tomentose; lfts. 6–8 pairs, oblong, 2–4 cm. long, each pair with a gland at base;
fls. deep yellow, 2.5 cm. in diam.; fertile stamens 7; pod 12 cm. long.—Established in Marin Co. and at Santa Barbara; native of Mex., S. Am.

CERCÍDIUM

1. C. flóridum Benth. $2n = 14$ pairs (Raven, Kyhos & Hill, 1965).

p. 802.   PAPILIONOÌDEAE
In Key to Genera, after CC, change D to "Rachis of lf." and after EE, FF,
delete "35. *Pisum*" and insert:

> G. Calyx-lobes leafy; pod many-seeded. . . . . 35. *Pisum*
> GG. Calyx-lobes long-subulate; pod 1–2 seeded. . . . . 36. *Lens*

p. 803.   THERMÓPSIS
3. T. macrophỳlla H. & A. Add:
Var. agnìna J. T. Howell. Plants to 2 m. tall; lfts. ± villous-pubescent on
both sides; lower calyx-lobes deltoid, 3.5–4 mm. long.—Santa Ynez Mts., Santa
Barbara Co.

p. 804.   PICKERÍNGIA
1. P. montàna Nutt. $2n = 14$ pairs (Raven, Kyhos & Hill, 1965).

p. 804.   LUPÌNUS
In Key delete word *fragrantissimus* in line 15 from bottom of page, in the 1959
printing.
In Key, the last word on the page should be *polycarpus,* not *micranthus.*

p. 805.   In Key, under JJ. about two-thirds of way from top of page, change "19. *L.
Moranii*" to "19. *L. guadalupensis.*"

p. 806.   In Key, after BB, C, D, EE insert:

> EEE. Stems and lvs. subglabrous or slightly strigose; corolla yellow, 10
>   mm. long. Se. Shasta Co. . . . . . . 71. *L. Andersonii* var. *Christinae*

Just below the above, "74. *L. latifolius*" should be "76. *L. latifolius,*" in the
1959 printing.

p. 807.   About one-third way down the page "56. *L. Grayii*" should be "58. *L. Grayii.*"
p. 809.   2. L. rùber Heller occurs in Monterey Co., *Howitt & Howell.*
p. 811.   5. Walter Knight (Four Seasons 1(3): 8–9. 1965) thinks that *Lupinus* Mìlo-
Bàkeri C. P. Sm. is a distinct sp. from *L. luteolus* Kell.: (1) *L. M.-B.* not yet in
full bloom on June 27, while *L. l.* is past; (2) *L. M.-B.* to ca. 165 cm. tall, *L. l.*
to 75 cm.; (3) lfts. on *L. M.-B.* oblanceolate, keeled to 45°, on *L. l.* largely
obovate, keeled to 90°; (4) fls. on *L. M.-B.* blue, yellowish in age only, on *L. l.*
yellow throughout; (5) stem on *L. M.-B.* with pith until old and in seed, on
L. l. generally hollow from early. *L. M.-B.* he finds to be a local endemic in
Round Valley at Covelo, Mendocino Co.

p. 812.   12. L. concínnus J. G. Agardh. Dunn, Christian and Dziekanowski after sev-
eral years of work on the *L. concinnus* complex, make the following changes
(Cf. Aliso 6: 45–50. 1966):
L. concínnus Agardh.
L. concínnus ssp. optàtus (C. P. Sm.) Dunn
L. concínnus ssp. Orcúttii (Wats.) Dunn
L. Agardhiànus Heller
L. pállidus Bdg.
L. brévior (Jeps.) Christian & Dunn.
They find *L. pallidus* and *L. Agardhianus* intersterile with the rest of the com-
plex, but *L. pallidus* interfertile with *L. sparsiflorus* Benth. (no. 18 of the
FLORA). L. brévior is an obligate selfer and ranges from Imperial Co. n.
13. L. Stìversii Kell. ascends to 5500 ft. in King's River Canyon.

p. 813.   18. L. sparsiflòrus Benth. was also studied by Dunn, Christian and Dziekanowski who report as follows:
L. sparsiflòrus Benth. is of cismontane S. Calif.

Ssp. **inopinàtus** (C. P. Sm.) Dziekanowski & Dunn is of the San Diego region and adjacent L. Calif.

Ssp. **mohavénsis** Dziekanowski & Dunn occurs in the Mojave Desert and into Ariz. and Sonora. Generally smaller than cismontane plants and in its fls. They give the following Key:

A. Keel glabrous.
   B. Lfts. linear spatulate, mostly subglabrous above; plants sparsely spreading-pilose; fls. bluish-purple. . . . . *L. Agardhianus*
   BB. Lfts. spatulate-oblanceolate to obovate, amply pubescent above; plants abundantly spreading-pilose; fls. pinkish-white to lavender. . . . . *L. concinnus*
AA. Keel ciliate above and/or below the claws.
   B. Fls. off-white to bluish or purplish, 5–7 mm. long or less; plants usually less than 15 cm. tall.
      C. Plants silky to strigose, often decumbent or prostrate; lfts. pubescent on both sides. . . . . *L. pallidus*
      CC. Plants glabrous or sparsely pilose; lfts. glabrous above. . . . . *L. brevior*
   BB. Fls. blue to pink or purple, 7–13 mm. long; plants generally more than 15 cm. tall.
      C. The fls. pink to magenta with a yellow center spot; lfts. obovate to oblanceolate with the tip rounded, fleshy in texture; plants appearing succulent.
L. arizonicus
      CC. The fls. blue or purplish, with a yellowish-white center spot; lfts. linear to filiform, not fleshy; plants not appearing succulent.
         D. Fls. 10–13 mm. long. Cismontane, Ventura to Riverside cos. *L. sparsiflorus*
         DD. Fls. 7–11 mm. long.
            E. Banner oblong-oval, longer than wide. San Diego Co. and n. L. Calif.
L. sparsiflorus inopinatus
            EE. Banner orbicular, emarginate. Mojave Desert to Ariz. ond Son.
L. sparsiflorus mohavensis

(I am very grateful to Dr. David Dunn for making the above information available to me.)

p. 814.   19. *L. Moranii* Dunkle should be changed to **L. guadalupénsis** Greene according to *Dunn.*

        22. **L. nànus** Dougl. in Benth. In the Key, change "Largest lfts. 1.5–5 mm." to "5–7.5 mm." for the 1959 printing.

p. 816.   28. Change name to **L. polycárpus** Greene. [*L. micranthus* Dougl. in Lindl., not Gussone, fide *Dunn.*]

p. 817.   32. **L. séllulus** Kell. var. **ártulus** (Jeps.) Eastw. has a range from Plumas Co. to Modoc Co.

p. 818.   35. **L. Culbertsònii** Greene. has been collected in Mono Co., *Hardham.*

p. 823.   61. **L. arbòreus** Sims. Add as synonym: *L. macrocarpus* H. & A.

p. 824.   62. **L. albifróns** Benth. is apparently on Santa Cruz and Santa Catalina ids. $2n = 24$ pairs (Raven, Kyhos & Hill, 1965).

p. 827.   76. **L. latifòlius** Agardh. Add to synonymy *L. lasiotropis* Greene ex Eastw.

p. 828.   78. **L. polyphýllus** Lindl. ssp. **superbus** (Heller) Munz occurs in the Piute and Greenhorn mts., Kern Co., *Twisselmann.*

p. 829.   82. **L. magníficus** Jones var. **glarécola** Jones, not *glareola.*

p. 830.   CÝTISUS

Change Key to:

A. Fls. white; banner hairy on the back. . . . . 1. *C. proliferus*
AA. Fls. yellow; banner mostly glabrous.
   B. Stems sharply angled, leafless or nearly so; pods hairy along margins only.
2. *C. scoparius*
   BB. Stems obtusely angled or ridged, leafy; pods hairy all over.
      C. Racemes nearly capitate, 3–9-fld., at the ends of short lateral branchlets.
         D. Shrub 10–30 dm. high; lfts. flat, obovate; fls. 10–12 mm. long.
3. *C. monspessulanus*
         DD. Shrub 2–8 dm. high; lfts. revolute, linear-oblong; fls. 12–14 mm. long.
3a. *C. linifolius*
      CC. Racemes ± elongate, 6–many-fld., secund, terminal and lateral; fls. 12–14 mm. long.
         D. Lfts. less than 2 cm. long, usually obovate; petioles to 8 mm. long.
            E. The racemes dense, 2–5 cm. long; lfts. glabrous above, densely silky-villous beneath, often only 3–6 mm. long; calyx-lobes ± ovate, rather abruptly narrowed to an acuminate apex. . . 4. *C. canariensis*
            EE. The racemes lax, 5–10 cm. long; lfts. silky-pubescent above and be-

neath, 8–18 mm. long; calyx-lobes lanceolate, gradually narrowed to
  the acuminate tip. .... 4a. *C.* × *racemosus*
DD. Lfts. 1.5–5 cm. long, oblong-obovate; petioles often 12 or more mm.
  long; fls. 13–15 mm. long. .... 5. *C. stenopetalus*

2. **C. scopàrius** (L.) Link. Specimens of a shrub spreading on a road bank
ca. 3 miles down Page Mill road from intersection with Moody road, 4 mi. s. of
Palo Alto, Santa Clara Co., with sharply angled stems and solitary yellow fls.
with deep red tips to the wings, has been distributed as **C.** × **Dallimorei** Rolfe.
[*C. multiflorus* × *C. scoparius* var. *Andreanus.*] In some ways it more closely
resembles descriptions and plates of *C. scoparius* var. *Andreanus* (Puissant), a
shrub originating apparently in Normandy.
3. **C. monspessulànus** L. Abundant in San Luis Obispo Co.; near Placerville,
Eldorado Co., *Thorne*; Santa Catalina Id., *Wolf.*
3a. **C. linifòlius** (L.) Lam. [*Genista l.* L.] Low shrub 2–8 dm. high, with
erect, appressed-silky branches; lfts. linear or linear-lanceolate, revolute at margin, nearly glabrous and shining above, silvery-pubescent beneath, 12–25 mm.
long; fls. 12–14 mm. long; pod torulose.—Adventive in Santa Barbara Co. and
on Santa Catalina Id., *Fuller.* From Medit. region.
4. **C. canariénsis** (L.) Kuntze. Amend to: lfts. glabrous above, densely silky-
villous beneath, often only 3–6 mm. long; calyx-lobes lance-ovate, abruptly narrowed to the acuminate tip.
4a. **C.** × **racemòsus** Nichol. Near to *C. canariensis* in appearance, but with
longer more lax racemes; lfts. silky-pubescent above and beneath, largely 8–18
mm. long; calyx-lobes lanceolate, gradually attenuate.—Monterey and Santa
Clara cos., *Fuller.* Probably of garden origin.
5. *C. maderénsis* Masf. Change to **C. stenopétalus** (Webb) Christ. and amend
description to: lfts. to 3.5 cm. long; petioles to 15 mm. long; racemes to 10 cm.
long.—Found also at Pacific Grove, Monterey Co., *Fuller.* Native of Canary Ids.

p. 831. MEDICÁGO
Insert after generic description: Heyn, C. C. The annual spp. of Medicago.
Scripta Hierosolymitana 12: 1–154. 1963.
  2. **M. lupulìna** L. $2n = 16$ (Mulligan, 1957).
  4. Change *M. hispida* Gaertn. to **M. polymórpha** L. and var. *confìnis* (Koch)
Burnat to **M. p.** var. **brevispìna** (Benth.) Heyn.

p. 832. MELILÒTUS. The noun is feminine, not masculine as in the FLORA.
  2. **M. índica** (L.) All. $2n = 8$ pairs (Raven, Kyhos & Hill, 1965).
  TRIFÒLIUM
In Key, after A, B, C, and D, insert:

D′. Fls. few in a head, becoming reflexed and surrounded by later sterile fls.
  forming a bur. .... 1a. *T. subterraneum*
D′D′. Fls. more numerous and not forming a bur.
E. "Stipules lance-oblong," etc. as in FLORA.

p. 833. In Key, line 12 from bottom of page, *T. oreganum* should be no. 16, not 6.
p. 834. In Key after CC. "Invol. flat, rotate," D, EE, insert:

F. Invol. 12–15 mm. broad; calyx not inflated and vesiculose in
  fr. Native. .... 39. *T. Wormskjoldii*
FF. Invol. 5–6 cm. broad; calyx conspicuously inflated and vesiculose in fr. Introd. .... 39a. *T. fragiferum*

In Key, after CC, DD, EE, FF insert:

G. Calyx teeth triangular, abruptly spine-pointed; fls. pur-
  plish; corolla 4 mm. long. ...... 44a. *T. glomeratum*
GG. Calyx teeth not abruptly spine-pointed, dilated.
H. Corolla 12–15 mm. long; plants erect to ± de-
  cumbent. Widely distributed. 43. *T. tridentatum*
HH. Corolla 8–10 mm. long; plants subprostrate. Mon-
  terey Peninsula. .... 42. *T. polyodon*
GGG. Calyx teeth not dilated, etc. replacing GG. in the
  FLORA.

1a. **T. subterràneum** L. Hairy annual; prostrate; lfts. obovate, apically notched, to 1 cm. long; fertile fls. ca. 2–5 in a head without an invol., 8–12 mm. long, cream-yellow, conspicuously reflexed after anthesis and then surrounded by sterile fls. forming a bur-like cluster.—Introd. in Humboldt, Sonoma and Santa Cruz cos., *Howell*; from Eu.

2. **T. procúmbens** L. In Monterey Co., *Howitt & Howell. n =* 7 (Larsen, 1955).

4. **T. bìfidum** Gray. As far s. as Monterey Co., *Howitt & Howell.* 2n = 16 (Mosquin & Gillett, 1965).

p. 835.
6. **T. Pálmeri** Wats. 2n = 16 (Gillett & Mosquin, 1967).

7. **T. ciliolàtum** Benth. *n* = 8 (Gillett & Mosquin); 2n = 16 (Mosquin & Gillett, 1965).

8. **T. Brèweri** Wats. 2n = 16 (Mosquin & Gillett, 1965); *n* = 8 (G. & M., 1967).

11. **T. Beckwíthii** Brew. ex Wats. 2n = ca. 48 (Gillett & Mosquin, 1967).

p. 836.
14. **T. prodúctum** Greene. *n* = 8 (Gillett & Mosquin, 1967).

15. **T. eriocéphalum** Nutt. *n* = 8 (Gillett & Mosquin, 1967).

17. **T. lóngipes** Nutt. *n* = 16, 24 (Mosquin & Gillett, 1965); *n* = 8, 16, 24 (Gillett & Mosquin, 1967).

p. 837.
18. **T. macrocéphalum** (Pursh) Poir. *n* = 16, ca. 84 (Gillett & Mosquin, 1967).

19. **T. Andersònii** Gray. *n* = 8 (Gillett & Mosquin, 1967).

20. **T. monoénse** Greene. 2n = 16 (Gillett & Mosquin, 1967).

25. **T. arvénse** L. Reported from Monterey Peninsula, *Howitt & Howell.*

26. **T. incarnàtum** L. Reported from Monterey Co., *Howitt & Howell* and from several cos. from Fresno Co. and Monterey Co. north, *Weiler.*

p. 838.
27. **T. hírtum** All. In the Santa Ynez Mts., Santa Barbara Co., *Raven*; Santa Lucia Mts., Monterey Co., *Howitt & Howell*; Mariposa Co., *Howell*; Fresno and Madera cos., *Weiler*; Kern Co., *Twisselmann.*

28. **T. Macràei** H. & A. 2n = 16 (Gillett & Mosquin, 1967).

30. **T. dichótomum** H. & A. In San Luis Obispo Co., *Hardham.*

33. **T. cyathíferum** Lindl. *n* = 8 (Gillett & Mosquin, 1967).

p. 839.
35. **T. Gràyii** Loja. At Atascadero, San Luis Obispo Co., *Eastwood.*

36. **T. mìcrodon** H. & A. 2n = 16 (Mosquin & Gillett, 1965).

37. **T. microcéphalum** Pursh. *n* = 8 (Gillett & Mosquin, 1967).

38. **T. monánthum** Gray. 2n = 16 (Mosquin & Gillett, 1965; G. & M. 1967).

p. 840.
39. **T. Wormskíoldii** Lehm. *n* = 16 (Mosquin & Gillett, 1965; G. & M. 1967).

39a. **T. fragíferum** L. Perennial with creeping, rooting stems; lfts. cuneate-obovate, 6–12 mm. long; fls. pink to white, in dense globose heads ca. 12 mm. in diam., on very long peduncles; calyx inflated and vesiculose in fr.—Found at King City, Monterey Co., *Howell*; Davis, Yolo Co., *Skaggs*; North Highland, Sacramento Co., *Fuller*; from Medit. region.

44. should be **T. variegàtum** Nutt. in T. & G.

p. 841.
44a. **T. glomeràtum** L. Glabrous annual; lfts. 5–8 mm. long, obovate-cuneate, sharply serrate; stipules usually ovate with long points; heads sessile, globular; fls. purplish; calyx strongly ribbed, whitish, the teeth triangular, spinescent; corolla 4 mm. long.—Natur. in Yuba Co., *Crampton*; from Eu.

45. **T. tridentàtum** Lindl. 2n = 16 (Mosquin & Gillett, 1965).

p. 842.
49. **T. depauperàtum** Desv. 2n = 16 (Mosquin & Gillett, 1965). Reported from Temblor Range, Kern Co., *Twisselmann* and from Madera and Fresno cos., *Weiler.*

LOTUS

In 1959 printing of the FLORA, in the Key, under A, BB, CC, D, line F belongs after EE, not before it.

p. 845.
10. **L. grandiflòrus** (Benth.) Greene. 2n = 7 pairs (Raven, Kyhos & Hill, 1965); *n* = 7 (Grant & Sidhu,, 1967).

11. **L. rígidus** (Benth.) Greene. 2n = 7 pairs (Raven, Kyhos & Hill, 1965).

p. 846.
13. **L. strigòsus** (Nutt.) Greene. 2n = 7 pairs (Raven, Kyhos & Hill, 1965).

15. **L. salsginòsus** Greene. $2n = 7$ pairs (Raven, Kyhos & Hill, 1965); $n = 7$ (Grant & Sidhu, 1967). The sp. reported as in the San Emigdio Range, Kern Co., *Twisselmann*.

Var. **brevivexíllus** Ottley. $2n = 7$ pairs (Raven, Kyhos & Hill, 1965). Has been found in the El Paso Range, Kern Co., *Twisselmann*.

16. **L. denticulàtus** (E. Drew) Greene. $n = 6$ (Grant & Sidhu, 1967).

p. 847.   17. **L. subpinnàtus** Lag. $n = 6$ (Grant & Sidhu, 1967).

18. **L. humistràtus** Greene. $n = 6$ (Grant & Sidhu, 1967).

21. **L. Purshiànus** (Benth.) Clem & Clem. $n = 7$ (Grant & Sidhu, 1967).

p. 848.   24. **L. nevadénsis** Greene. $n = 7$ (Grant & Sidhu, 1967).

25. **L. Douglásii** Greene. $2n = 14$ (Grant, 1965).

27. **L. argophÿllus** (Gray) Greene. $2n = 7$ pairs (Raven, Kyhos & Hill, 1965); $n = 7$ (Grant & Sidhu, 1967).

Ssp. **adsúrgens** (Dunkle) Raven. [*L. a.* var. *adsurgens* Dunkle.] A beautiful silvery suffrutescent plant with densely crowded ascending lvs. San Clemente Id.

Ssp. **ornithòpus** (Greene) Raven. [*Hosackia o.* Greene.] $2n = 7$ pairs (Raven, Kyhos & Hill, 1965).

p. 849.   29. **L. hamàtus** Greene. Occurs in San Luis Obispo Co., *Hardham*.

30. **L. Benthàmii** Greene. [*L. cytisoides* Benth., not *cystoides*.] $2n = 7$ pairs (Raven, Kyhos & Hill, 1965).

31. **L. scopàrius** (Nutt. in T. & G.) Ottley. $n = 7$ (Grant & Sidhu, 1967).

Var. **dendroìdeus** (Greene) Ottley. $n = 7$ (Grant & Sidhu, 1967). Add:

Ssp. **Tráskiae** (Eastw. ex Abrams) Raven. [*L. T.* Eastw. ex Abrams.] Pods mostly 3–5 cm. long and 4–8-seeded.—San Clemente Id.

p. 850.   34. **L. corniculàtus** L. $n = 12$ (Grant & Sidhu, 1967).

35. **L. uliginòsus** Schk. Add to synonymy *L. trifoliolatus* Eastw. *L. pedunculatus* auth., not Cav.

PSORÀLEA

In Key, delete "6. *P. rigida*" and on next line insert:

Fls. racemose; calyx short-pubescent; plant 3–6 dm. high. . . . . 6. *P. rigida*
Fls. subcapitate or subumbellate; calyx conspicuously white-hairy; plant to 20 dm. high. Introd. . . . . 6a. *P. bituminosa*

p. 851.   1. **P. califórnica** Wats. $2n = 11$ pairs (Raven, Kyhos & Hill, 1965).
p. 851.   3. **P. lanceolàta** ssp. **scabra** (Nutt.) Piper. $2n = 11$ pairs (Raven, Kyhos and Hill, 1965).—At 6500 ft., 5.5 mi. w. of state line, along Highway 31, Mono Co., *Reveal*.

5. **P. physòdes** Dougl. $n = 11$ (Raven, Kyhos & Hill, 1965).

6a. **P. bituminòsa** L. Half shrub to 2 m. tall; lvs. 3-foliolate; lfts. lanceolate, 2–5 cm. long; stipules lance-subulate, 5–7 mm. long; fls. lilac with an almost white keel and banner somewhat red in age.—Millard Canyon, San Gabriel Mts., Los Angeles Co., *Griesel*. Possibly established here and at Pleasanton, Alameda Co., after being tested as a fire-resistant plant by forest personnel, *Fuller*. From Old World.

7. **P. macrostàchya** DC. $2n = 11$ pairs (Raven, Kyhos & Hill, 1965).

p. 853.   DÀLEA

In Key, AA, B, C and CC, change "lfts." to "lvs."

3. **D. Párryi** T. & G. $2n = 10$ pairs (Raven, Kyhos & Hill, 1965).

5. **D. Schóttii** var. **puberula** (Parish) Munz. $n = 10$ (Turner, 1963); $2n = 10$ pairs (Raven, Kyhos & Hill, 1965).

6. **D. polyadènia** Torr. ex Wats. $2n = 10$ pairs (Raven, Kyhos & Hill, 1965).

p. 854.   PETALOSTEMON, not *Petalostemum* in 1959 printing. Cf. Taxon 8: 293. 1959.
p. 855.   SESBANIA. Authority for genus is Adans., corr. Scop.
p. 856.   ASTRÁGALUS

Before the Key, insert Barneby, R. C. Atlas of N. Am. Astragalus 2 vols., 1188 pages, 1964.

In Key, change *A. Hornii* from 81 to no. 82.

p. 864.   In Key, after S at top of page, delete "84. *A. iodanthus*" and insert:

T. Stems decumbent, not zigzag; lfts. 5–15 mm.
long; petals ochroleucous with purple keel-tip;
pods 2–4 cm. long. . . . . 84. *A. iodanthus*
TT. Stems prostrate, abruptly zigzag; lfts. 5–9 mm.
long; petals red-violet; pods 2 cm. long.
84a. *A. pseudiodanthus*

1. **A. Gambeliànus** Sheld. Reported from Kern Co., *Twisselmann.*

2. **A. didymocárpus** H. & A. $2n = 12$ pairs (Raven, Kyhos & Hill, 1965).

p. 865.   Var. **obispénsis** (Rydb.) Jeps. $2n = 13$ pairs (Raven, Kyhos & Hill, 1965).

3. **A. Brèweri** Gray. $n =$ ca. 12 (Raven, Kyhos & Hill, 1965).

p. 866.   9. **A. Nuttalliànus** DC. var. **imperféctus**, not no. 3 as in 1959 printing.

p. 867.   12. **A. calycòsus** Torr. $2n = 22$ (Ledingham & Fahselt, 1964).

p. 868.   17. **A. inyoénsis** Sheld. $2n = 22$ (Ledingham & Fahselt, 1964).

p. 870.   25. **A. Serènoi** (Kuntze) Sheld. $2n = 24$? (Ledingham & Fahselt, 1964).

p. 871.   29. **A. dasyglóttis** Fisch. ex DC., not *A. agrestis* Dougl. Cf. Barneby, Leaflets
W. Bot. 9: 51. 1959.

p. 873.   40. **A. coccíneus** Bdg. $2n = 22$ (Ledingham & Fahselt, 1964).

41. **A. funèreus** Jones [*Xylophacos f.* Rydb.] was omitted from the FLORA.
Cespitose perennial with stems to ca. 1 dm. long, the plant densely villous with
tangled hairs; lfts. 13–17, oval to obovate, obtuse, 5–8 mm. long, silky- or
cottony-tomentose with tangled hairs; racemes subcapitate, 3–10-fld.; calyx-
tube 7–8 mm. long, black-hairy, the subulate teeth ca. 3 mm. long; corolla rose-
purple, the keel 21–26 mm. long, the wing-petals equaling or shorter; pod 2.5–
4 cm. long, densely hairy.—At 4000–5000 ft., Death Valley region. March–Apr.

p. 873.   42. **A. Púrshii** Dougl. In 1964 Barneby reduced var. *longilobus* Jones to
synonymy under typical **A. Purshii** and included the concept named *longilobus*
in the FLORA in var. **tínctus** Jones.

p. 874.   Var. **léctulus** Jones. $2n = 22$ (Ledingham & Fahselt, 1964).

46. **A. Johánnis-Howéllii** Barneby $2n = 22$ (Ledingham & Fahselt, 1964).

p. 875.   49. **A. Ravènii** (Barneby. $2n = 24$ (Ledingham & Fahselt, 1964); $2n = 22$
(Raven, Kyhos & Hill, 1965).

p. 877.   58. **A. miguelénsis** Greene. $2n = 22$ (Ledingham & Fahselt, 1964).

p. 878.   62. **A. asymmétricus** Sheld. Occurs in the Temblor Range, Kern Co., *Twisselmann.*

p. 879.   65, 66, 69. Barneby called in 1964 sp. 66 of the FLORA **A. trichópodus** (Nutt.)
Gray, with *A. capíllipes* Jones as a synonym. Sp. 65 of the FLORA became **A.
trichópodus** var. **lónchus** (Jones) Barneby with *Phaca canescens* Nutt. and *P.
encenadae* Rydb. as synonyms. $2n = 11$ pairs (Raven, Kyhos & Hill, 1965).
Sp. 67 was called **A. trichópodus** var. **phóxus** (Jones) Barneby. [*A. Antiselli*
var. *phoxus* Jones; *A. Antiselli* Gray; *Homalobus Antiselli* Rydb.; *A. trichopodus*
var. *A.* Jeps.; *A. Hasseanthus* Sheld., *A. gaviotus* Elmer; and *A. Antiselli* var.
gaviotus Munz.]

p. 880.   71. **A. Vaseyi** Wats. changed by Barneby (1964) to **A. Pálmeri** Gray. [*A.
Vaseyi* Wats.; *A. metanus* Jones; *A. Vaseyi* var. *Johnstonii* Munz & McBurn.]

p. 881.   74. **A. oóphorus** Wats. $2n = 24$ (Ledingham & Fahselt, 1964).

p. 883.   83. *A. lentiginosus* var. **carinatus** Jones reduced to synonymy under typical
A. lentiginòsus Dougl. by Barneby (1964).

p. 884.   83. **A. lentiginòsus** var. **Fremóntii** (Gray) Wats. $2n = 22$ (Ledingham &
Fahselt, 1964).

p. 884.   **A. lentiginòsus** var. **coachéllae** Barneby in Shreve & Wiggins used for our
material referred in the FLORA to var. *Coulteri.*

84a. **A. pseudiodánthus** Barneby. Near to *A. iodanthus* Wats., but with prostrate, abruptly zigzag stems; villous-pubescent; lfts. 5–9 mm. long; fls. red-
violet, 8–9 mm. long; pods 2 cm. long.—Old beach, n. side of Mono Lake,
Mono Co., *Reveal*; w. Nev. June.

p. 886.   92. **A. Whítneyi** Gray. $2n = 22$ (Ledingham & Fahselt, 1964).

p. 888.   ORNITHÒPUS

2. **O. pinnàtus** (Mill.) Druce. Differs from *O. roseus* by having lvs. glabrous;
fls. yellow; pods strongly bent. Taken at same station as *O. roseus.* Native of Eu.

ALHÀGI

1. **A. camelòrum** Fisch. $n = 8$ (Baquar et al., 1965).—Reported from Contra Costa Co. and Afton Canyon, Mojave Desert, San Bernardino Co., *Fuller*.

p. 889.   LÁTHYRUS

In Key, AA, B, C, D, E, delete "2. *L. sphericus*" at end of line and add:

F. Stems winged; fls. 10–13 mm. long.	2a. *L. Cicera*
FF. Stems angled, not winged; fls. 10 mm. long. . . .	2. *L. sphericus*

p. 890.   2a. **L. Cicèra** L. Annual, 2–6 dm. high, glabrous; stems winged; lfts. 2, lanceolate to linear; fls. reddish, 10–13 mm. long, solitary; pods 3–4 cm. long, 8–10 mm. wide.—Reported from San Mateo Co., *Howell*, and Amador Co., *Fuller*. From Eurasia.

p. 891.   4. **L. tingitànus** L. Lfts. 2, not 4.

p. 892.   11. **L. vestìtus** Nutt. ex T. & G. and ssp. **Bolánderi** (Wats.) C. L. Hitchc. are both in Monterey Co., *Howitt & Howell*.

13. **L. laetiflòrus** Greene. $2n = 7$ pairs (Raven, Kyhos & Hill, 1965).—Found in the San Emigdio Range, Kern Co., *Twisselmann*.

p. 896.   VÍCIA

8. **V. benghalénsis** L. $2n = 12$ (Srivastaoa, 1963).—Reported from Monterey Co., *Howitt & Howell*.

11. **V. dasycárpa** Ten.—Reported from Catalina Id., *Thorne*; Monterey Co., *Howitt & Howell*.

16. **V. angustifòlia** Reichard (Not *angusifolia* as in 1959 printing of the FLORA). $2n = 6$ pairs (Raven, Kyhos & Hill, 1965).

p. 897.   36. **Léns** Moench. LENTIL

Like *Pisum*, but the fls. small, inconspicuous, whitish; calyx-lobes very narrow; seeds 1–2. Eurasia.

1. **L. culinàris** Medic. [*Ervum Lens* L.] Annual, to 4 dm. tall; lfts. 4–7 pairs; fls. 1–3, to ca. 6 mm. long; pod to 2 cm. long, almost as broad.—Occasional escape; reported from Ventura and San Francisco cos.

PLÁTANUS

1. **P. racemòsa** Nutt. $2n = 21$ pairs (Raven, Kyhos & Hill, 1965).

p. 898.   KRAMÈRIA

1. **K. Gràyii** Rose & Painter. $n = 6$ (Turner, 1959).

p. 900.   ÁLNUS

3. **A. oregòna** Nutt.—Reported from as far s. as Monterey Co., *Howitt & Howell*.

p. 901.   1. **Chrysolèpsis** Hjelmquist. CHINQUAPIN

Trees or shrubs, evergreen, the buds with imbricated scales. Lvs. simple. Catkins staminate or androgynous; fls. 3–7 (–11), fasciculate, staminate always bracteolate; calyx 5–6-parted; stamens several. Pistillate fls. at base of staminate, 3 in a cupule of 7 free valves (5 outer and 2 inner, the latter separating the 3 trigonous fruits from one another); styles 3. Fr. maturing in the second season, the spiny invol. inclosing the nuts, these angled. (Greek, *chrysos*, gold, and *lepis*, scale). Two spp. of w. N. Am. (Hjelmquist, Bot. Notiser, Suppl. 2: 117. 1948; 113: 377. 1960).

1. **C. chrysophýlla** (Dougl. ex Hook.) Hjelmquist. [*Castanopsis c.* A. DC. *Castanea c.* Dougl. ex Hook.] See description in the FLORA under *Castanopsis*.—Extends s. to Marin Co., possibly Santa Cruz Mts.

Var. **mìnor** (Benth.) Munz, comb. nov. [*Castanea chrysophylla* var. *minor* Benth., Pl. Hartweg., 337. 1857. *Castanopsis c.* var. *m.* A. DC.]

p. 902.   2. **C. sempervìrens** (Kell.) Hjelmquist. [*Castanopsis s.* Dudl. *Castanea s.* Kell.] For description see *Castanopsis* in the FLORA.

LITHOCARPUS

p. 904.
1. **L. densiflorus** (H. & A.) Rehd. at De Sabla, Butte Co., *Vesta Holt.*

QUÉRCUS

3. **Q. agrifòlia** Neé. $2n = 12$ pairs (Raven, Kyhos & Hill, 1965). Var. **frutéscens** Engelm., not Jeps. as in 1959 printing.

p. 905.
6. **Q. Douglásii** H. & A. A supposed hybrid with *Q. lobata* Neé has been described as **Q. × jolonensis** Sarg., from Monterey Co.

9. **Q. dumòsa** Nutt. A hybrid supposedly with *Q. lobata* Neé is **Q. × Townei** Palmer, once described from near Pasadena.

p. 907.
16. **Q. Dúnnii** Kell. seems to have priority as a sp. name over *Q. Palmeri* Engelm.

p. 909.
JÙGLANS

1. **J. califórnica** Wats. is in Monterey Co., *Howitt & Howell,* where it grows in the Santa Lucia Mts.

p. 910.
PÓPULUS

2. **P. trichocárpa** T. & G. is sometimes treated as a ssp.; *P. balsamifera* L. ssp. *t.* Brayshaw. (Cf. Brayshaw, Can. Field-Naturalist 79: 95. 1965).

P. acuminàta Rydb. is reported by *Twisselmann* from the upper Kern R. and by *DeDecker* from Lone Pine Creek. Lvs. much longer than wide, not toothed near apex. A sp. from e. of Calif. in Rocky Mt. region. Sometimes considered a hybrid.

p. 912.
SÀLIX

In Key, line 9 from top of page, change HH to:

> HH. Shrub to ca. 1 m. high, with gray-tomentose twigs; lvs. obovate to elliptic.
> I. Lvs. mostly 2–3 cm. long; fils. mostly free; style 0.5–0.8 mm. long. E. slope of Sierra Nevada.
> 29a. *S. brachycarpa*
> II. Lvs. 1.5–8 cm. long; fils. ± united; style ca. 1 mm. long. Del Norte Co. ... 29. *S. delnortensis*

In Key, after AA, B, CC, D, EE, F, GG, insert:

> H. Margins of lf.-blades and petioles near the apex with conspicuous yellowish glands; branchlets and upper surface of lvs. shiny. .... 1. *S. lasiandra*
> HH. Margins of lf.-blades and petioles not or not conspicuously glandular; branchlets and upper surface of lvs. not shiny. .... 4. *S. laevigata*

In Key, after AA, BB, C, insert:

> C'. Plants with "weeping" habit, having long pendulous branches; lvs. largely 10–15 cm. long, very long-acuminate. Escape from cult. .. 3. *S. babylonica*
> C'C'. Plants not conspicuous in the pendulous branches. Native.
> D. Stamens 4–6; etc. as in the FLORA.

3. **S. Goòddingii** Ball. $2n = 19$ pairs (Raven, Kyhos & Hill, 1965).

p. 193.
3a. **S. babylónica** L. WEEPING WILLOW. Broad-headed large tree with long flexible hanging branches; lvs. 8–15 cm. long, long-acuminate, finely serrulate; stipules rarely developed.—Escape from cult., as at Santa Barbara, *Pollard.* Native of Cuba.

p. 914.
7. **S. melanópsis** Nutt. is referred to *S. exigua* ssp. *m.* Cronq. in vol. 2 of Vasc. Pls. Pac. N. W. 1964. *Twisselmann* reports from along Kern R. above Lake Isabella and from Tehachapi Mts.

9. **S. lùtea** Nutt. is made a synonym of *S. rigida* Muhl. by Cronquist. Var. **Watsònii** (Bebb) Jeps. on Kern Plateau, *Twisselmann.*

p. 915.
12. **S. pseudocordàta** Anderss. is referred to *S. myrtillifolia* Anderss. by Cronquist.

13. **S. lasiólepis** Benth. $2n = 38$ pairs (Raven, Kyhos & Hill, 1965).

p. 916.
20. **S. anglòrum** Cham. var. **antiplásta** C. K. Schneid. is referred to *S. arctica* Pall. by Cronquist.

22. **S. planifòlia** Pursh var. **mònica** (Bebb) C. K. Schneid. is referred to *S. phyllicifolia* var. *monica* Jeps.

p. 918. 29a. **S. brachycárpa** Nutt. Erect shrub 2–10 dm. tall; young twigs dark or reddish under the villous tomentum; lvs. entire, obovate to elliptic, hairy when young, mostly 2–3 cm. long; ament scales mostly brown; stamens 2; caps. hairy, 3–5 mm. long.—Convict Creek, Mono Co. at 9900–10,600 ft., *Major and Bamberg*; Ore. to Alaska, Rocky Mts.; Quebec.

31. **S. Geyeriàna** Anderss. var. **argéntea** C. K. Schneid. found at Pine Flat, Kern Co., *Twisselmann*.

ÚLMUS

Change Key to Species to:

A. Lvs. doubly serrate, unequal at base.
    B. Lvs. with scattered pubescence, scabrous above; branchlets pubescent until the second year. . . . . 1. *U. procera*
    BB. Lvs. with axillary tufts beneath, smooth above; branchlets subglabrous.
                                                    2. *U. carpinifolia*
AA. Lvs. usually simply serrate; subequal at base.
    B. Branchlets soon glabrous; fls. in spring before the lvs.; samara ca. 12 mm. long.
                                                    3. *U. pumila*
    BB. Branchlets pubescent; fls. in late summer; samara ca. 8 mm. long. 4. *U. parvifolia*

p. 919. 3. **U. pùmila** L. Siberian Elm. Small tree; branchlets soon glabrous; lvs. elliptic to oblong-lanceolate, 2–3.5 cm. long, short-acuminate; fls. in the spring. —Cult. in interior and desert areas; native of Siberia.

4. **U. parvifòlia** Jacq. [*U. chinensis* Pers.] Chinese Elm. Partially evergreen in mild climate; branchlets pubescent; lvs. elliptic to ovate, 2–3.5 cm. long, acute; fls. in late summer.—Seeding itself as at Pasadena, *Howell*, Santa Barbara, *Pollard*; native of e. Asia.

CÉLTIS

1. **C. reticulàta** Torr. is probably the better name for *C. Douglasii* Planch.

MORÀCEAE

In Key to Genera, add a third line:

Plant a tree; lvs. lobed, alternate. . . . . 3. *Morus*

p. 920. HÙMULUS

1. **H. Lùpulus** L. Hops. $2n = 20$ (Jacobsen, 1957).

3. Mòrus L. Mulberry

Trees with milky juice, alternate lobed lvs.; monoecious or dioecious; fls. in small cylindrical catkin-like spikes, the ♂ soon falling, the ♀ ripening into a blackberry-like juicy cluster; perianth 4-parted; stamens 4; each ovary becoming a drupelet inclosed in the enlarged fleshy perianth. Ca. a dozen spp. (*Morus*, the classical name.)

1. **M. álba** L. White Mulberry. Tree to 15 m.; lvs. broad-ovate, the blade 5–15 cm. long, largely scallop-toothed, often irregularly lobed; fr. 2–5 cm. long, whitish to purple, sweet.—Kern R., near Stockdale Country Club, Kern Co., *Twisselmann*. Natur. from China.

Fìcus carìca L., the Common Fig, sometimes escapes, as on Catalina Id., *Thorne*.

URTICÀCEAE

In Key to Genera, delete "3. *Parietaria*" from end of third line and add:

Fls. in axillary glomerate clusters. . . . . 3. *Parietaria*
Fls. solitary. . . . . 4. *Helxine*

ÚRTICA

1. **U. holoserícea** Nutt. Hitchcock (Vasc. Pl. Pac. N.W. 2: 91. 1964) uses *U. dioica* L. ssp. *gracilis* vars. *holosericea, Lyallii* and *californica*.

p. 921.   HESPEROCNIDE

1. **H. tenélla** Torr. reported from Temblor Range and Greenhorn Range, Kern Co., *Twisselmann.*

PARIETARIA

3. **P. pensylvánica** Muhl. $n = 8$ (E. B. Smith, 1963).

4. Helxìne Req. BABY'S-TEARS

Delicate creeping herb; lvs. alternate; monoecious; fls. minute, solitary in axils; ♂ fls. with 4-parted calyx and 4 stamens; ♀ calyx tubular, contracted at mouth; ♂ fls. with a 3-lvd. invol., ♀ with a 3-lobed invol.; ak. ovoid, included in the invol. One sp., from Corsica, Sardinia.

1. **H. Soleiròlii** Req. Lvs. mostly less than 6 mm. long, unequal-sided.—Natur. at Cambria, San Luis Obispo Co., *Hardham,* and at other stations from Lake Co. to Santa Barbara Co., *Howell.*

p. 922.   AMMÁNNIA

1. **A. coccínea** Rottb. Reported from Marin Co., *Howell.*

p. 923.   PÉPLIS

1. **P. Pórtula** L. [*Lythrum P.* (L.) D. A. Webb.]

LYTHRUM

In Key to Species, under "Fls. sessile or nearly so," insert:

Petals 1.5–2 mm. long; plant annual. . . . . 1. *L. Hyssopifolia*
Petals 7–10 mm. long; plant perennial. . . . . 1a. *L. Salicaria*

1a. **L. Salicària** L. PURPLE LOOSESTRIFE. Stout erect perennial 6–12 dm. tall; lvs. opposite or whorled, sessile, ± lanceolate, 3–10 cm. long; spikes 1–4 dm. long; petals red-purple, 7–10 mm. long.—Natur. in e. U.S. and adventive 0.5 mi. e. of Grass V., Nevada Co., *Fuller* and 2.5 mi. s. of Oroville, Butte Co., *Heinrichs.* Native of Eu.

2. **L. tribracteàtum** Salzm. ex Ten. Reported from Lake Co., *Fuller.*

ONAGRÀCEAE

In Key at bottom of page, change to

Sepals persistent. . . . . 1. *Ludwigia*
Sepals deciduous after anthesis.
  Fls. 4–merous normally, etc. as in the FLORA.

pp. 924–925.   Combine *Jussiaea* and *Ludwigia* as follows:

1. Ludwígia L.

Our spp. herbaceous, mostly of wet places, sometimes floating in open water, sometimes with basal vegetative shoots creeping and rooting at the nodes. Underwater parts often swollen and spongy. Lvs. alternate or opposite, rarely whorled, mostly simple, membranaceous or rarely coriaceous. Stipules present, at least in upper part of plant. Fls. yellow or white, solitary and axillary, or in terminal spikes or heads. Fl.-tube not prolonged beyond the ovary, usually with 2 bracteoles at the base of the ovary or summit of the pedicel. Fls. diurnal, regular, 3–7-merous, but mostly 4-merous. Sepals persistent after anthesis. Petals 0–7, caducous. Stamens in 1 or 2 series, each series usually as many as the sepals; anthers usually versatile, basifixed in very small fls. Ovary with as many locules as sepals; style simple, ± produced above the disc; stigma capitate or hemispheric, often slightly lobed. Ovary cylindrical to obconic, many-ovuled, the ovules pluriseriate to uniseriate in each locule. Pluriseriate seeds naked and with evident raphe, the uniseriate surrounded by an endocarp. Caps. dehiscing by a terminal pore or by flaps separating from the valvelike top or more irregularly.

A.   Stamens in 2 series, mostly 8 or 10 in number; petals 10–20 mm. long.
  B.   Flowering stems usually floating or creeping; lvs. oblong, 1–10 cm. long; bracteoles
      at base of ovary deltoid; caps. mostly 2–3 mm. thick. Well distributed.

1. *L. peploides*

BB. Flowering stems usually erect; lvs. ± lanceolate, mostly 5–10 cm. long; bracteoles
   lanceolate; caps. 3–4 mm. thick. Local. . . . .   2. *L. uruguayensis*
AA. Stamens in 1 series, 4–5 in number; petals none or small and quickly shed.
   B. Ovary with 4 evident longitudinal green bands; basal bracteoles from not evident
       to ca. 1 mm. long; petals none. . . . .   3. *L. palustris*
   BB. Ovary lacking green bands; bracteoles above the base and 1–5 mm. long; petals
       present, but easily shed. . . . .   4. *L. repens*

p. 925.   **1. L. peploìdes** (HBK) Raven. [*Jussiaea p.* HBK. *J. repens* var. *p.* Griseb.
J. r. var. *californica* Wats. *J. c.* Jeps.] Description as in the FLORA.
      Ssp. **montevidénsis** (Spreng.) Raven. [*J. m.* Spreng.] In Eldorado Co., *Fuller.*
      2. L. uruguayénsis (Camb.) Hara. [*Jussiaea u.* Camb. in St. Hil. *J. grandi-
flora* Michx. *J. Michauxiana* Fern.] Description as on p. 925.
      3. L. palústris (L.) Ell. [*Isnardia p.* Ell. *L. p.* var. *americana* Fern. & Gris-
com.] Description as for var. *americana* on p. 925.
      Var. **pacífica** Fern. & Griscom, as on p. 925.
p. 926.   **4. L. rèpens** Forster var. **stipitàta** (Fern. & Griscom) Munz. [*L. natans* Ell.
var. *s.* Fern. & Griscom.] Use description on p. 926.

ZAUSCHNÈRIA

In Key, change Z. *californica* to Z. *c. mexicana* and Z. *c. angustifolia* to
Z. *californica.*
      3. Z. califórnica Presl. [*Z. c.* ssp. *angustifolia* Keck.] Amend description to:
Suffrutescent at base, often much branched, the stems 3–7 dm. long, tomentose-
canescent, ± glandular; lvs. linear, densely tomentose-canescent, the lower
opposite or subopposite, lateral veins usually not evident; fls. 3–4 cm. long; fl.-
tube largely 2–3 cm. long; sepals erect, lanceolate, 8–10 mm. long, scarlet;
petals 2-cleft, scarlet, 8–15 mm. long; stamens well exserted; style and stigma
surpassing stamens; caps. sessile or nearly so, linear, 4-angled, 8-nerved, often
curved, with a short beak and 1–2 cm. long; $n = 30$.—Dry slopes below 2000
ft., Coastal Sage Scrub, Chaparral, etc., Coast Ranges from Monterey Co. to
San Diego Co.; Catalina Id. Aug.–Oct.
      Ssp. **mexicàna** (Presl) Raven. [*Z. m.* Presl. *Z. villosa* Greene. *Z. californica*
var. *v.* Jeps. *Z. Eastwoodae* Moxley. *Z. velutina* Eastw. ex Moxley.] Suffrutescent at base, the stems to 9 dm. long; lvs. lanceolate to linear-lanceolate or
oblong-lanceolate, mostly 3–5 mm. wide, green to gray-pilose; $n = 30$.—Dry,
mostly stony or gravelly places below 3800 ft., Sonoma and Lake cos. to L.
Calif. Variable, the var. *villosa* having been used to designate plants from the
Santa Barbara Ids. with long soft hairs.
p. 927.   Use Ssp. **latifòlia** and Z. **càna** as they are in the FLORA.

EPILÒBIUM

In Key, line 4 from bottom of page, change to "Stems 3–20 dm. tall."
p. 928.   In Key, after DD, E, insert:

E′.   Petals yellow, 14–18 mm. long; stems mostly 3–7 dm. tall. Siski-
      you Mts. . . . .   7b. *E. luteum*
E′E′. Petals pink to white, 2–10 mm. long.
   F.   Petals 5–10 mm. long, etc. as in the FLORA.

      1. E. angustifòlium L. Mosquin (Brittonia 18: 167–187. 1966) proposes:

A. Abaxial lf. midribs glabrous; lvs. (3)–10–(30) mm. wide, (35)–85–(170) mm. long;
    pollen grains commonly less than 85μ diam. Circumpolar, s. to ca. the s. limits of the
    boreal forest and in Rocky Mts. to Wyo. . . . . Ssp. *angustifolium*
AA. Abaxial lf. midribs glabrous to pubescent; lvs. (5)–20–(40) mm. wide, (60)–110–
    (220) mm. long; pollen grains over 85μ diam. S. Canada and U.S., as well as Eurasia.
                                                                        Ssp. *circumvagum*

      Subsp. **angustifòlium** includes var. *intermedium* of the FLORA. $n = 18$ (Mos-
quin).
      Subsp. **circumvàgum** Mosquin includes var. *macrophyllum* of the FLORA. $n =
36$ (Mosquin).
p. 929.   **3. E. obcordàtum** Gray. Transpose lines 8 and 9 of 1959 printing. Lvs. glaucous, 6–16 mm. long; fl. tube 2–4 mm.—Sierra Nevada to Ida.

Ssp. **siskiyouénse** Munz. [*E. o.* var. *laxum* (Hausskn.) Dempster in Jeps.] Plants more greenish; lvs. mostly 10–22 mm. long, subacute; fl.-tube 2–2.5 mm. long; longer stamens ca. half as long as petals.—Siskiyou and Trinity cos.; to Jackson Co., Ore.

p. 930.

7. **E. minùtum** Lindl. ex Hook. *n* = 13. Reported from as far s. as Ventura Co., *Hardham.*

7a. **E. foliòsum** (Nutt. ex T. & G.) Suksd. [*E. minutum* var. *f.* T. & G. *E. m.* var. *Biolettii* Greene.] Resembling *E. minutum,* but lvs. linear to lance-linear, sharply pointed, somewhat toothed, with more tendency to axillary fascicles and narrow petioles; fls. smaller; sepals ca. 1 mm. long; petals scarcely 2 mm. long; caps. short-pedicelled; *n* = 16. Ranging with *E. minutum,* particularly northward.

7b. **E. lùteum** Pursh. Perennial with creeping underground rootstock and well developed turions; stems subsimple, erect, 2–7 dm. tall; lvs. ± ovate, 2–7 cm. long, very slightly reduced up the stem; fls. few, nodding in the bud; petals yellow, obcordate, 14–18 mm. long.—Moist places, Siskiyou Co., *Bacigalupi;* to B.C., Alta.

p. 931.

11. **E. Pringleànum** Hausskn. In line 2 of description delete "slender" from middle of line.

12. **E. Halleànum** Hausskn. Reported from Marin and Santa Cruz cos.

p. 932.

19. **E. adenocaúlon** Hausskn. var. **occidentàle** Trel. in Monterey Co., *Howell.*

p. 933.

BOISDUVÁLIA

New reference to literature: Raven, P. H. and D. M. Moore. A revision of Boisduvalia. Brittonia 17: 238–253. 1965.

p. 934.

3. **B. glabélla** (Nutt.) Walp. *n* = 15 (Kurabayashi, 1962).

4. **B. strícta** (Gray) Greene occurs in the Greenhorn Mts., Kern Co., *Twisselmann;* in Monterey Co., *Howitt & Howell;* San Bernardino Mts., *Charlotte Bringle.*

6. Reduce *B. pállida* Eastw. to synonymy under 5. **B. macrántha** Heller.

p. 935.

CLÁRKIA

In Key, after AA, B, C, change to:

D. Petals 6–12 mm. long, 3–7 mm. broad.
    D'. Pollen dull yellow-gray to dark blue-gray; petals 6–12 mm. long, lanceolate to rhombic, with or without dark spots. Widely distributed.
                                                      27. *C. rhomboidea*
    D'D'. Pollen yellow, petals 6–7.5 mm. long, obovate, not spotted. Plumas and Yuba cos. .... 28a. *C. stellata*

In Key, after AA, BB, CC, D, E, change to:

F. Some long hairs present on ovary and calyx; lf.-width ¼–⅖ the length; petal-width ½–¾ the length; style usually well exserted. Lake and Plumas cos. to San Diego Co.
                                             24. *C. unguiculata*
FF. Long hairs absent; lf.-width less than ⅓ the length; petal-width usually less than ½ the length; leafy bracts width usually less than ¼ the length.
    G. Style usually well exserted; sepals dark red-purple; petals usually with a large dark red-purple spot at base of blade; often with 5–6 fls. open on one stem at same time. Tulare Co. .... 25a. *C. springvillensis*
    GG. Style seldom well exserted; sepals mostly green or only slightly reddish; petal spot, if present, small and well defined or, if large, not sharply defined; usually 1–3 fls. open on stem at the same time.
        H. The style equaling or only slightly exceeding the anthers; lvs. usually bright green; petals pink, with or without a purple spot at the base of the blade, or white. S. Tulare and n. Kern cos. .... 25. *C. exilis*
        HH. The style equaling the anthers to well exserted; lvs. usually gray-green; petals pink, sometimes with a darker blotch at base of blade, or petals reduced, sepal-like, unexpanded and wrinkled. Inner Coast Ranges, Alameda Co. to w. Kern Co.
                                        25b. *C. tembloriensis*

In Key, AA, BB, CC, D, EE, F, G, HH, I, insert at end of line 2:
"5. *C. gracilis*" (for 1959 printing).

p. 936.   In Key, AA, BB, CC, D, EE, FF, G, H, I, petals should be 10–30, not 10–13 mm. long (for 1959 printing).

In Key, after DD, E, F, G, delete "2. *C. rubicunda*" and insert:

> H. Fl.-tube 4–10 mm. long; petals 10–30 mm. long, obovate to fan-shaped. Monterey Co. to Marin Co.
> 2. *C. rubicunda*
> HH. Fl.-tube 1–3 mm. long; petals 5–13 mm. long, wedge-shaped. San Francisco. .. 2a. *C. franciscana*

p. 938.   2a. **C. franciscàna** Lewis & Raven. Short description in the FLORA.

5. **C. grácilis** (Piper) Nels. & Macbr. in the synonymy *G. a.* var. *pygmaea* Jeps. should be forma (1959 printing).

p. 939.   10. **C. Dàvyi** (Jeps.) Lewis & Lewis In Santa Cruz Co.; on Santa Rosa Id., *Raven*.

p. 940.   12. **C. purpùrea** ssp. **quadrivúlnera** (Dougl.) Lewis & Lewis. In the synonymy var. *capitata* Jeps. and var. *flagellata* Jeps. should read forma. (1959 printing.)

p. 941.   16. **C. bilòba** (Durand) Nels. & Macbr. ssp. **Brandègeae** (Jeps.) Lewis & Lewis. In the synonymy, for 1959 printing change "var." to "f."

p. 942.   21. **C. símilis** Lewis & Ernst. In Monterey Co., *Howitt & Howell*.

24. **C. unguiculàta** Lindl. Line 4 from bottom of description, change "short-petioled" to "short-pediceled."

25a. **C. springvillénsis** Vasek. Near to *C. unguiculata*; lf.-blades bright green, 2–9 cm. long, 5–20 mm. wide; fl.-tube 3–4 mm. long; sepals 12–16 mm. long, puberulent, usually dark red; petals 13–16 mm. long, including a narrow red claw 7–9 mm. long and a limb 6–8 mm. long, 7–10 mm. broad, lavender-pink and usually with a dark purplish spot at base of limb; style exceeding stamens; $n = 9$.—Foothill Wd., near Springville, Ranger Station, Tulare Co.

25b. **C. temblorriénsis** Vasek. Near to *C. unguiculata*, erect, to 8 dm. tall; lf.-blades gray-green, 2–7 cm. long, 3–13 mm. wide; fl.-tube 2(3) mm. long; sepals 9–16 mm. long, 2–3 mm. wide, puberulent; petals expanded, 13–17 mm. long, including a narrow claw 5–11 mm. long 1(2) mm. wide, the limb scarcely wider than the base; style often not exceeding the stamens; $n = 9$.—Inner Coast Ranges from e. Alameda and w. San Joaquin cos. to w. Kern and e. San Luis Obispo cos.

p. 943.   28a. **C. stellàta** Mosquin. Erect, to 1 m. tall, simple or branched, subglabrous to strigulose; lf.-blades lanceolate to elliptic or ovate, 1–5 cm. long, 5–20 mm. broad, on petioles 5–30 mm. long; infl.-rachis recurved in bud; fl.-tube 1.5–2 mm. long; sepals 5–7 mm. long; petals obovate, 6–7.5 mm. long, 3–4 mm. broad, shallowly 3-lobed, the central lobe ca. 1 mm. longer than the lateral, lavender-purple, not flecked, red-purple at the base; anthers pale; pollen yellow; style shorter than the stamens; mature caps. 2–2.5 cm. long, 2–3 mm. broad, dry and quadrangular, often with red streaks, straight or slightly curved; $n = 7$. —Plumas and Yuba cos.

p. 944.   OENOTHÈRA

References to literature: Raven, Brittonia 16: 276–299. 1964 and Munz, N. Am. Flora, Series II, Part 5: 79–177. 1965.

In Key, A, B, CC, change to:

> CC. Fls. white to rose, the buds often nodding.
> D.   Caps. sterile and slender in lower part, thicker, fertile and ± winged in upper part; seeds in more than 2 rows in each locule; fl.-tube 0.4–2 cm. long.
> E.   Petals white to pink, 2.5–4 cm. long; plants with running underground rootstocks; buds nodding. .... 7. *Oe. speciosa*
> EE. Petals rose to red-violet, 0.5–1 cm. long; plants from a ± woody caudex; buds erect. .... 7a. *Oe. rosea*
> DD. Caps. cylindric, sessile, not sterile in lower part; seeds in 1 row in a locule; fl.-tube 2–4 cm. long.
> E.   Plants annual or surviving longer, from a deep taproot; basal lvs. ± rhombic, the blades 2–10 cm. long; caps. usually woody, with exfoliating epidermis. .... 8. *Oe. deltoides*

EE. Plants perennial, largely from running underground rootstocks; basal
    lvs. tending to be smaller and more narrow; caps. usually not
    woody.
    F.   Plants greenish and subglabrous to strigose; caps. 2.5 mm. thick
        at base. S. Calif., mostly west of the deserts. 9. *Oe. californica*
    FF. Plants canescent to hoary, usually with some spreading hairs
        especially in the upper parts.
        G. Stems 4–8 dm. long; lvs. runcinate-pinnatifid, 3–12 cm.
            long; free sepal-tips 1–3 mm. long. Sand dunes about
            Antioch. .... 8. *Oe. deltoides Howellii*
        GG. Stems 1–5 dm. long; lvs. subentire to deeply sinuate-
            dentate, 1–6 cm. long; free sepal-tips lacking or 1 mm.
            long. Deserts. .... 9a. *Oe. avita*
BB. Caps. crested etc., as in the FLORA.

p. 945.   In Key, AA, BB, CC, D, E, FF, GG, delete H and HH. and end GG. in 27.
          Oe. Boothii.
          In Key, near bottom of page, keep F, G and GG, omitting H and HH and
          change to:

    H. Fls. small, the petals 2–5 mm. long.
        I. The plants low, commonly less than 15 cm. tall,
            with stems less than 1 mm. in diam. and gla-
            brous or finely pubescent; lvs. less than 2 mm.
            wide.
            J. Sepals 1.5–2 mm. long; petals 1.5–2.5 mm.
               long. Mojave Desert to e. Wash.
                            29. *Oe. contorta*
            JJ. Sepals 2–3 mm. long; petals 3.5–5 mm.
               long. Central Valley and adjacent areas to -
               the west. .... 29a. *Oe. cruciata*
        II. The plants taller or coarser, with stems more
            than 1 mm. in diam.
            J. Lvs. rather broad, the principal 2–5 mm.
               broad, often coarsely and sharply serrate;
               petals 3–4 mm. long; plant with an abun-
               dant spreading pubescence. E. middle Calif.
                            29b. *E. pubens*
            JJ. Lvs. mostly 1–2 mm. broad, scarcely or not
               toothed; petals 2–3 mm. long; plant sub-
               glabrous to strigulose or finely spreading-
               pubescent. W. of the Cordillera, from L.
               Calif. to s. Ore. .... 29c. *Oe. dentata*
    HH. Fls. larger, the petals usually 5–14 mm. long.
        I. Caps. sessile; petals mostly 5–8 mm. long; lvs.
            narrow, mostly 1–2.5 mm. broad. Contra Costa
            and Butte cos. to Mojave Desert and s. Calif.
                         30a. *Oe. campestris*
        II. Caps. tending to be pediceled and often some-
            what clavate, the fls. larger, with petals 10–14
            mm. long; lvs. mostly wider, denticulate. Mo-
            jave Desert and borders. .... 31. *Oe. kernensis*

p. 946.   In Key, change G and GG at top of page to:

    G. Mature caps. oblong-pyramidal, 12–15 mm. long, almost
        straight. San Clemente Id. ...... 32. *Oe. guadalupensis*
    GG. Mature caps. curved or contorted, 15–40 mm. long.
        H. Plants pallid with a closely appressed pubescence,
            mostly prostrate or nearly so. Deserts.
            I. Sepals 3–4 mm. long; petals 3–6 mm. long.
               From Inyo and e. San Diego cos. to Ariz.
                            33a. *Oe. Abramsii*
            II. Sepals 7–9 mm. long; petals 8–12 mm. long.
               W. edge of Colo. Desert. ..... 34a. *Oe. Hallii*
        HH. Plants green, not pallid (or if so, growing on Coastal
            Strand), the pubescence largely spreading, sometimes
            almost lacking.
            I. Fls. small, the petals 1.5–7 mm. long.
               J. Petals 2–4 mm. long; stems prostrate to
                 ascending or erect, not reddish; cauline lvs.
                 sessile; foliage hirsutulous or villous. Men-
                 docino and Glenn cos. to L. Calif.
               K. Stems semiprostrate; cauline lvs. oblong-

lanceolate, obtuse, sessile but not
clasping. .... 33. *Oe. micrantha*
KK. Stems erect or ascending; cauline lvs.
oblong-ovate to broadly ovate, acute
with subcordate clasping base.
33a. *Oe. hirtella*
JJ. Petals 5–7 mm. long; stems nearly erect,
slender, reddish, subglabrous or nearly so.
Central Calif. to L. Calif. 33c. *Oe. ignota*
II. Fls. larger, the petals mostly 8–22 mm. long.
J. Plants of sea-bluffs and inland, greenish;
greenish cauline lvs. lanceolate to lance-
ovate, acute, wavy-margined, thin.
34. *Oe. bistorta*
JJ. Plants of sea-beaches, usually grayish to
silvery; cauline lvs. lance-oblong to orbicu-
lar-ovate, obtuse, not wavy-margined, thick
in texture. .... 35. *Oe. cheiranthifolia*

In Key, DD, EE, change to:

F. Lvs. all cauline, well distributed, simple, mostly cordate-orbicu-
lar; caps. short-pediceled, coarse-cylindrical; pollen shed in
tetrads.
G. Fl.-tube 5–14 mm. long; style 8–23 mm. long.
37. *Oe. cardiophylla*
GG. Fl.-tube 18–40 mm. long; style 30–58 mm. long.
37a. *Oe. arenaria*
FF. Lvs. mostly basal, often pinnatifid, largely ovate, oblong or
lanceolate; caps. usually prominently pediceled; pollen grains
shed individually.
G. Caps. linear, usually over 2 cm. long and less than 2 mm.
in diam.
H. Stigma surrounded by anthers at anthesis; petals less
than 6 mm. long; style less than 6 mm. long; infl.
erect in bud. .... 41. *Oe. Walkeri*
HH. Stigma elevated above anthers at maturity; petals
usually more than 6 mm. long; style over 6 mm. long.
38. *Oe. brevipes*
GG. Caps. distinctly clavate, usually more than 2 mm. in diam.
H. Corolla lavender in anthesis; flowering mostly in late
summer and fall. .... 42. *Oe. heterochroma*
HH. Corolla yellow or white at anthesis; flowering mostly
in spring and early summer.
I. Mature pedicels and caps. ascending or spreading; corolla yellow or white. Widespread on deserts. .... 39. *Oe. claviformis*
II. Mature pedicels and caps. sharply deflexed;
corollas bright yellow. Region s. of Death Valley.
39a. *Oe. Munzii*

p. 948.   5. **Oe. strícta** Ledeb. ex Link. Now reported from Santa Barbara, Monterey
and Santa Cruz cos.

7a. **Oe. ròsea** L'Hérit. ex Ait. [*Hartmannia r.* G. Don.] Perennial, blooming
the first year, from a somewhat woody caudex, freely branched, to 1 m. or more
tall, ± strigulose throughout; lvs. not crowded, the lower oblanceolate or wider,
subentire to pinnatifid, 2–5 cm. long, the cauline gradually reduced up the stem;
fls. in simple slender erect bracteate racemes; fl.-tube 4–8 mm. long; sepals
5–8 mm. long; petals rose to red-violet, 5–10 mm. long; caps. proper obovoid,
8–10 mm. long, 3–4 mm. thick, with 4 wings to ca. 1 mm. wide, caps. passing
at base into a hollow ribbed pedicel 5–20 mm. long; $n = 7$.—Texas to S. Am.
Increasingly found as an adventive in Calif.

p. 949.   8. **Oe. deltoìdes** Torr. & Frém. The varieties *cognata, Piperi, Howellii* have
been raised to subspecies, with W. Klein as the authority. Var. *cineràcea* (Jeps.)
Munz is reduced to synonymy under *Oe. deltoides*.

Ssp. *eurekénsis* becomes 9a. **Oe. ávita** W. Klein ssp. **eurekénsis** (Munz) Klein.

9. **Oe. califórnica** Wats. is retained for the tetraploid plants ($n = 14$) of cismontane s. Calif. and

9a. **Oe. ávita** W. Klein should be used for the desert plants of e. Calif. and
w. Ariz. with $n = 7$. These tend to be shaggier, with more long spreading hairs
especially in the upper parts.

p. 950.   10. *Oe. caespitòsa* Nutt. var. *longiflora* (Heller) Munz can be reduced to
synonymy under **Oe. caespitòsa** var. **marginàta** (Nutt.) Munz. $n = 7$ (Kurabayashi et al., 1962).
        12. **Oe. primivèris** Gray can be keyed out as follows:

Plants practically acaulescent; fl.-tube 3–5 cm. long. Deserts, mostly above 1500 ft.
    Petals 10–22 mm. long; sepals 10–20 mm. long; caps. 17–30 mm. long. St. George,
    Utah to extreme e. San Bernardino Co., then se. to Texas, Son. . . . . *Oe. primiveris*
    Petals 25–40 mm. long; sepals 20–25 mm. long; caps. 25–50 mm. long. Sw. Nev. and
    Inyo Co., Calif. to Riverside Co. . . . . Ssp. *bufonis*
Plants with stems 1–4 dm. long; fl.-tube 4–6 cm. long; petals mostly 3–4 cm. long. From
below 900 ft., Imperial Co., Calif. to Yuma and Pima cos., Ariz. . . . . Ssp. *caulescens*

Synonymy is as follows:
    Oe. primivèris Gray. [*Lavauxia p.* Small. *Oe. Johnsoni* Parry.]
    Oe primivèris Gray ssp. **bufònis** (M. E. Jones) Munz. [*Oe. b.* Jones. *La-
vauxia lobata* A. Nels.]
    Oe. primivèris ssp. **cauléscens** (Munz) Munz. [*Oe. p.* var. *c.* Munz.]
        15. **Oe. leptocárpa** Greene. Add as synonym *Camissonia californica* Raven.
p. 951.   16. **Oe. Pálmeri** Wats. Add as synonym *Camissonia P.* Raven.
        17. **Oe. graciliflòra** H. & A. Add as synonym *Camissonia g.* Raven.
        18. *Oe. heterántha* Nutt. Change name to **Oe. subacaúlis** (Pursh) Garrett
with synonyms: *Jussiaea s.* Pursh. *Camissonia s.* Raven. *Oe. heterantha* Nutt.
        19. **Oe. ovàta** Nutt. in T. & G. Additional synonym *Camissonia o.* Raven.
        20. **Oe. tanacetifòlia** T. & G. Additional synonym *Camissonia t.* Raven.
p. 952.   21. **Oe. breviflòra** T. & G. Additional synonym *Camissonia b.* Raven.
        22. **Oe. refrácta** Wats. Additional synonym *Camissonia r.* Raven.
        23. **Oe. chamaenerioìdes** Gray. Additional synonym *Camissonia c.* Raven.
        24. **Oe. mìnor** (A. Nels.) Munz. Additional synonym *Camissonia m.* Raven.
        25., 26., and 27. combined under **Oe. Boòthii** for which the following key is
presented:

A. Mature caps. merely curved or bent, not distinctly coiled or contorted, subfusiform or
    linear in shape.
    B. Lvs. well distributed, glandular-pubescent to -villous; stem epidermis exfoliating
        tardily if at all; caps. 10–15 mm. long.
        C. Stems largely 1.5–4 dm. tall, the central one usually more prominent than
            the lateral; basal lvs. ovate to lance-ovate; fl.-tube 4–8 mm. long; petals
            3.5–9 mm. long. Northeast and east of Calif. . . . . 25. *Oe. Boothii*
        CC. Stems largely 1–2 dm. tall, the branches sometimes as prominent as the cen-
            tral stem; basal lvs. lanceolate to lance-ovate; fl.-tube 3–5 mm. long; petals
            4–4.5 mm. long. Mono and Inyo cos. and adjacent Nev. . . . . Ssp. *intermedia*
    BB. Lvs. largely near the base of the plant, subglabrous to strigulose, lance-ovate to
        oblanceolate; stem epidermis exfoliating promptly; caps. 15–25 mm. long.
        C. The caps. not more than 2 mm. thick at base, not conspicuously quadrangu-
            lar or thickened and indurated at the angles, scarcely woody; plant slender,
            2–5 dm. tall.
            D. Caps. with simple curve about ½ the way from the base, so that the tip
                spreads away from the stem axis.
                E. Base of mature caps. ca. 2 mm. thick, the body curved and with
                    spreading tips.
                    F. Exfoliating epidermis of stem straw- or flesh-color; petals 4.5–
                        5 mm. long, white except possibly when aging. Monterey and
                        Stanislaus cos. to Kern and Los Angeles cos. . . Ssp. *decorticans*
                    FF. Exfoliating epidermis of stems white to reddish; petals 3.5–4
                        mm. long, red. Mts. about the w. end of the Mojave Desert.
                                                                                    Ssp. *rutila*
                EE. Base of mature caps. ca. 1 mm. thick, the body straight or curved;
                    petals 3–3.5 mm. long. Inyo Mts., Inyo Co. . . . . Ssp. *inyoensis*
            DD. Caps. often contorted so that the tip points down; base of caps. 1–1.5
                mm. thick; epidermis of stems white. W. Mojave Desert. Ssp. *desertorum*
        CC. The caps. 2.5–3 mm. thick at base, conspicuously quadrangular and much
            thickened and indurated at the angles, quite woody; plants low and coarse,
            rarely more than 2 dm. high. Deserts from e. Inyo Co. to Imperial and e. San
            Diego cos., thence to Utah, Ariz. . . . . Ssp. *condensata*
AA. Mature caps. usually distinctly coiled or contorted, not merely bent and curved, not
    subfusiform in shape; lateral stems often prominent; plants finely pubescent to short-
    villous. E. Ore. to San Bernardino Co. and Ariz. and Utah. . . . . Ssp. *alyssoides*

pp. 952.–   27. Synonymy for the sspp. of **Oe. Boòthii** Dougl. ex Lehm. in Hook.
953.   [*Sphaerostigma B*. Walp. *Camissonia B*. Raven. *Sphaerostigma senex* A. Nels.
S. *Lemmonii* A. Nels.]

Ssp. **intermèdia** Munz.

Ssp. **decórticans** (H. & A.) Munz. [*Gaura d*. H. & A. *Oe. d*. Greene. *Sphae-rostigma d*. Small. *Camissonia Boothii* ssp. *d*. Raven.]

Ssp. **rùtila** (Davidson) Munz. [*Oe. r*. Davidson. *Oe. decorticans* var. *r*. Munz.]

Ssp. **inyoénsis** Munz.

Ssp. **desertòrum** (Munz) Munz. [*Oe. decorticans* var. *d*. Munz. *Camissonia Boothii* ssp. *desertorum* Raven.]

Ssp. **condensàta** (Munz) Munz. [*Oe. decorticans* var. *c*. Munz. *Camissonia Boothii* ssp. *c*. Raven.]

Ssp. **alyssoìdes** (H. & A.) Munz. [*Oe. a*. H. & A. *Oe. a*. var. *villosa* Wats. *Camissonia Boothii* ssp. *a*. Raven.]

28. **Oe. andìna** Nutt. Add to synonymy *Camissonia a*. Raven.

29. **Oe. contórta** Dougl. ex Hook. Use following key:

Caps. sessile, curved or straight, 25–35 mm. long, ending in a definite beak; $n = 7$. Siski-you and Lassen cos. to B.C., Ida. .... *Oe. contorta*
Caps. definitely pediceled, not attenuate into a beak, 17–25 (–30) mm. long, frequently curved into a half circle; $n = 7$. Mojave Desert to Wyo., Utah, e. Wash. ..... var. *flexuosa*

p. 954.   Add to synonymy under Var. **flexuòsa**: *Camissonia parvula* (Nutt.) Raven.

29a. **Oe. cruciàta** (Wats.) Munz. [*Oe. dentata* var. *c*. Wats. *Oe. campestris* var. *c*. Greene. *Sphaerostigma campestre* var. *minus* Small.] Bushy, slender-stemmed annual, 5–15 cm. tall, subglabrous or with some spreading hairs, rather leafy; lvs. linear to oblong-linear, 10–25 mm. long, 1–2.5 mm. wide, subentire to denticulate, with appressed or spreading hairs; fls. few, solitary in axils of foliose bracts; fl.-tube 1–2 mm. long; sepals 2–3 mm. long; petals 3.5–5 mm. long, yellow, aging orange; caps. linear, 1.5–2.5 cm. long, sessile, short-beaked, straight or somewhat contorted.—Open places below 3500 ft., Central Valley from Butte Co. to Kern Co. and w. to Lake Co.

29b. **Oe. pùbens** (Wats.) Munz. $n = 14$. Use instead of *Oe. contorta* var. *pubens* (Wats.) Cov.

29c. Instead of *Oe. contorta* var. *epilobioides* (Greene) Munz use **Oe. den-tàta** Cav. [*Sphaerostigma d*. Walp. *Camissonia d*. Reiche. *Oe. contorta* vars. *strigulosa* and *epilobioides* Munz.] Much like *Oe. contorta*, the stems commonly 1.5–3 dm. tall, subglabrous to strigulose or spreading-pubescent, mostly not over 1 mm. in diam., freely branched, often glandular in the infl.; lvs. well distributed, linear, 1–2 mm. wide, 2–3 cm. long; caps. 1.5–2.5 cm. long, sessile, beaked or not; $n = 14$, 21.—Dry disturbed places mostly below 5000 ft., L. Calif. to s. Ore., w. of the Cordillera; Chile.

30. **Oe. campéstris** Greene. [*Oe. dentata* var. *c*. Jeps. *Camissonia c*. Raven.]— From Butte and Contra Costa cos. s. to Kern and Santa Barbara cos.

Ssp. **Paríshii** (Abrams) Munz. [*Oe. dentata* var. *P*. Munz.] Stem subglabrous or with short appressed hairs; petals 5–8 mm. long; $n = 7$.—Santa Barbara to Los Angeles Co. and from San Bernardino to w. Riverside Co.

Oe. dentata var. *Johnstonii* Munz is an uncertain quantity and approaches Var. *Gilmanii* which is now transferred to

p. 955.   31. **Oe. kernénsis** Munz. This is keyed as follows:

A.   Plants canescent with short spreading nonglandular hairs in the lower parts; caps. often pediceled, cylindric-clavate, not beaked. Walker Pass region, Kern Co. .. Ssp. *kernensis*
AA. Plants finely glandular-pubescent almost throughout or somewhat strigulose below; caps. sessile or pediceled, linear, ± beaked.
  B.   Central stem tending to be the most prominent; plants usually strongly glandular throughout; lvs. plane, mostly ca. 2–3 mm. wide. S. Death Valley region, Inyo Co.
                                                                    Ssp. *Gilmanii*
  BB. Central stem not more prominent than the principal branches; plant weakly glandu-lar; lvs. ± crisped on margins, often 3–4 mm. wide. Mojave Desert from Pilot Knob to Kelso. .... Ssp. *mojavensis*

Synonymy as follows:

Oe. kernénsis Munz. [*Camissonia k.* Raven.] $n = 7$.

Oe. kernénsis ssp. Gilmánii (Munz) Munz. [*Oe. dentata* var. *G.* Munz.] $n = 7$.

Oe. kernénsis Munz ssp. mojavénsis Munz. $n = 7$.

32. Oe. guadalupénsis Wats. ssp. clementìna Raven. [*Camissonia g.* ssp. *c.* Raven.] Plants from San Clemente Id. differ from the Guadalupe Id. ones in being more pubescent.

33. Oe. micrántha Hornem. Additional synonym *Camissonia m.* Raven.

33a. Oe. Abrámsii Macbr. [*Oe. micrantha* var. *exfoliata* (A. Nels.) Munz. *Camissonia pallida* Raven.]

33b. Oe. hirtélla Greene. [*Oe. micrantha* var. *h.* Jeps. *Oe. m.* var. *Jonesii* Munz. *Camissonia h.* Raven. *Oe. m.* var. *Reedii* Jeps.] $n = 7$.

33c. Oe. ignòta (Jeps.) Munz. [*Oe. micrantha* var. *i.* Jeps. *Oe. hirta* var. *i.* Munz. *Camissonia i.* Raven.]

p. 956.   34. Oe. bistórta Nutt. ex T. & G. Add to synonymy *Camissonia b.* Raven.

34a. Oe. Hállii (Davidson) Munz. [*Sphaerostigma H.* Davidson. *Oe. bistorta* var. *H.* Jeps. *Camissonia H.* Raven.]

35. Oe. cheiranthifòlia Hornem. ex Spreng. ssp. suffruticòsa (Wats.) Munz instead of var. *s.* Wats. Add to synonyms *Camissonia c.* ssp. *s.* Raven. $n = 7$ (Kurabayashi et al., 1962).

p. 957.   37. Oe cardiophýlla Torr. Add synonym *Camissonia c.* Raven. Plants rather slender; pubescence mostly villous.—San Bernardino Co. southward and eastward.

Ssp. robústa Raven. [*Camissonia cardiophylla r.* Raven.] Coarse, the pubescence mostly glandular.—Inyo Co.

37a. Oe. arenària (A. Nels.) Raven. [*Chylismia a.* A. Nels. *Oe. cardiophylla* var. *splendens* Munz & Jtn. *Oe. c.* var. *longituba* Jeps. *Camissonia arenaria* Raven.] Fl.-tube 18–40 mm. long; style 30–58 mm. long.—From Riverside Co. to sw. Ariz. and adjacent Son.

38. Oe. brévipes Gray. Insert the following key:

Buds not individually pendulous before opening; petals not fading red, usually more than 6 mm. long.

   Plants villous, stout-stemmed; sepals villous as well as glandular and with subapical free tips; caps. usually 2–3 mm. in diam. Deserts of se. Calif. to sw. Utah and Ariz.   *Oe. brevipes*

   Plants strigose, rather villous below; sepals glandular-pubescent to canescent, without free caudate tips; caps. mostly 1–1.5 mm. in diam. Inyo and Riverside cos. to Ariz. and Utah.

                                               ssp. *pallidula*

Buds individually pendulous before opening; petals often fading red, less than 6 mm. long. Imperial Valley to Yuma Co., Ariz. .... ssp. *arizonica*

Add following synonymy.

Oe. brévipes Gray. [*Camissonia b.* Raven. *Oe. divaricata* Greene.]

Ssp. pallídula (Munz) Raven. [*Oe. b.* var. *p.* Munz. *Oe. p.* Munz. *Camissonia brevipes* ssp. *p.* Raven.]

Ssp. arizónica Raven. [*Camissonia brevipes* ssp. *a.* Raven.]

39. Oe. clavifórmis Torr. & Frém. Use the following key:

A. Lower parts of plant villous with spreading pubescence; sepals with free caudate tips arising below the apices; petals usually yellow and not changing color when fading. San Diego and Imperial cos. .... ssp. *Peirsonii*

AA. Lower parts of plant strigose or glabrous, but not with spreading hairs; sepals with or without free tips.

   B. Petals white, the fl.-tube orange-brown.

      C. Plants variously pubescent on stems and in infl.

         D. Lateral lfts. reduced in number, the lvs. nearly simple; basal rosette compact. E. central Calif. to s. Ore. .... ssp. *integrior*

        DD. Lateral lfts. generally well developed and numerous, the basal rosette not compact.

           E. Sepals often with free subapical tips; terminal lfts. often large and nearly cordate; buds and infl. often silky-strigose. Death Valley region. .... ssp. *funerea*

           EE. Sepals usually lacking free tips; terminal lfts. usually inconspicuous; buds and lfts. not silky. Well distributed. .... ssp. *aurantiaca*

CC. Plants usually glabrous in infl. and on buds; lateral lfts. usually well developed. W. deserts of Calif. . . . . *Oe. claviformis*
BB. Petals yellow, the fl.-tube yellow or orange-brown.
   C. Plants strigose above and in the infl.; sepals sometimes with free tips. Se. Imperial Co. to Son. . . . . ssp. *yumae*
   CC. Plants usually glabrous above; sepals without free tips.
      D. Lvs. lanceolate, narrow, evenly dentate, often almost without lateral lfts.; fl.-tube dark. Mono and Inyo cos. . . . . ssp. *lancifolia*
      DD. Lvs. pinnate, the terminal lfts. ovate, often blunt, the lateral lfts. often well developed. Ne. Calif. to Ore., Ida. . . . . ssp. *cruciformis*

Add to synonymy of *Oe. claviformis*:

Oe. claviformis Torr. & Frém. [*Chylismia scapoidea c.* Small. *C. c.* Heller. *Camissonia c.* Raven.]—Largely of the w. Mojave Desert.

Ssp. **aurantiàca** (Wats.) Raven. [*Oe. scapoidea* var. *a.* Wats. *Chylismia s.* var. *a.* Wats. ex Davids. & Moxley. *Oe. claviformis* var. *a.* Munz. *Camissonia c.* ssp. *a.* Raven. *Chylismia a.* Johansen.]—Lincoln Co., Nev. to L. Calif.

Ssp. **yùmae** Raven. [*Camissonia claviformis* ssp. *y.* Raven.]—Se. Imperial Co., to adjacent Ariz. and Son.

Ssp. **Peirsònii** (Munz) Raven. [*Oe c.* var. *P.* Munz. *Chylismia P.* Johansen. *Camissonia c.* var. *P.* Raven.]—Colo. Desert e. of Salton Sea, to n. L. Calif.

Ssp. **intégrior** Raven. [*Camissonia c.* ssp. *i.* Raven. *Oe. scapoidea* var. *purpurascens* Wats.]—E. central Calif. to w. Nev., se. Ore.

Ssp. **cruciförmis** (Kell.) Raven. [*Oe. cruciformis* Kell. *Camissonia claviformis* ssp. *cruciformis* Raven. *Oe. c.* ssp. *citrina* Raven.]—Ne. Calif. to se. Ore., Ida., w. Nev.

Ssp. **lancifòlia** (Heller) Raven. [*Chylismia l.* Heller. *Camissonia c.* ssp. *l.* Raven.]

39a. **Oe. Múnzii** Raven. [*Camissonia M.* Raven.] Like *Oe. claviformis*, with numerous branches at base and above, ± strigose; lvs. pinnate, with well developed lfts.; fls. yellow; mature pedicels and caps. sharply deflexed.—Region s. of Death V., Inyo Co.

p. 958.   41. Change to **Oe. Wálkeri** (A. Nels.) Raven ssp. **tórtilis** (Jeps.) Raven. [*Oe. scapoidea* var. *t.* Jeps. *Camissonia W.* ssp. *t.* Raven.] Annual to short-lived perennial, with well developed basal rosette, etc.—E. cent. Calif. to w. Utah and Nev.

42. **Oe. heterochròma** Wats. Add synonym *Camissonia h.* Raven.

Ssp. **monoénsis** (Munz) Raven. [*Oe. h.* var. *m.* Munz. *Camissonia h.* ssp. *m.* Raven.] $n = 7$ (Kurabayashi et al., 1962).

GAYOPHÝTUM

Cite: Lewis, H. and J. Szeykowski, The genus Gayophytum. Brittonia 16: 343–391. 1964.

Substitute the following key:

A. Plants flowering from near the base, the first fls. at 1–4 nodes above the cotyledons.
  B. The plants branched only in their lower portion, secondary branches few or none, the branching not dichotomous.
    C. Caps. with dorsal and ventral valves remaining attached to the septum at maturity, the lateral valves free; seeds usually obliquely placed in the caps, and often ca. 15–18 in each locule. . . . . 1. *G. humile*
    CC. Caps. with all 4 valves free from the septum at maturity, the seeds usually vertically placed in the caps. and 5–10 in each locule. . . . . 2. *G. racemosum*
  BB. The plants branched throughout, the secondary branches evident.
    C. Branches mostly separated by 2–8 nodes; seeds in even rows, not staggered; caps. not torulose. . . . . 3. *G. decipiens*
    CC. Branches mostly at every node or every other node; seeds often plainly staggered, those in one row alternate with those in the other; caps. often plainly torulose. . . . . 7. *G. diffusum parviflorum*
AA. Plants not flowering near the base, but only several to many nodes above the cotyledons.
  B. Caps. irregularly lumpy by failure of part of the ovules to develop; a high percentage of pollen grains empty. Wash. to Nev. and Calif. . . . . 4. *G. heterozygum*
  BB. Caps. ± regular in outline, entire or torulose, all of the ovules developing; pollen grains almost all good.
    C. Petals 0.5–1 mm. long; caps. 2–5 mm. long, mostly shorter than the pedicels. Wash. to cent. Calif., Mont., Colo. . . . . 5. *G. ramosissimum*

CC. Petals mostly 1.5–7 mm. long; caps. 3–12 mm. long, equaling or longer than the pedicels.
  D.   Seeds 1–5 (–6) in a caps., each ca. 1.5 mm. long; caps. ca. as long as pedicels; petals mostly 1.5–2 mm. long. Mts. of s. Calif.
                              6. *G. oligospermum*
  DD. Seeds usually 6–10 or more in a caps.; each ca. 1–1.2 mm. long; petals mostly 1.5–7 mm. long.
    E.   Petals generally 1.5–2.5 mm. long; style not surpassing stamens. B.C. to Mont., S. Dak., New Mex., L. Calif.
                              7. *G. diffusum parviflorum*
    EE. Petals 3–7 mm. long; style surpassing stamens.
      F.   The petals largely 3–4.5 mm. long; sepals 2–3 mm. long. Wash. to Plumas Co., Calif. and to e. Mont. and Wyo., also in San Bernardino Mts. .... 7. *G. diffusum*
      FF. The petals 4–7 mm. long; sepals 3–4 mm. long. Sierra Nevada and Greenhorn Mts. .... 8. *G. eriospermum*

1. **G. hùmile** Juss. [*G. pumilum* Wats. *G. Nuttallii* T. & G. as to lectotype.] Use description on p. 959. Change range as s. to the San Bernardino Mts.

2. **G. racemòsum** T. & G. [*G. caesium* T. & G. *G. rasemosum* var. *c.* Munz. *G. Helleri* Rydb. *G. ramosissimum* var. *pygmeum* Jeps. *G. Helleri* var. *glabrum* Munz. *G. humile* var. *hirtellum* Munz.] Use description on p. 959, changing range as from Ventura Co. n.

3. **G. decípiens** Lewis & Szweykowski. Plants 1–3 dm. tall, simple or branched at base and ± throughout, the branches mostly separated by 2–8 nodes, subglabrous throughout, or finely strigulose especially above, or occasionally with short spreading hairs; lvs. well distributed, the lower 2–3 cm. long, the uppermost 0.5–1.2 cm. long and bractlike; fls. from near the base of the plant or beginning higher; sepals ca. 1 mm. long; petals mostly 1–1.2 mm. long; lower stamens ca. ⅔ the length of the petals; pistil slightly shorter than the petals; caps. erect or recurved, somewhat flattened, not strongly constricted between the seeds; seeds evenly spaced, not staggered, usually more than 10 in a caps.; $n = 7$.—Occasional in dry sandy and gravelly places, Sagebrush Scrub and Pine F., San Bernardino and San Gabriel mts., through the Sierra Nevada and desert ranges to Wash., Ida., Utah, n. Ariz.

4. **G. heterozỳgum** Lewis and Szweykowski. [*G. diffusum* var. *villosum* Munz.] Mostly 1.5–5 dm. tall, freely and repeatedly branched, usually in the upper half, the successive branches often at succeeding internodes, the central axis more prominent than the lateral branches, often ± zigzag, subglabrous throughout or strigulose or spreading-pubescent especially toward the tips; lower lvs. to 6 or 7 cm. long and 4–6 mm. wide; cauline half as long, the uppermost are linear bracts; pedicels mostly 2–7 mm. long; sepals largely 1.5–2.5 mm. long; petals 2–4 mm. long; longer stamens ca. equaling the petals, with many of the pollen grains empty; caps. 5–10 mm. long, irregularly lumpy; seeds 1–1.5 mm. long; $n = 7$.—Local in Chaparral and Montane F., San Jacinto Mts. n. through the Coast Ranges and Sierra Nevada; to Wash., w. Nev.

5. **G. ramosíssimum** T. & G. Use description on p. 958. S. to Inyo Co.

6. **G. oligospérmum** Lewis and Szweykowski. Plants 2–8 dm. tall, repeatedly branched in upper parts, sometimes also below, erect, with the principal axis ± zigzag; lower lvs. early deciduous, cauline linear, 2–5 cm. long; pedicels filiform, 3–6 mm. long, arising only in the most distal axils, ascending to reflexed; sepals often strigulose, 1–1.5 mm. long; petals 1.5–2 mm. long; longer stamens ca. ⅔ as long as petals; style slightly exceeding stamens; caps. ca. equaling pedicels, mostly strigulose, conspicuously constricted between the seeds; seeds 1–5 (–6), those in one locule alternating with those in the other, ca. 1.5 mm. long; $n = 7$.—Dry ridges and slopes, 4500–7500 ft., Montane Coniferous F., San Gabriel and San Bernardino mts. to Cuyamaca Mts.

7. **G. diffùsum** T. & G. Erect, simple or usually branched and mostly above and repeatedly, largely at successive nodes, 1–5 or more dm. tall, strigulose or with spreading hairs above; lower lvs. lance-linear to linear, petioled, largely 2–4 cm. long, the cauline gradually reduced up the stem; pedicels 3–8 mm. long, ascending to erect; sepals 2–3 mm. long; petals 3–4 (–5) mm. long;

longer stamens ca. equaling petals; style somewhat surpassing longer stamens; caps. 5–12 mm. long, glabrous or pubescent; seeds 1–1.2 mm. long; $n = 14$.— Coniferous F., Plumas Co. to Wash., Mont., Wyo.; also in San Bernardino Mts.

Ssp. **parviflòrum** Lewis & Szweykowski. [*G. Nuttallii* auth., not T. & G. *G. ramosissimum* var. *strictipes* Hook. *G. lasiospermum* var. *Hoffmannii* Munz. *G. Helleri* var. *rosulatum* Jeps. *G. Nuttallii* vars. *Abramsii* & *intermedium* Munz. *G. i.* Rydb.] Pedicels 1.5–5 mm. long, erect to spreading or deflexed; petals 1–2.5 mm. long; longer stamens not surpassing petals; style nearly as long as petals; caps. with or sometimes without constrictions between seeds, largely 4–12 mm. long; seeds mostly 3–10, often staggered, those in one locule alternating with those in the other, ca. 1 mm. long; $n = 14$.—Montane Coniferous F., B.C. to L. Calif., New Mex., S. Dak.

8. **G. eriospérmum** Cov. [*G. lasiospermum* var. *e.* Munz.] Closely resembling *G. diffusum* as to stature, habit and foliage; fls. larger; sepals 3–4 mm. long; petals 4–7 mm. long; $n = 7$.—Coniferous F., Sierra Nevada and Greenhorn Range.

p. 960. GÁURA

4. **G. odoràta** Ses. ex Lag. In Santa Cruz Co., *Fuller*.

5. **G. coccínea** Pursh. $2n = 14$ (Taylor, 1967).

p. 961. HETEROGÁURA

1. **H. heterándra** (Torr.) Cov. Also in S. Coast Ranges, from Santa Lucia Mts. and Diablo Range south.

CIRCAÈA

1. **C. alpìna** L. ssp. **pacífica** (Asch. & Magnus) Raven.

HALORAGÀCEAE

Change Key to Genera to:

A. Plants aquatic, with some submerged lvs.
   B. Submerged lvs. pinnatifid; stamens 4 or 8 . . . . 1. *Myriophyllum*
   BB. Submerged lvs. simple, entire; stamen 1. 2. *Hippuris*
AA. Plants terrestrial.
   B. Lvs. large, round to subreniform. . . . . 3. *Gunnera*
   BB. Lvs. medium in size, lance-ovate. . . . . 4. *Haloragis*

p. 962. MYRIOPHÝLLUM

1. **M. brasiliénse** Camb.—In San Francisco and Marin cos., *Howell*.

4. **M. hippuroìdes** Nutt. ex T. & G.—At 7200 ft. in Fresno Co., *Quibell*.

p. 963.

3. Gúnnera L.

Perennial herbs with creeping rhizomes. Lvs. radical, petioled, large, round to subreniform, entire to lobed. Infl. scapose, the upper fls. ♂, the lower ♀, with bisexual between. Calyx-lobes 2–3. Petals 2, hooded, or 0. Ca. 25 spp. of the S. Hemis. (J. E. *Gunner*, 1718–1773, Norwegian botanist).

1. **G. chilénsis** Lam. Rhizome short, thick; petiole large, fleshy; laminae to 2 m. diam., palmately lobed and incised; infl. a large spike to 1 m. tall; fls. apetalous; fr. red.—Escaped in Marin Co., *Howell*; native of Chile.

4. Haloràgis Forst.

Herbs or shrubs. Lvs. entire to serrate. Fls. small, pedicelled to subsessile. Calyx-lobes 2–4. Petals 2–4, concave. Stamens 4–8. Ovary 2–4-loculed; styles 2–4. A rather large genus of the S. Hemis. (Greek, *halos*, round, and *rhagos*, berry.)

1. **H. erécta** (Murr.) Schindler. [*Cercodia e.* Murr.] Erect low leafy shrub; lvs. opposite, lance-ovate, serrate; fls. small, nodding; petals carinate, ca. 3 mm. long.—Reported from San Francisco as natur. plants.

p. 963. MYRTÀCEAE

Fr. a dehiscent caps.; calyx-lobes and petals united to form a lid or cap which dehisces transversely. . . . . 1. *Eucalyptus*
Fr. fleshy, black, sweet; perianth not forming a lid. . . . . 2. *Eugenia*

EUCALÝPTUS

In Key to Species, delete "3. *E. tereticornis*" at end of last line and add:

Lid 2–4 times longer than the calyx-tube. . . . . 3. *E. tereticornis*
Lid ca. as long as calyx-tube. . . . . 4. *E. camaldulensis*

4. **E. camaldulénsis** Dehnhardt. [*E. rostrata* Schlecht., not Cav.] Tall tree, with smooth deciduous bark; lvs. narrowly lanceolate; fls. 6–12 mm. across, 4–8 together in a stalked umbel; lid conical not beaked; fr. subglobular.—Reported as natur. at Santa Barbara, *Pollard* and El Paso Creek, Kern Co., *Twisselmann*.

2. Eugènia L.

Evergreen trees or shrubs closely related to *Myrtus*. Fls. solitary or clustered in the axils. Calyx 4–5-lobed. Stamens many. Ovary 2–3-loculed with many to few ovules. Fr. a berry crowned by the calyx. A large genus in warmer regions. (Prince *Eugene* of Savoy, 1663–1736, patron of hort.)
    1. **E. apiculàta** DC. Shrub or small tree, finely pubescent; lvs. 1–2.5 cm. long, ovate, sharply pointed; fls. white, solitary, ca. 2 cm. wide; stamens crowded in a ring; fr. fleshy, black, sweet.—Natur. in Marin Co., *Howell*. From Chile.

p. 964. CALLÍTRICHE
    3. The comb. **C. heterophýlla** Pursh ssp. **Bolánderi** Calder & Taylor has been published.

p. 966. ARISTOLÒCHIA
    1. **A. califórnica** Torr. has been collected at Millerton Lake, Madera Co., 22 mi. ne. of Friant, *Barbara Brock*. $2n = 28$ (Gregory, 1956); $2n = 16$ pairs (Raven, 1965).

p. 969. VITÀCEAE
Key to Genera:

Lvs. simple, palmately lobed. . . . . 1. *Vitis*
Lvs. palmately compound. . . . . 2. *Parthenocissus*

p. 970.   ## 2. Parthenocíssus Planch.

Climbers with tendrils, which are often disk-like at their tips. Fr. a small 1–4-seeded berry. Ca. one doz. spp. of N. Am. and Asia. Gr., *virgin-ivy*.)
    1. **P. insérta** (Kerner) Fritsch. [*P. vitacea* (Knorr) Hitchc.] A high climbing woody vine with long-petioled palmately compound lvs. and few-branched tendrils; fls. in terminal umbellate clusters; berries almost black, ca. 6 mm. diam. —Reported from lower Kern Canyon, Kern Co., *Twisselmann*. Native in e. N. Am.

94A. Balsaminàceae. JEWEL-WEED FAMILY

Succulent herbs. Lvs. alternate, simple. Fls. irregular, showy or the later fls. small and apetalous. Sepals 3, the 2 lateral small, greenish, the posterior sepal large, petaloid, saccate and spurred. Petals 3 or 5, with 2 cleft into unequal lobes. Stamens 5, short; fils. with scalelike appendages on inner side and ± united; anthers connivent or coherent. Ovary oblong, 5-loculed; style short or obsolete; stigma 5-lobed. Ovules several in each locule. Caps. slender, elastically dehiscent into 5 coiled valves. Two genera and ca. 200 spp., largely of trop. Asia.

1. Impàtiens L.

Characters of the family:

Fls. pale yellow. Humboldt Co. . . . . 1. *I. occidentalis*
Fls. pink-purple. San Bernardino Co. . . . . 2. *I. Balfouri*

1. **I. occidentàlis** Rydb. Annual, ca. 1 m. high; lvs. oval, 2–10 cm. long, coarsely few-toothed (serrate-dentate); infl. 3–5-fld.; lateral sepals 6 mm. long; spur ca. 1.5 cm. long; anterior petal pale yellow, ca. 7 mm. long, 10 mm. wide; caps. 15–20 mm. long.—Apparently once reported from Humboldt Co.; W. Wash. to Alaska.

2. **I. Balfoùrii** Hook. f. Perennial, to 1 m. tall; lvs. 7–12 cm. long, with many sharp recurved teeth; infl. 6–8-fld.; lateral sepals ca. 6–7 mm. long; spur ca. 2 cm. long; anterior petal pink-purple.—Along stream near Mentone, San Bernardino Co., *Roos*; Felton and Santa Cruz, Santa Cruz Co., *Hasse*; Humboldt Co., *Pollard*. Himalayan.

p. 971.   CONDÀLIA

Under **Condalia** add as synonyms *Condaliopsis lycioides* (Gray) Suesseng. and *Condaliopsis Parryi* (Torr.) Suesseng.

p. 972.   RHÁMNUS

2. **R. crocèa** ssp. **ilicifòlia** C. B. Wolf. $2n = 12$ pairs (Raven, Kyhos & Hill, 1965).

p. 975.   CEANÒTHUS

In Key A, BB, CC, D, EE, change "lvs. white" to "fls. white," in the 1959 printing.

p. 976.   1. **C. velutìnus** Dougl. ex Hook. var. *laevigàtus* (Hook) T. & G.; change to var. **Hoòkeri** M. C. Johnston.

p. 977.   3. **C. integérrimus** var. **califórnicus** (Kell.) G. T. Benson. Kern Co., (Greenhorn Pass, Tejon Canyon), *Twisselmann*.

p. 978.   8. **C. incànus** T. & G. occurs in Monterey Co., *Howitt & Howell*.

C. × **Van Rensselaeri** Roof. [*C. incanus* × *C. thyrsiflorus*.]Ca. 5 m. tall, evergreen; some branches sometimes streaked with red-brown; lvs. prominently 3-veined from base, dark green, dull, lighter underneath, 1–3.5 cm. long, 1–2 cm. wide; fls. white, in panicles.—Sandy slope near Lake Merced, San Francisco.

11. **C. oligánthus** Nutt. in T. & G. is reported from Monterey Co., *Howitt & Howell*.

p. 980.   19a. **C. Hearstiòrum** Hoov. & Roof. Proposed for small colonies of plants from near Arroyo de la Cruz, Hearst Ranch, nw. San Luis Obispo Co. Reported as near to *C. dentatus*, but prostrate and matted; branchlets villous when young; lvs. oblong, green and glabrous above, white-tomentose beneath, glandular-dentate, 10–17 mm. long, on petioles 1–2 mm. long; infl. 5–9 mm. long; fls. deep vivid blue; caps. ca. 4 mm. diam.

p. 981.   25. The combination *C. megacarpus* ssp. *insularis* has been made by Raven.

p. 983.   33. **C. rígidus**; add:

Var. **álbus** Roof. Procumbent, with low arcuate branches; lvs. bright green; fls. white.—Yankee Point, Carmel Highlands, Monterey Co.

p. 984.   41. **C. pùmilus** Greene. Plants taken in Eldorado Co. at 2000 ft. elev., on n. slope of Pine Hill, 3–4 mi. east-northeast of Rescue, by *Thorne*, have lvs. like *C. pumilus* in size and shining upper surface, but with broader blunter teeth.

p. 985.   SIMMÓNDSIA

1. **S. chinénsis** C. K. Schneid. $2n = 26$ pairs (Raven, Kyhos & Hill, 1965).

p. 986.   STAPHYLÈA

1. **S. Bolánderi** Gray. $2n = 13$ pairs (Raven, Kyhos & Hill, 1965).

p. 987.   DÍRCA

1. **D. occidentàlis** Gray. $2n = 38$ (Stebbins & Major, 1965).

ELAEAGNÀCEAE should be OLEASTER FAMILY in 1959 printing.

p. 988.   COMÁNDRA

1. **C. pállida** DC. Piehl (Mem. Torrey Bot. Club 22: 65. 1965) uses **C. umbellàta** (L.) Nutt. ssp. **califórnica** (Rydb.) Piehl. [*C. californica* Eastw. ex Rydb. *C. nudiflora* A. Davids.] Ranging from Vancouver Id. through Wash., w. Ore., to Kern Co., Calif. and in Ariz. The name *pallida* is restricted as **C. umbellàta** ssp. **pallida** (A. DC.) Piehl, to n. Ariz. and the n. Rocky Mts. and Cascades. It has grayer lvs. than ssp. **califórnica**.

p. 989.   LORANTHÀCEAE
In Key to Genera add third line:

Berry subsessile, rounded; ♀ sepals 4; anthers several-celled. .... 3. *Viscum*

ARCEUTHÒBIUM
In Key to Species, for hosts add *Tsuga* for *A. campylopodum*.

p. 990.   1. **A. americànum** Nutt. ex Engelm. in Gray. $n = 14$ (Wiens, 1964).—Ranging from Tulare Co. n., *Kujet*.
2. **A. Douglásii** Engelm.—From Siskiyou and Shasta cos.
3. **A. campylopòdum** Engelm. in Gray. $n = 14$ (Wiens, 1964).

PHORADÉNDRON
(Wiens, D. Revision of acatophyllous species of Phoradendron. Brittonia 16: 11–54. 1964.)
1. **P. califórnicum** Nutt. $n = 14$ (Wiens, 1964).
2. **P. juniperìnum** Engelm. [*P. ligatum* Trel.] Internodes usually less than 1 cm. long; plant usually erect; $n = 14$. Parasitic on *Juniperus*.

p. 991.   Ssp. **Libocèdri** (Engelm.) Wiens. [*P. j.* var. *L.* Engelm. *P. L.* Howell.] Internodes usually over 1 cm. long; plant often pendulous in age; $n = 14$. Parasitic on *Libocedrus,* now *Calocedrus*.
3. Change **P. Bolleànum** (Seem.) Eichler var. *densum* (Torr.) Fosb. to ssp. **dénsum** (Torr.) Wiens, with $n = 14, 27$ and
Var. *pauciflòrum* (Torr.) Fosb. to ssp. **pauciflòrum** (Torr.) Wiens, with $n = 14$.
4. Change *P. flavescens* (Pursh) Nutt. var. *macrophyllum* Engelm. to **P. tomentòsum** (DC.) Engelm. ex Gray ssp. **macrophýllum** (Engelm.) Wiens, with $n = 14$, and change
Var. *villòsum* (Nutt.) Engelm. to **P. villòsum** (Nutt.) Nutt., with $n = 14$.

3. Víscum L.

Fls. unisexual. Sepals much reduced; petals sepaloid, usually 4. Stamens sessile, opening by pores. Berries white, viscous. Genus of Old World. (Latin, *mistletoe.*)
1. **V. álbum** L. Woody evergreen; lvs. narrowly obovate, leathery, 5–8 cm. long; fls. 3–5, subsessile; berry 1 cm. diam.—Reported as on apple trees and maple, ca. 1 mi. n. of Sebastopol, Sonoma Co., *Howell*. Native, Eurasia.

p. 992.   CNEORÍDIUM
1. **C. dumòsum** Hook. f. $2n = 18$ pairs (Raven, Kyhos & Hill, 1965).

p. 994.   AÉSCULUS
1. **A. califórnica** Nutt. $n = 20$ (Ornduff & Lloyd, 1965).

p. 996.   ÀCER
3. **A. macrophýllum** Pursh. $2n = 26$ (Wright, 1957).

p. 998.   RHÙS
2. **R. diversilòba** T. & G. $2n = 15$ pairs (Raven, Kyhos & Hill, 1965). Add to synonymy: *Toxicodendron radicans* L. ssp. *diversiloba* (T. & G.) Thorne.

p. 1000.   Fig. 99 illustrates *Angelica* sp., not *Sphenosciadium capitellatum*.

p. 1003.   HYDROCÓTYLE
H. sibthorpioìdes Lam. Native of Asia, Afr., not of Eu.

p. 1004.   BÒWLESIA
After the generic description insert: Mathias, M. E. & L. Constance. A revision of the genus Bowlesia Ruiz & Pavon and its relatives. Univ. Calif. Publ. Bot. 38: 1–73. 1965.
1. **B. incàna** R. & P. $n = 16$ (Bell & Constance, 1960).

p. 1005.   SANÍCULA
5a. **S. símulans** Hoov. Proposed for plants from Monterey Co. to Santa Barbara Co., said to differ from *S. arguta* Greene in the bractlets not being cuspidate, but ovate to oblong, 1.5–2 mm. in maximum width and the fls. a paler yellow.

p. 1007.   TÓRILIS
Use the following key:

A.   Umbels sessile or short-pedunculate, capitate, opposite the lvs. . . . . 1. *T. nodosa*
AA. Umbels usually long-pedunculate, spreading, terminal and lateral.
    B.   Invol. of several bracts, 1 to each ray; bristles incurved-ascending, shorter than
         the width of the fr. . . . . .2. *T. japonica*
    BB. Invol. none or of one bract.
        C.   Plant appressed-hispid throughout; rays 2–10; both carpels uncinate-bristly.
                                                                                        3. *T. arvensis*
        CC. Plant spreading-pubescent; rays 2–3, one carpel with a glochidiate append-
             age. . . . . 4. *T. heterophylla*

2. **T. japónica** (Houtt.) DC. is probably not in Calif.
3. **T. arvénsis** (Huds.) Link has little or no invol., but has 2–10 rays and both carpels are uncinate-bristly.
4. **T. heterophýlla** Guss. Annual, spreading-pubescent, 2–6 dm. high; lvs. bipinnatisect, the uppermost much different from the lower, undivided or 3-parted; umbels long-pedunculate, terminal; rays 2–3; invol. none; fls. white or pink; carpels usually dimorphic, usually only one with glochidiate appendage. —Reported from Butte, Sonoma and Humboldt cos., *Howell*. From the Medit. region.

ANTHRÍSCUS
1. Change *A. scandicina* (Weber) Mansf. to **A. neglécta** Boiss. & Reuter var. **Scándix** (Scop.) Hylander. [*A. scandicina* Calif. auth.]

p. 1008.   OSMORHÌZA
3. **O. depauperàta** Phil. $n = 11$ (Bell & Constance, 1960).

p. 1011.   SÌUM
1. **S. suáve** Walt. $n = 6$ (Bell & Constance, 1960).

p. 1012.   PERIDERÍDIA
2. Insert "P." before "Kellóggii."—Occurs in Monterey Co., *Howitt & Howell*.

p. 1013.   3. **P. Gáirdneri** (H. & A.) Math. $n = 17$ (Bell & Constance, 1960).
4. **P. oregàna** (Wats.) Math. $n = 18$ (Bell & Constance, 1960).
5. **P. Paríshii** Nels. & Macbr. $n = 17, 18, 19$ (Bell & Constance, 1960).
6. **P. Bolánderi** Nels. & Macbr. $n = 18, 19, 20$ (Bell & Constance, 1960). Reported from Greenhorn Range, Kern Co., *Twisselmann*.
7. **P. Prínglei** Nels. & Macbr. Reported from Monterey Co., *Howitt & Howell*.

p. 1014.   LIGÚSTICUM
1. **L. apiifòlium** (Nutt.) Gray. $n = 11$ (Bell & Constance, 1960).
3. **L. Gràyii** Coult. & Rose. $n = 11$ (Bell & Constance, 1960).

p. 1015.   CICÙTA
2. **C. Douglásii** Coult. & Rose. $n = 12$ (Bell & Constance, 1960).

OREONANA
1. **O. Cleméntis** (Jones) Jeps. Flowers from late May to Aug., *Buckalew*.

p. 1018.   LOMÀTIUM
Additional reference: Theobald, W. L. Lomatium dasycarpum-mohavense complex. Brittonia 18: 1–18. 1966.

p. 1019.   In Key AA, BB, CC, D, E, FF, GG, HH, I, JJ, change to:

JJ. Fls. white.
    K.   Lf.-blades ± oblong, 4–10 cm. long, the ultimate segms. 1–4 mm. long, not crowded. At ca. 5000 ft., e. Lassen Co. . . . . 21a. *L. Ravenii*
    KK. Lf.-blades narrow-ovate in outline, 1.5–5 cm. long, the ultimate segms. 1–2 mm. long, crowded. At 10,000 ft. or higher, Inyo Mts.
                                                    22. *L. inyoense*

p. 1012.   1. **L. lùcidum** (Nutt.) Jeps. $n = 11$ (Bell & Constance, 1960).
4. **L. parvifòlium** var. **pállidum** Jeps. $n = 22$ (Bell & Constance, 1960).
9. **L. leptocárpum** Coult. & Rose. $n = 11$ (Bell & Constance, 1960).

p. 1023.   16. **L. caruifòlium** (H. & A.) Coult. & Rose. Occurs in the Greenhorn Range, Kern Co., *Twisselmann.*

19. **L. nevádense** (Wats.) Coult. & Rose. $n = 11$ (Bell & Constance, 1960).

p. 1024.   21. Theobald uses **L.**ꞏ **foeniculàceum** (Nutt.) Coult. & Rose ssp. **fimbriàtum** Theobald for Calif. plants heretofore treated as *L. MacDougallii* and reduces *L. inyoense* Math. & Const. to L. **foeniculàceum** ssp. **inyoénse** Theobald. He separates the two sspp. as follows:

Petals glabrous. . . . . ssp. *inyoense*
Petals pubescent along the margins. . . . . ssp. *fimbriatum*

21a. **L. Ravènii** Math. & Const. Acaulescent perennial, 1.5–4 dm. high, villous; lvs. ± oblong, 4–10 cm. long, ternate-bipinnate, the ultimate divisions linear, 1–4 mm. long; petioles 2–10 cm. long; peduncles 1–3 dm. long; fertile rays of umbel 5–18, unequal, 2–7 cm. long; involucel of several linear, ± scarious, distinct, villous or ciliolulate bractlets 2–4 mm. long; petals white; anthers purple; fr. oval, 6–8 mm. long, with narrow thin wings.—Near Ravendale, Lassen Co.

23. **L. dasycárpum** (T. & G.) Coult. & Rose is maintained by Theobald with ssp. **tomentòsum** (Benth.) Theobald, which is sp. no. 26 in the FLORA.

24. **L. mohavénse** (Coult. & Rose) Coult. & Rose. Theobald distinguishes:

Ultimate divisions of lvs. obovate, rarely more than 2–3 times longer than broad; petals purple or yellow; fr. pubescent. Mojave Desert and higher elevs., of Ventura and Santa Barbara cos. . . . . ssp. *mohavense*
Ultimate divisions of lvs. oblong to oblong-obovate, usually more than 3 times longer than broad; petals usually yellow; fr. pubescent to glabrate. Higher elevs., s. margin of Mojave Desert, w. and nw. Colo. Desert, into L. Calif. . . . . ssp. *longilobum* Theobald

p. 1025.   26. **L. tomentòsum** (Benth.) Coult. & Rose. $n = 11$ (Bell & Constance, 1960).

30. **L. disséctum** (Nutt.) Math. & Constance. $n = 11$ (Bell & Constance, 1960).

Var. **multífidum** Math. & Constance. $n = 11$ (Bell & Constance, 1960).

p. 1026.   33. **L. triternàtum** var. **macrocárpum** (Coult. & Rose) Math. $n = 11$ (Bell & Constance, 1960).

35. **L. nudicáule** (Pursh) Coult. & Rose. $n = 11$ (Bell & Constance, 1960).

p. 1027.   ANGÉLICA

2. **A. linearilòba** Gray var. **Culbertsònii** Jeps. occurs in the Greenhorn Range, Kern Co., *Twisselmann.* The variety is a taxon of questionable validity based on a collection from Little Kern R., with lf.-segms. 8–9 mm. wide.

p. 1028.   5. **A. tomentòsa** Wats. $n = 11$ (Bell & Constance, 1960).
p. 1029.   SPHENOSCIÀDIUM

1. **S. capitellàtum** Gray. $n = 11$ (Bell & Constance, 1960).

p. 1030.   PTERÝXIA

1. **P. terebinthìna** (Hook.) Coult. & Rose. var. **califórnica** Math. $n = 11$ (Bell & Constance, 1960).

p. 1031.   CYMÓPTERUS

2. **C. desertícola** Bdg. $n = 11$ (Bell & Constance, 1960).

5. **C. panaminténsis** Coult. & Rose. Reported from the El Paso Range, Kern Co., *Twisselmann.*

Var. **acutifòlius** (Coult. & Rose) Munz. $n = 11$ (Bell & Constance, 1960).

p. 1032.   ERÝNGIUM

3. **E. pinnatiséctum** Jeps. $n = 16$ (Bell & Constance, 1960).

p. 1033.   4. **E. alismifòlium** Greene. $n = 16$ (Bell & Constance, 1960).

6. **E. aristulàtum** Jeps. $n = 16, 32$ (Bell & Constance, 1960).

7. **E. Vàseyi** var. **castrénse** (Jeps.) Hoov. $n = 32$ (Bell & Constance, 1960).

Var. **globòsum** (Jeps.) Hoov. [*E. spinulosum* Math.] Found in the Greenhorn Range, Kern Co., *Twisselmann.*

p. 1034.   CÓRNUS

2. **C. stolonífera** Michx. $2n = 22$ (Taylor, 1967).

140

p. 1035.   5. C. Nuttallii Aud. has been found in the Greenhorn Range, Kern Co., *Twisselmann.*

p. 1036.   GÁRRYA

3. **G. flavéscens** Wats. var. **pállida** (Eastw.) Bacig. ex Ewan. Reported from the Tehachapi and Greenhorn ranges, Kern Co., *Twisselmann.*

p. 1037.   4. **G. ellíptica** Dougl. $2n = 22$ (Van Horn, 1963).

RUBIÀCEAE

Substitute the following Key to Genera:

```
A.  Lvs. in whorls mostly of 4 or more; plants herbs or low shrubs.
    B.  Fls. solitary or in cymes, pedicelled; fls. lacking 3 basal bracts.
        C.  Corolla rotate.
            D.  The corolla with 4 free lobes; fr. dry or fleshy, of 2 1-seeded mericarps.
                                                                    1. Galium
            DD. The corolla with 5 free lobes; fr. berry, 1-seeded and derived from 1
                mericarp. ........................................ 1a. Rubia
        CC. Corolla funnelform.
            D.  Calyx of 4(-6) distinct teeth, persistent in fr.; corolla pinkish-lilac.
                                                                    2. Sherardia
            DD. Calyx an inconspicuous ridge; corolla whitish or bright blue.
                                                                    2a. Asperula
        BB. Fls. in elongate spikes, sessile, each fl. with 3 basal bracts. .... 2b. Crucianella
AA. Lvs. opposite, or if whorled, on large shrubs.
    B.  Plants low perennial herbs; fls. in cymes. ..................... 3. Kelloggia
    BB. Plants large shrubs.
        C.  Fls. in heads. Plants native. ........................ 4. Cephalanthus
        CC. Fls. in compound clusters. Escape from gardens. ........... 5. Coprosma
```

p. 1038.   GÀLIUM

Insert the following references to literature:

Ehrendorfer, F. Evolution of the G. multiflorum complex in w. N. Am. I. Diploids and polyploids in this diverse group. Madroño 16: 109–122. 1961. Dempster, L. T. New names and combs. in the genus Galium. Brittonia 10: 181–192. 1958. A re-evaluation of G. multiflorum and related taxa. Brittonia 11: 105–122. 1959. Dempster, L. T. & G. L. Stebbins. The fleshy-fruited Galium spp. of Calif. I. Cytological findings and some taxonomic conclusions. Madroño 18: 105–112. 1965.

In Key, under AA, B, CC, change to:

```
CC. Plants perennial; fr. often glabrous.
    C'.   Lvs. 15–50 mm. long, in 4's, elliptic to elliptic-ovate; fr. with hooked
          bristles. Del Norte Co. ....................... 8c. G. oreganum
    C'C'. Lvs. less than 20 mm. long; fr. glabrous.
        D.  The lvs. 2–4 mm. long; fls. greenish or yellow. Santa Lucia Mts.
                                                        16a. G. Hardhamiae
        DD. The lvs. 5–20 mm. long, 4–6 at a node.
            E.  Fls. 1.5–2 mm. broad, 1–3 in upper axils or on bractlets;
                pedicels strongly arcuate in age. Widespread.  9. G. trifidum
            EE. Fls. 2.5–3.5 mm. broad, in small cymes; peduncles often
                curved, but pedicels straight. Nw. Calif. .. 10. G. cymosum
```

p. 1039.   In Key at top of page, FF, GG, HH, II, delete "Sierra Nevada." In Key under CC, change D as follows:

```
D.  Corolla-lobes glabrous or minutely pubescent.
    E.  Hairs of fr. ascending and subappressed. At 7000 ft. or more, San
        Gabriel and San Bernardino mts. .............. 29. G. Jepsonii
    EE. Hairs on fr. spreading.
        F.  Corolla reddish, with lance-acuminate lobes; plants often
            polygamous. E. Mojave Desert. ........... 26. G. Wrightii
        FF. Corolla greenish-white, the lobes mostly acute.
            G.  Lvs. linear to lanceolate.
                H.  Infl. merely bracteate, the fls. abundant; pedicels
                    short to none. Cismontane. .. 27. G. angustifolium
                HH. Infl. leafy, the fls. rather few. Modoc and Siskiyou
                    cos. ...................... 38. G. serpenticum
            GG. Lvs. ovate to orbicular.
                H.  Herbage glabrous and shiny; lvs. acuminate, ± ar-
                    cuate; infl. divaricately branched. Modoc Co. to
                    Mono Co. ................. 33. G. multiflorum
```

HH. Herbage minutely pubescent or glabrous, dull; lvs. merely acute, not arcuate; infl. divaricately branched.
    I. Lvs. fusiform or ovate, commonly thin. E. Mono Co. .... 38. *G. Watsonii*
    II. Lvs. round to broadly ovate, usually thickish.
        J. Frs., including hairs, 5–9 mm. wide, included or scarcely exserted from the lvs. Lake and Placer cos. n. 36. *G. Grayanum*
        JJ. Frs., including hairs, 3–4 mm. wide, exserted well beyond the lvs. Mts. of e. central Calif. .... 37. *G. hypotrichium*
DD. Corolla-lobes mostly hairy to hispid.
    E. Lvs. acerose-acute or -acuminate, the midveins prominent, lateral veins mostly lacking, margin often strongly revolute. Deserts, mostly below 4500 ft. .... 30. *G. stellatum*
    EE. Lvs. acute, but not acerose-acuminate, the lateral veins usually present, sometimes as prominent as the midvein.
        F. Fl.-clusters drooping; mature frs., including hairs, 4–5 mm. in diam.; corolla-lobes silky-hairy without. Mts. about w. end of Mojave Desert. .... 31. *G. Hallii*
        FF. Fl.-clusters not drooping; frs. mostly smaller; corolla-lobes mostly bristly hairy.
            G. Lvs. linear-oblong to oblong, 1–2 mm. wide; plants tufted, 0.5–2 dm. tall, cinereous-pubescent. San Gabriel Mts. to San Jacinto Mts. .... 28. *G. gabrielense*
            GG. Lvs. lance-ovate to roundish, mostly wider.
                H. Herbage glabrous, except uppermost bracts.
                    I. Lvs. 2–8 mm. long. Kern and San Bernardino cos. to Inyo Co. .... 34. *G. Matthewsii*
                    II. Lvs. 6–17 mm. long. Inyo Co. to Utah.
                          32a. *G. magnifolium*
            HH. Herbage hispid.
                I. Lvs. of a given whorl unequal, 3–7 mm. long; fls. ca. 1.5 mm. in diam., borne in sessile glomerules on a virgate or sparsely branched infl. San Gabriel Mts. to Santa Rosa and Kingston mts. .... 35. *G. Parishii*
                II. Lvs. of a given whorl subequal, 5–12 mm. long.
                    J. The lvs. elliptical or ovate, tapering at both ends, not arcuate, generally 1-nerved. 32. *G. Munzii*
                    JJ. The lvs. broadly ovate, mostly round at the base, abruptly narrowed to a sharp apex, ± arcuate, the broader pair often 3-nerved. .... 33. *G. multiflorum*

p. 1040.   **G. parisiénse** L. in Santa Barbara Co., *Raven*; Monterey Co., *Howitt and Howell*; Kern Co., *Twisselmann*.

    3. Change *G. tricorne* Stokes to **G. tricornùtum** Dandy.

    4. **G. Aparìne** L. $2n$ = ca. 66 (Löve & Löve, 1956); 44 (Kliphius, 1962).

    5. **G. spùrium** L., the smooth-fruited form reported from Marin Co., *Howell*.

    6. **G. Mollùgo** L. $2n$ = 44 (Kliphuis, 1962).

    8. Change *G. asperrimum* Gray to **G. mexicànum** HBK. var. **aspérulum** (Gray) Dempster.

    8a. **G. oregànum** Britt. Perennial with slender creeping rootstocks; stems arising singly, erect, 1–4 dm. tall, glabrous; lvs. in 4's, hispid-ciliate on margins, elliptic to elliptic-ovate, 1.5–5 cm. long; infl. branched; corolla 3 mm. diam.; fr. 2 mm. high, with many hooked bristles.—Del Norte Co.; to Wash.

p. 1041.   13. **G. muràle** (L.) All. Sierran foothills, *Howell*.

    14. **G. Andrèwsii** Gray. $2n$ = 22. Add:

Var. **gaténse** Dempster. Strikingly hairy; $2n$ = 88.—Los Gatos Creek, w. Fresno Co. and San Carlos Peak above New Idria, San Benito Co.

    15. **G. ambíguum** Wight. $2n$ = 22.

Var. **siskiyouénse** Ferris. $2n$ = 66.

    16a. **G. Hardhàmiae** Dempster. Dioecious perennial herb with hispid internodes 0.5–2.5 cm. long; lvs. 6 at a node, ovate, acute, sparsely hispid, 2–4 mm. long; infl. narrow, with short branches; corolla rotate, 2 mm. across, yellow or green; fr. fleshy, glabrous, didymous; $2n$ = 22.—Santa Lucia Mts. of San Luis Obispo and Monterey cos.

p. 1042.   17. **G. califórnicum** H. & A. $2n = 88$ or 132. Add:
Ssp. **luciénse** Dempster & Stebbins. Plants to 1.5 dm. tall, soft-pubescent,
pale green; lvs. 4–6 (–10) mm. long, not armed at apex; ovary densely pubescent; fr. white, fleshy; $2n = 44$.—Region of Cone Peak, Santa Lucia Mts.,
Monterey Co.
          18. **G. muricàtum** Wight. $2n = 22, 44$.
          19. **G. Bolánderi** Gray. [*G. pubens* Gray, sp. no. 21 in the FLORA.] $2n = 66$. *G. pubens* proves to be hexaploid forms of *G. Bolanderi*.
          20. **G. sparsiflòrum** Wight. $2n = 22$.
          21a. **G. gránde** McClatchie treated as a sp. by Dempster. $n =$ more than
110.
          22. Under **G. Nuttállii** Gray ($2n = 22$) insert the following key:

A.   Lvs. acute at apex, tipped with a stoutish hair or bristle.
   B.   The lvs. linear or lanceolate to narrowly ovate, 3–8 mm. long, narrowed gradu-
       ally to the apex. Near the coast, San Diego Co. to San Benito Co. Channel Ids.
       (Include ssp. *insulare* Ferris as synonym). . . . . *G. Nuttallii*
AA. Lvs. obtuse or rounded at the apex, tipped with a weak hair or none.
   B.   The lvs. oval or oblong. Coast Ranges, San Diego Co. to Ore.
                                    Var. *ovalifolium* Dempster
   BB. The lvs. linear, Sierra Nevada foothills and inner Coast Ranges.
                                    Var. *tenue* Dempster

          22a. **G. Cliftonsmíthii** (Dempst.) Dempst. & Stebbins. [*G. Nuttallii* var. *C. Dempster*.] Principal stems acutely angled; internodes 3–10 cm. long; lvs.
6–14 mm. long, long-acuminate; secondary herbage in large tufts; fls. very
few, green or pale yellow, with long-acuminate lobes; $2n =$ ca. 182–189.—
Mts. below 4000 ft., Santa Barbara Co. to Monterey Co.

p. 1043.   24. **G. buxifòlium** Greene is treated by Dempster as *G. catalinense* var. *b.*
Dempster.
          27. **G. angustifòlium** Nutt. Insert:
Var. **onycénse** Dempster. Low tufted masses, gray in color, 12–25 cm. tall;
fr. 2 mm. diam.—Onyx, Kern Co.

p. 1044.   30. **G. stellàtum** ssp. **erèmicum** Ehrend. $2n = 22$ (Ehrendorfer, 1961).
          32. **G. Múnzii** Hilend & Howell. Delete *G. Matthewsii* var. *scabridum* Jeps.
from synonymy. Add:
Var. **kingstonénse** Dempster. Corolla campanulate, not rotate as in *G. Munzii*, larger, clear pink; $2n = 44$.—Kingston Mts., Mojave Desert.
Var. **cárneum** Hilend & Howell. A variable series, often tall and wiry, pos-
sibly representing hybrids between *G. Munzii* and *G. Matthewsii*.—Panamint
Mts.
          32a. **G. magnifòlium** (Dempster) Dempster. [*G. Matthewsii* var. *m.* Demp-
ster. *G. Munzii* f. *glabrum* Ehrend.] To 4 dm. tall, wiry, suffrutescent lvs.
glabrous, acute or mostly acuminate, lanceolate to ovate, 6–17 mm. long; infl.
much branched, divaricate; corollas and ultimate bracts hispid.—Between
2700 and 7300 ft., s. Inyo Co. to se. Utah and n. central Ariz.
          33. **G. multiflòrum** Kell. [*G. Bloomeri* Gray and var. *hirsutum* Gray. *G. Matthewsii* var. *scabridum* Jeps.] $2n = 22$ (Ehrendorfer, 1961).
          34. **G. Matthèwsii** Gray. $2n = 22$ (Ehrendorfer, 1961).—Reported from the
Walker Pass region, Kern Co., *Twisselmann*.
          35. **G. Paríshii** Hilend & Howell, $2n = 22$ (Ehrendorfer, 1961).

p. 1045.   36. **G. Grayànum** Ehrend. $2n = 22, 44$ (Ehrendorfer, 1961). [*G. G.* ssp.
glabrescens Ehrend.]
          37. **G. hypotríchium** Gray. $2n = 22$. Ssp. **subalpìnum** Ehrend. $2n = 44$.
Intermediate between *G. hypotrichium* and *G. Munzii*.
          38. **G. Watsonii** (Gray) Heller. [*G. multiflorum* var. *W.* Gray.] Plants mod-
erately low, not at all stiff, usually lax; lvs. generally fusiform, thin, 12–24 mm.
long, glabrous or with scant microscopic pubescence, not shiny; infl. little
branched, not divaricate; corollas glabrous or nearly so. $2n = 22$ (Ehrendorfer,
1961).—E. Mono Co., between 7500 and 10,000 ft.; to Utah.
          39. **G. serpénticum** Dempster. [*G. Watsonii* (Gray) Heller f. *scabridum*

Ehrend.] Cespitose perennial with erect branches 12–28 cm. tall; lvs. linear or lanceolate, 5–20 mm. long, glabrous to hispidulous, acute; panicles leafy, the straight branches 2.5 cm. long; corolla rotate, glabrous, ± yellowish to greenish; fr. with long brown hairs, thus 6 mm. diam.; $2n = 22$ (Ehrendorfer, 1961).—Modoc and Siskiyou cos.; to Wash., Ida.

1a. Rùbia L.

Perennial herbs, frequently rather stiff, hispid or prickly. Lvs. in whorls of 4–8, rarely opposite. Fls. small, in cymes, 5-merous. Invol. none. Calyx-tube ovoid or globose, without limb. Corolla rotate or slightly campanulate. Ovary 2-loculed with 1 ovule in each locule; fr. fleshy. Ca. 40 spp. of Old and New Worlds. (Latin *red*, a dye extracted from the root.)

1. **R. tinctòrum** L. MADDER. To ca. 1 m. high, glabrous; lvs. lanceolate, with a conspicuous network of lateral veins beneath; fls. yellow, in axillary and terminal cymes; fr. a red-brown berry.—Escape at Niles, Alameda Co., *Howell.* From Medit. region.

SHERÁRDIA

1. **S. arvénsis** L. $2n = 22$ (Löve & Löve, 1956).

p. 1046.   ## 5. Coprósma J. R. & G. Forst.

Evergreen shrubs or small trees. Lvs. shining, commonly opposite, obtuse or notched at apex. Fls. small, solitary or fascicled, imperfect, white or greenish. Corolla funnelform or campanulate, 4–5-lobed. Fr. an ovoid or globose usually 2-celled drupe. Ca. 60 spp., largely of S. Hemis. (Greek name, referring to the usually foetid odor of the plants.)

1. **C. rèpens** A. Rich. Shrub or to 8 m. tall; lvs. ± fleshy, broad-oblong, 6–8 cm. long, with glandlike pits on undersurface at base of lateral veins; fls. ♂ and ♀, small; drupe orange-red, ca. 10 mm. long. Occasional escape from cult., near the coast.—From New Zealand. Cult. in Calif. as *C. Baueri.*

CAPRIFOLIÀCEAE

Line 1 of family description, insert "sometimes herbs" at end of first sentence.

p. 1047. SAMBÙCUS

1. Originally spelled S. cerùlea Raf.
2. **S. mexicàna** Presl. $2n = $ ca. 36 (Raven, Kyhos & Hill, 1965).
3. **S. callicárpa** Greene. Add as synonym S. *racemosa* var. *arborescens* Gray.
4. **S. microbòtrys** Rydb. Add as synonym, S. *racemosa* var. *m.* Kearney & Peebles.

p. 1049. SYMPHORICÁRPOS

1. **S. rivularis** Suksd. Add as synonym, S. *albus* var. *laevigatus* (Fern.) Blake. Reported from Greenhorn Range, Kern Co., *Twisselmann.*
3. **S. hespérius** G. N. Jones. Insert as synonym, S. *mollis* Nutt. ssp. *h.* Abrams ex Ferris.
4. **S. acùtus** (Gray) Dieck. Reported from Greenhorn and Piute mts., Kern Co., *Twisselmann.*
6. **S. Paríshii** Rydb. Extends through the Tehachapi and Piute mts. and to Mt. Pinos, *Twisselmann.*

p. 1050. LONÍCERA

In Key, AA, B, change to:

B. Fls. mostly in 1 whorl, sometimes 2–3; lvs. glabrous except for the ciliate margins.
　　C. Corollas with a short, nearly regular limb; lvs. deciduous. . . . . 5. *L. ciliosa*
　　CC. Corollas conspicuously 2-lipped, the limb ca. as long as the tube; lvs. ±
　　　　　evergreen. . . . . 5a. *L. etrusca*

p. 1051.   4. **L. utahénsis** Wats. Probably not in Calif.; the old collection referred to it probably was wrongly identified and was a specimen of **L. tatárica** L., a deciduous shrub to 3 m. tall, with ovate lvs. 2–6 cm. long, and with pink or white to crimson bilabiate fls. 2–2.5 cm. long, borne in pairs on slender axillary peduncles.—From Eurasia.

5a. **L. etrúsca** Santi. Vigorous evergreen vine; lvs. 4–9 cm. long, not connate except just below the infl.; infl. stipitate-glandular; bracts subtending fls. round; fls. 3–5 cm. long, yellowish white tinged with purplish red.—Reported from Del Norte and Humboldt cos., w. Ore. Introd. from Eu.

6. **L. subspicàta** H. & A. in Monterey Co., *Howitt & Howell*.

p. 1054.   VALERIANÉLLA

1. Change *V. olitòria* (L.) Poll. to **V. Locústa** (L.) Betcke.

PLECTRÌTIS

To literature citations add: Dempster, L. T. Dimorphism in the fruits of Plectritis, and its taxonomic implications. Brittonia 10: 14–27. 1958. Morey, D. H. Changes in nomenclature in the genus Plectritis. Contr. Dudley Herb. 5: 119–121. 1959.

Change the treatment in the FLORA to:

A. Corolla bilabiate, funnelform, pale to medium pink, the spur obsolete to usually less than ⅓ the length of the corolla; fr. keeled, the keel rarely grooved, acutely angled or smoothly rounded, winged or wingless, the wings thin, pubescent, the hairs flexible, evenly tapered, ± obtuse. . . . . 1. *P. congesta*
AA. Corolla regular, white to bilabiate, red, tubular or ± funnelform, the spur usually more than ⅓ the length of the corolla; fr. keeled, the keel often with a dorsal groove, obtusely angled, winged or wingless, the wings stiff and often thick, the margins thickened, often grooved, pubescent, the hairs slightly clavate, cylindrical or long and curly.
   B. Corolla essentially regular, white or light pink, usually lacking red spots at the base of the ventral lip, stout and with a clavate spur; keel of the fr. without 2 brush-like rows of hairs. . . . . 2. *P. macrocera*
   BB. Corolla strongly bilabiate, pink to light red, usually with 2 red spots at the base of the ventral lip, slender and with a slender spur; keel of the fr. often with 2 brush-like rows of hairs. . . . . 3. *P. ciliosa*

1. **P. congésta** (Lindl.) DC. [*Valerianella congesta* Lindl.] Erect, 1.5–6 dm. tall; lvs. obovate to ovate, 1–5 cm. long; corolla pale pink to pink, subcampanulate to funnelform, 4.5–9.5 mm. long, strongly bilabiate, the spur short to obsolete, usually with expanded tip; fr. pale yellow to brown, 2–4.5 mm. long, the keel sharply angled, acute, very slightly indented dorsally, wings broad to obsolescent, with thin subscarious margins that are basally connivent and spreading above.—Shaded places at low elevs., near the coast, San Luis Obispo Co. n.; to B.C. Apr.–May.

Ssp. **nítida** (Heller) Morey. [*P. n.* Heller.] Frs. shining, the keel smoothly rounded, the wings, when present, connivent at base and apex.—Shaded, ± wet places, coastal lowlands, Monterey Co. to Mendocino Co.

Ssp. **brachystèmon** (F. & M.) Morey. [*P. b.* F. & M. *Betckea major* F. & M. *P. samolifolia* Calif. refs. *Valerianella anomala* Gray. *V. aphanoptera* Gray. *V. magna* Greene. *P. involuta* Suksd.] Fls. 1–3.5 mm. long, often spurless, the corolla tubular-funnelform.—Brushy montane areas, Monterey Co. n.; to B.C.

2. **P. macrócera** T. & G. [*P. Jepsonii* (Suksd.) Davy. *P. glabra* Jeps. *P. Eichleriana* (Suksd.) Heller. *P. collina* Heller.] Plants slender, 1–6.5 dm. tall; lvs. obovate to lance-ovate; corolla white to pale pink, 2–3.5 mm. long, stout, subcampanulate to broadly tubular, regular to weakly bilabiate, the spur stout, ca. twice as long as broad, 1–1½ times as long as the tube, not or slightly expanded at the tip; fr. pale straw-yellow to red-brown, 2–4 mm. long, ± pubescent; keel rounded to rather angular, obtusely angled, often with a dorsal groove; wings thick, expanded to obsolete, with a usually grooved marginal thickening. $n = 18$ (Raven, Kyhos & Hill, 1965).—Usually shaded places below 4000 ft., Foothill Wd., Oak Wd., Yellow Pine F., etc., S. Calif. to s. Wash. Apr.–May.

Ssp. **Gràyii** (Suksd.) Morey. [*Aligera G.* Suksd. *A. mamillata* Suksd.] Expanded wings thin, with a narrow marginal thickening scarcely grooved; fr. with a median ridge on ventral surface usually bearing a multiseriate row of bristles.—Open or shaded places, s. Calif. to Wash., Mont., Utah.

3. **P. ciliòsa** (Greene) Jeps. [*Valerianella c.* Greene. *Aligera macroptera* Suksd. *A. californica* Suksd.] Slender, 1–5.5 dm. tall; lvs. obovate to oblong-fusiform; corolla deep pink with dark spots at base of ventral lobes, 5.5–8.5 mm. long, slender, bilabiate, the spur slender, usually exceeding ovary; fr. pale straw-yellow to brown, 3–4 mm. long, ± pubescent; keel rounded, obtusely angled, with a deep dorsal groove; wings variously expanded, bounded with a usually grooved, marginal thickening.—Open sunny places below 6000 ft., many Plant Communities, San Benito and Monterey cos. to Mendocino Co. and w. base of Sierra Nevada. Apr.–May.

Ssp. **insígnis** (Suksd.) Morey. [*Aligera i.* Suksd. *A. rubens* Suksd. *A. patelliformis* Suksd. *P. Davyana* Jeps.] Corolla 1.5–3.5 mm. long.—Yellow Pine F. and below, inland coastal valleys, San Diego Co. to Napa Co.; sparingly to Wash.; n. L. Calif.

p. 1056. CENTRÁNTHUS

Change spelling to **Kentránthus** Neck.

p. 1057. DÍPSACUS

1. **D. sylvéstris** Huds. has been incorrectly named in books and should be called **D. fullònum** L.

2. **D. satìvus** (L.) Honckeny is the correct name for the cult. or FULLERS' TEASEL.

p. 1058. CUCURBITÀCEAE

In Key to Genera, A, change BB by deleting "4. Citrullus" and inserting:

    C.   Anther-connective without terminal appendage; seeds with obtuse margin.
                                              4. *Citrullus*
    CC. Anther-connective terminated by an appendage; seeds not margined.
                                              5. *Cucumis*

p. 1060. BRYÒNIA

After the genus *Marah* add **Bryònia dioìca** Jacq. BRYONY. Like *Marah*, but with small red globular berries. In cultivation and an escape in Golden Gate Park, San Francisco. From the Old World.

CUCÚRBITA

1. **C. foetidíssima** HBK. Occurs in Monterey Co., *Howitt & Howell.*

p. 1061. 3. **C. palmàta** Wats. Occurs in Monterey Co., *Howitt & Howell.*

CITRÚLLUS

1. Change *C. vulgaris* Schrad. var. *citroides* Bailey to **C. lanàtus** (Thunb.) Mansf. var. **citroìdes** (Bailey) Mansf. as the name for CITRON. For the WATERMELON the correct name is **C. lanàtus** (Thunb.) Mansf.

5. Cucùmis L.

Herbaceous scabrous plants; tendrils simple; lvs. 3–7-lobed, rounded-obtuse; pepo globose. (Greek, *kykyon*, cucumber.) An Afr. genus of ca. 40 spp.

1. **C. myriocárpus** Naud. Green trailing annual with angulate-striate, rough-hairy branches; lvs. 4–5 cm. long, long-petioled, the prominent lobes and sinus rotundate, the middle lobe large; fls. very small; pepo ca. 2 cm. in diam., subglobose, marked with darker green bands and beset with weak deciduous prickles; $2n = 24$ (Shimotsuma, 1965).—Native of S. Afr. An infestation of some size was reported from near Ballard, Santa Barbara Co., *Fuller.*

2. **C. Mèlo** L. var. **Dudaím** (L.) Dunal. [*C. D. L. C. odoratissimus* Moench.] Lvs. scarcely lobed; fls. relatively large; fr. medium orange, smooth, 5–6 cm. in diam., very fragrant.—Weed in Asparagus fields w. of El Centro, Imperial Co., *Fuller.*

p. 1062. CAMPÁNULA

In Key AA, B, C, add "n. to Ore." for *C. prenanthoides.*

p. 1063. 3. **C. prenanthoìdes** Durand. Add synonym *Asyneuma p.* McVaugh; $2n = 34$ (Gadella, 1963).

4. **C. Scoùleri** Hook. For the 1959 printing of the FLORA, transpose line 6 and lines 7 and 8.

7. **C. califórnica** (Kell.) Heller. Reported from the Santa Cruz Mts., *Howell*.

p. 1064. TRIODÀNIS

1. **T. biflòra** (R. & P.) Greene. $2n = 28$ (Löve & Solbrig., 1065).

p. 1065. CITHÓPSIS

3. **G. specularioìdes** Nutt. reported from the Greenhorn Mts., Kern Co., *Twisselmann*; Madera and Fresno cos., *Weiler*.

p. 1066. NEMÁCLADUS

In Key after first DD insert:

> D′.   Plants 0.5–1 cm. tall; pedicels exceeded by the subtending bract; no glands evident on the ovary. . . . . 6a. *N. Twisselmannii*
> D′D′. Plants 3–12 cm. tall; pedicels not exceeded by the subtending bract; ovary-glands evident.
> E, EE, etc. for spp. 4, 5, 6.

1. **N. longiflòrus** Gray. In line 4 of description, delete "fls. 4–7 mm. long."

p. 1067. 6a. **N. Twisselmánnii** J. T. Howell. Rosulate, 0.5–1 cm. tall, grayish, hirsutulose; lvs. entire, the basal spatulate, 2–3 mm. long, the cauline oblong, 3 mm. long; fls. 2–3 mm. long at anthesis, 4–5 mm. in fr.; corolla 2–3 mm. long, the tube 1 mm., the lobes hirsutulose; glands of ovary obsolete; seeds 0.75 mm. long, with rows of ca. 8 pits.—Sw. of Pine Flat, Kern Plateau, Kern Co., at 7350 ft.

p. 1068. 10. Appendages apparently are present in **N. glandulíferus** Jeps.

11. **N. capillàris** Greene occurs in Ventura Co., *Hardham*; and in Monterey Co., *Howitt & Howell*.

p. 1069. DOWNÍNGIA

In the Key, under A, BB insert:

> C.   Corolla bright blue, the lower lip with a central bilobed white spot; lobes of upper lip narrow, usually parallel or crossed over each other. 2. *D. elegans*
> CC. Corolla lavender-blue, the lower lip with a central white area containing 2 bright orange-yellow spots; lobes of upper lip broader, widely divergent.
>   2a. *D. Bacigalupii*

p. 1070. 1. **D. insígnis** Greene. $n = 11$ (Wood, 1961).

2a. **D. Bacigalùpii** Weiler. Plants 5–30 cm. tall; corolla lavender-blue, usually with prominent, more deeply colored veins especially on lower corolla-lobes except in the central white area and orange-yellow spots; lobes of lower lip rounded, abruptly pointed.—Sierra Co., Calif. to sw. Ore., sw. Ida. In *D. elegans* $n = 10$; in *D. Bacigalupii* $n = 12$.

3. **D. pusílla** (G. Don) Torr. $n = 11$ (Wood, 1962).

5. **D. bicornùta** Gray. $n = 11$ (Wood, 1961).

Var. **pícta** Hoov. $n = 11$ (Wood, 1961).

6. **D. pulchélla** (Lindl.) Torr. $n = 11$ (Wood, 1961).

p. 1071. 7. **D. ornatíssima** Greene. $n = 11$ (Wood, 1961).

8. **D. cuspidàta** (Greene) Greene. $n = 11$ (Wood, 1961).—In Fresno and Kern cos., *Weiler*.

9. **D. bélla** Hoov. occurs on Mt. Abel Road, Ventura Co., *Twisselmann*.

10. **D. concólor** Greene. $n = 8, 9$ (Wood, 1961).

p. 1073. Family number for COMPOSITAE is 119.

p. 1074. In Key to Tribes of Compositae, under G insert "usually" after "style-branches." In Key, A, B, C, D, E, FF, GG, H, *Anthemideae*, change to p. 1227 and in HH, II the third word is "aks." not "ask."

p. 1075. In Artificial Key, under A, "Anthers tailed or sagittate at their base" under BB add:

> C.   Style without ring of hairs or distinct thickened ring below the branches; plants not prickly; receptacle naked. . . . . *Inuleae* p. 1257
> CC. Style with a ring of hairs or a thickened ring below the papillate branches, the branches generally connate near the tip; plants usually prickly; receptacle usually densely bristly. . . . . *Cynareae* p. 1271

In Key under **Group A**, after AA, B, C, and D, insert:

> E.   Phyllaries 1–3; head usually 1-fld. Introd. . . . . 50a. *Flaveria*
> EE. Phyllaries several; head several-fld. Native. . . . . 51. *Baeria*

p. 1077.   In Key under **Group B**, after AA, BB, etc. EE, FF, GG, HH, insert:

> H'.   Plants rather succulent, glabrous except for a microscopic glandular pubescence and very sparse flocs of wool in lf.-axils and below the heads.
> 65. *Blennosperma*
> H'H'. Plants not as above.
> I.   Herbage not white-woolly; annual herbs.
>   J.   Lvs. 1–3 times ternately divided; plants 3–6 dm. high. San Bernardino and San Jacinto mts. . . . . 54. *Bahia*
>   JJ. Lvs. coarsely sinuate-dentate; plants 1–3 dm. high. Garden escape.
> 121a. *Dimorphotheca*

In Key to **Group C**, follow through A, BB, CC, DD "Awns or teeth retrorsely barbed. Herbaceous"; delete "12. *Bidens*" and add:

> E.   Inner phyllaries free essentially to the base. . . . . 12. *Bidens*
> EE. Inner phyllaries connate to the middle or higher.
> 12a. *Thelesperma*

p. 1079.   In Key under **Group D**, after AA, BB, CC, D, EE, FF, G, change to:

> H.   Plants 1–4 dm. tall.
> I.   Branches filiform; lvs. linear, entire.
> 86. *Tracyina*
> II. Branches coarser; lvs. broader, dentate to pinnatifid. . . . . 111. *Senecio*
> HH. Plants taller, coarse; lvs. dentate to lobed.
> 117. *Erechtites*

p. 1083.   In Key, FF, G insert "usually" after "pappus."

p. 1084.   WYÈTHIA
  1. **W. ovàta** T. & G. Greenhorn Mts., Kern Co., *Twisselmann.*

p. 1086.   BALSAMORHÌZA
  4. **B. macrolèpis** Sharp ssp. **platylèpis** (Sharp) Ferris. [*B. p.* Sharp.] Pubescence unusually dense, silvery; pinnae of lvs. not or scarcely lobed; outer phyllaries shorter than to equaling the disk.—Nevada Co. to Modoc and Siskiyou cos.; sw. Ore., w. Nev. (Delete *B. platylepis* from synonymy under **B. Hookeri**).

p. 1087.   VIGUIÈRA
  1. **V. deltoìdea** var. **Paríshii** (Greene) Vasey & Rose. $n = 18$ (Heiser, 1960).

p. 1089.   HELIÁNTHUS
  4. **H. ciliàris** DC. At Hayward, Alameda Co., *Fuller* and in Orange Co., *Fuller.*

p. 1090.   RUDBÉCKIA
  2. **R. califórnica** Gray. In line 4 change "peduncles" to "petioles" in the 1959 printing.

p. 1092.   ENCÈLIA
  1. **E. farinòsa** Gray var. **ràdians** Bdg. ex Blake reported from se. Calif. by Wiggins. Lvs. soon glabrate; invol. essentially glabrous; disk fls. purplish.
  2. **E. frutéscens** (Gray) Gray. $n = 17$ (Jackson, 1960).

p. 1093.   VERBESÌNA
The combination **V. encelioìdes** ssp. **auriculàta** (Rob. & Greenm.) Coleman has been published.

p. 1094.   ECLÍPTA
  1. **E. álba** (L.) Hassk. $n = 12$ (Mehra et al., 1965).—Found in moist and cult. places, Kern Co., *Twisselmann.*
BÌDENS
In Key, change first line to:

"Aks. (at least the central ones) linear-tetragonal" and add:
  Lvs. pinnate with 3–5 lfts. Common in s. Calif. . . . . 1. *B. pilosa*
  Lvs. mostly entire. Rare, San Joaquin Co. . . . . 1a. *B. connata*

1. **B. pilòsa** L. *n* = 12, 14 (Powell & Turner, 1963).—Occurs in Santa Cruz Co., *Howell.*

1a. **B. connàta** Muhl. var. **petiolàta** (Nutt.) Farwell. Lvs. mostly unlobed, tapering to slender or narrowly margined petioles; inner aks. to 8 mm. long, the awns retrorsely barbed.—Stanislaus River, Caswell Memorial State Park, San Joaquin Co., *Rubtzoff.* Native of e. U.S.

2. **B. laèvis** (L.) BSP. *n* = 11 (Torres, 1958).—In Marin and adjacent counties, *Howell.*

3. **B. cérnua** L. At Greenfield, Kern Co., *Twisselmann.*

p. 1095. 4. **B. frondòsa** L. 2*n* = 48 (Löve, 1964).

12a. Thelespérma Less.

Mostly perennial, smooth, glabrous. Lvs. opposite, usually finely dissected. Heads pedunculate, invol. double, the outer phyllaries often narrow, the inner broader, connate in at least the lower half. Rays yellow, if present; disk fls. mostly yellow; aks. papillose, with 2 narrow, retrorsely barbed teeth. A genus of several spp., largely of sw. N. Am. (Greek, *thele,* nipple, and *sperma,* seed, referring to the papillose aks.)

1. **T. megapotàmicum** (Spreng.) Kuntze. [*Bidens m.* Spreng. *T. gracile* (Torr.) Gray.] Three to 6 dm. tall; lvs. twice 3–5-nately parted into linear lobes; peduncles commonly 1–2 dm. long; heads normally discoid, 1–1.5 cm. thick; outer phyllaries free, 2–3 mm. long; inner much longer, connate; aks. dark, subtended by scarious receptacular bracts.—Once established on Catalina Id. Ranging from Ariz. to Utah, Wyo., Nebr., Tex., Mex.; s. to S. Am.

p. 1096. COREÓPSIS
2a. **C. Atkinsoniàna** Dougl. reported from Escalon, San Joaquin Co., *Fuller.*

p. 1097. 9. **C. Bigelòvii** (Gray) Hall. Taken on road to Cedar Grove, Fresno Co., *Howell.*

p. 1098. GUIZÒTIA
1. **G. abyssínica** (L. f.) Cass. Reported from San Francisco, *Howell.*

GALINSÒGA
1. **G. parviflòra** Cav. *n* = 8, 16 (Turner, Powell & King, 1962). Recorded as occasional in San Francisco Bay area, *Howell.*

p. 1099. EASTWOÒDIA
1. **E. élegans** Bdg. *n* = 9 (Solbrig et al., 1964).

MELAMPÒDIUM
1. **M. perfoliàtum** HBK. *n* = 12 (Turner & King, 1962).

p. 1100. OXYTÈNIA
1. *O. acerosa* Nutt. is combined with Iva as **I. aceròsa** (Nutt.) Jackson in R. C. Jackson, A revision of the genus Iva. Univ. Kans. Sci. Bull. 41: 793–876. 1960. *n* = 18 (Jackson, 1960).

p. 1101. ÌVA
2. **I. axillàris** Pursh. 2*n* = 36, 54 (Mulligan, 1961).
Ssp. **robústior** (Hook.) Bassett. [*I. a.* var. *r.* Hook. *I. a.* var. *pubescens* Gray. *I. a.* Calif. refs.] *n* = 18, 27 (Payne et al., 1964).—Ranging from Calif. to B.C., S. Dak. and New Mex. Ssp. **axillàris** is east of the Continental Divide. Our Calif. plant is reported from Monterey Co., *Howitt & Howell.*

DICÒRIA
1. **D. canéscens** T. & G. *n* = 18 (Payne et al., 1964).

p. 1102. HYMENOCLÈA
1. **H. Salsòla** T. & G. *n* = 18 (Payne et al., 1964).
2. **H. monogỳra** T. & G. *n* = 18 (Payne et al., 1964).

pp. 1102–
  1105. AMBRÒSIA and FRANSÈRIA

Shinners (Field & Lab. 17: 170–176. 1949) unites *Ambrosia* and *Franseria.* W. W. Payne (A reëvaluation of the genus Ambrosia. Jour. Arn. Arb. 45: 401–438. 1964) also unites them and for California we have the following spp.:

1. **A. acanthicárpa** Hook. $n = 18$. Reported from Monterey Co., *Howitt & Howell.*

2. **A. ambrosioìdes** (Cav.) Payne. [*Franseria a.* Cav.] $n = 18$.

3. **A. artemisiifòlia** L. $2n = 36$ (Mulligan, 1965).

4. **A. Chamissònis** (Less.) Greene. $n = 18$. It occurs on the mainland s. to Point Sal, Santa Barbara Co., *C. F. Smith.* Payne does not recognize ssp. *bipinnatisecta* of the FLORA.

5. **A. chenopodiifòlia** (Benth.) Payne. [*Franseria c.* Benth. in Hinds.] $n = 36$.

6. **A. confertiflòra** DC. $n = 36, 54$. Reported from Monterey Co., *Howitt & Howell.*

7. **A. dumòsa** (Gray) Payne. [*Franseria d.* Gray in Torr. & Frém. in Frém.] $n = 18, 36, 54, 63, (72?)$.

8. **A. eriocéntra** (Gray) Payne. [*Franseria e.* Gray.] $n = 18$.

9. **A. ilicifòlia** (Gray) Payne. [*Franseria i.* Gray.] $n = 18$.

10. **A. psilostàchya** DC. var. **califórnica** (Rydb.) Blake in Tidestr. differs from var. **psilostàchya** in having spreading instead of appressed or ascending hairs on the stems. Both varieties may occur in Calif.

11. **A. trífida** L. $2n = 24$ (Mulligan, 1957). Reported from Byron, San Joaquin Co., *Fuller.*

p. 1111. LÀYIA

9a. **L. Ziègleri** Munz. sp. nov. Annual, divaricately branched from base, 1–3 dm. high, with spreading, both stiff and soft hairs, and others ± appressed, leafy especially in the lower parts; basal leaves 2–4 cm. long, 3–4 mm. wide, winged-petiolate, then slightly wider and dentate in distal part; cauline lvs. largely turned to 1 side, gradually reduced upward, entire, subsessile, lance-oblong or narrower, the lower ca. 2.5 cm. long, the upper less than 1 cm. long, mostly 2–3 mm. wide, blunt, short-hairy, not glandular; heads hemispheric, solitary at ends of branches, on naked peduncles 1–8 cm. long and ± black-stipitate-glandular toward tip as are the receptacle and phyllaries; phyllaries ca. 13–14, ± uneven in length, ca. 7–8 mm. long, oblong, obtuse, with short stiff hairs and the stipitate glands; rays golden, ca. 8 mm. long, rather sharply 3-lobed; ray-aks. black, epappose, glabrous, ca. 3 mm. long, completely enclosed in the subtending phyllaries; disk-fls. separated from the rays by a double row of green acute stiff lance-oblong bracts 6–7 mm. long, the fls. ca. 35 in number, yellow, the corolla 4–5 mm. long, the pappus bristles ca. 30, stiff, ca. 3 mm. long, scarcely plumose or flattened, without woolly hairs near the base; disk-aks. dark, ca. 3 mm. long, strigose with short white hairs.

Planta annua, base divaricate ramosa, 1–3 dm. alta, ± hirsuta et strigosa, foliosa; foliis basalibus oblongo-lanceolatis, 2–4 cm. longis, 3–4 mm. latis, pauce serratis, foliis caulium integris, lanceolato-oblongis, 1–2.5 cm. longis, non glandulosis; caputibus hemisphericis, solitariis; pedunculis 1–8 cm. longis, superne stipitato-glandulosis; phyllariis glandulosis, ca. 13–14, inaequalibus, 7–8 mm. longis, oblongis, acute 3-lobatis; akeniis nigris, glabris, obcompressis, ca. 3 mm. longis; bracteis inter flores ligulatos et flores disci in 2 seriebus, viridibus, acutis, 6–7 mm. longis; floribus disci ca. 35, aureis, corolla 4–5 mm. longa, setis pappi ca. 30, teretibus, vix plumosis, base non lanosis; akeniis disci ca. 3 mm. longis, strigosis.

Type from grassy-meadowy slope between Mountain Center and Keen Camp Summit, San Jacinto Mts., Riverside Co., at 4750 feet, *Louis B. Ziegler,* ca. June 1, 1966 (RSA). Isotype material being distributed to other herbaria.

This proposed sp. seems nearest to *Layia glandulosa* (Hook.) H. & A. ssp. *lutea* Keck and to *L. pentachaeta* Gray. It resembles the former in its basal

150   *Layia*

dentate leaves, entire cauline leaves, stipitate-glandular peduncles and involucres, ring of bracts between ray- and disk-fls., yellow anthers, setaceous pappus, etc., but differs in the more numerous subterete pappus-bristles which are
scarcely plumose and not wholly at the base. From *L. pentachaeta* (which it
resembles in lack of wool on the terete pappus-bristles) it differs in its involucre not being pustulate-hirsute and the less plumose pappus. From both
taxa it is well removed geographically.

p. 1120.   HEMIZÒNIA
           7. **H. Halliàna** Keck. Occurs at Cholame, San Luis Obispo Co., *Twisselmann.*
p. 1121.   12. **H. fasciculàta** (DC.) T. & G. Reported from Monterey Co., *Howitt &
           Howell.*
           16. **H. púngens** (H. & A.) T. & G. was found in Marin Co., *Howell.*
p. 1122.   20. **H. Fítchii** Gray. Reported from the Greenhorn Mts., Kern Co., *Twissel-
           mann.*
p. 1124.   HOLOCÁRPHA
           1. **H. macradènia** (DC.) Greene. Collected ca. 1961 at Watsonville, Santa
           Cruz Co., *Robbins.*
           2. **H. virgàta** (Gray) Keck; in Marin Co., *Howell.*
           3. **H. obcónica** (Clausen & Keck) Keck. Reported as common on low foot-
           hills on e. side of San Joaquin Valley s. to mesas e. of Bakersfield., *Twissel-
           mann.*
p. 1125.   CALYCADÈNIA
           In Key under AA, B, C change "more" to "none" for 1959 printing.
p. 1127.   4. **C. villòsa** DC. Between Brites Valley and Tehachapi Valley, Kern Co.,
           Twisselmann.
p. 1128.   11. **C. spicàta** (Greene) Greene. In Greenhorn Range, Kern Co., *Twissel-
           mann.*
p. 1130.   HELÈNIEAE
           Key under last F at bottom of page, insert:

              F'.   Phyllaries 1–3; head usually 1-fld. Introd. .. 50a. *Flaveria*
              F'F'. Phyllaries several; head several-fld. Native. .... 51. *Baeria*

p. 1131.   Genera 99. *Hymenopappus* and 100. *Hymenothrix* belong to the *Anthem-
           ideae,* p. 1227, and are keyed out there also.
p. 1132.   PSILÓSTROPHE
           1. **P. Coòperi** (Gray) Greene. $n = 16$ (Jackson, 1960; Raven & Kyhos,
           1961.
           BÀILEYA
           1. **B. pauciràdiata** Harv. & Gray. $n = 16$ (Raven & Kyhos, 1961).
           2. **B. pleniràdiata** Harv. & Gray. $n = 16$ (Raven & Kyhos, 1961).
           3. **B. multiràdiata** Harv. & Gray. $n = 16$ (Raven & Kyhos, 1961).
p. 1133.   WHÍTNEYA
           1. **W. dealbàta** Gray. $n = 8, 14$ (Stebbins & Major, 1965).
           VENEGÀSIA
           1. **V. carpesioìdes** DC. $n = 19$ (Raven & Kyhos, 1961).
           JAÚMEA
           1. **J. carnòsa** (Less.) Gray. $n = 19$ (Raven & Kyhos).
p. 1134.   EATONÉLLA
           2. **E. Congdònii** Gray. $n = 10$ (Raven & Kyhos, 1961).
           PERÍTYLE
           1. **P. Emòryi** Torr. $n = 53$–57 (Raven & Kyhos, 1961). Reported from El
           Paso Range, Kern Co., *Twisselmann.*
p. 1135.   LAPHÀMIA and PERÍTYLE
           Shinners (Southwestern Naturalist 4: 204–205. 1959) unites *Laphamia* and
           Perityle under the latter name and makes the combs. *Perityle villosa* (Blake)
           Shinners for **Laphàmia villòsa** Blake and *P. intricata* (Bdg.) Shinners for **Lap-
           hàmia intricàta** Bdg.
           Add **Laphàmia inyóensis** Ferris, differing from *L. villòsa* Blake by the lvs.

being triangular-toothed, mostly truncate at the base; longer hairs to 1–1.5 mm. instead of 0.6 mm.—Inyo Mts., Inyo Co.

p. 1136.   HÚLSEA

3a. **H. inyóensis** (Keck) Munz. stat. nov. [*H. californica* T. & G. ex Gray ssp. *inyoensis* Keck, Aliso 4: 101. 1958.] For the most part a much less robust plant than *H. californica* which is an annual and with stems to 7 or 8 mm. thick when well developed. *H. inyoensis* is perennial and often with several stems from an underground base, 3–4 dm. tall, 3–4 mm. in diam. Lvs. green and glandular, the lower tending to be more coarsely and deeply dentate than in *H. californica.* Phyllaries broadly oblong-lanceolate, acuminate to acute, less woolly than in *H. californica.* Aks. 7–7.5 mm. long instead of 5 mm., the pappus-paleae subequal, 1 mm. long, instead of 2–3 mm. long and unequal.

Known from the Inyo and Panamint ranges of Inyo Co., while *H. californica* occurs in the mountains of San Diego Co. To *H. inyoensis* can be referred *Mary DeDecker 356* from junction of Al Rose and Mazourka roads, west slope of Inyo Mts., at 6700 feet, June 10, 1956, and *Mary DeDecker 1371* from west of Goldbelt Springs, Panamint Mts., at 5400 feet, April 30, 1961.

5. **H. vestìta** Gray. $n = 19$ (Raven & Kyhos, 1961).

p. 1137.   6. **H. nàna** Gray. $n = 19$ (Raven & Kyhos, 1961).

GAILLÁRDIA

1. **G. pulchélla** Foug. $n = 17, 18$ (Biddulph, 1944).

2. Add **G. aristàta** Pursh. BLANKETFLOWER. Reported from 2 mi. west of Tehachapi, Kern Co., 7 mi. s. of Grass V., Nevada Co., and 2.4 mi. n. of Hallelujah Junction, Lassen Co., *Fuller.* It differs from *G. pulchella* Foug. in being perennial, with lvs. 5–15 cm. long; ligules 25–30 mm. long, purple at base, the remainder yellow. Native from Ore. to B.C. and N. Dak.

p. 1138.   HYMENÓXYS

2. Under **H. Lemmònii** (Greene) Ckll. the Ariz. reference pertains to *H. helenioides* (Rydb.) Ckll., not to *H. Lemmonii.*

4. **H. odoràta** DC. $n = 11$ (Raven & Kyhos, 1961).

p. 1139.   HELÈNIUM

1. **H. amárum** (Raf.) Rock. $n = 15$ (Turner & Ellison, 1960).

2. **H. Hoopèsii** Gray. $n = 15$ (Raven & Kyhos, 1961).

4. **H. pubérulum** DC. $n = 29$ (Raven & Kyhos, 1961).

5. **H. Bigelòvii** Gray. $n = 16$ (Raven & Kyhos, 1961). Reported from Greenhorn Mts., Kern Co., *Twisselmann.*

p. 1140.   50a. **Flavèria** Juss.

Glabrous to pubescent annuals, ± succulent. Lvs. opposite, entire or toothed, sessile, sometimes connate. Heads individually inconspicuous. Invol. narrow, prismatic; phyllaries 1–8, subequal. Ray mostly 1 and yellow, or 0. Disk-fls. 1–15. Ak. narrow, 8–10-ribbed. Pappus wanting or rarely of 2–4 scales. Ca. 10 spp., mostly American. (Latin, *flavus,* yellow.)

1. **F. trinérvia** (Spreng.) C. Mohr. Stem 2–12 dm. tall, widely branched, subglabrous; lvs. linear to linear-elliptic, 3–10 cm. long, serrate, 3-ribbed; heads usually 1-fld., in axillary or involucrate clusters; corolla of ♀ fls. 1.5 mm. long, the ligule oblique; corolla of perfect fl. 2 mm. long; ak. 2 mm. long.—Ala. to Ariz. & S. Am. Natur. at Calimesa, Riverside Co., *Fuller.*

p. 1140.   LASTHÈNIA

Dr. Ornduff (A biosystematic survey of the goldfield genus Lasthenia. Univ. Calif. Publ. Bot. 40: 1–92. 1966) combines the three genera of the FLORA: *Baeria, Lasthenia* and *Crockeria* under **Lasthènia.** Herewith is given his key for determination of spp.:

A.   Phyllaries free.
     B.   Receptable subulate; phyllaries usually 3–6; anther tips subulate or deltoid with wartlike glands.
         C.   Rays very short or apparently absent; invol. cylindrical; disk florets mostly with tetramerous corollas. .... 5. *L. microglossa*

CC. Rays longer, over 2 mm. long; invol. turbinate to campanulate; disk florets mostly with pentamerous corollas.
  D. Stems fine and wiry; lvs. linear and entire; anther tips subulate.
  4. *L. leptalea*
  DD. Stems coarser; lvs. with occasional very short lateral teeth; anther tips deltoid with wartlike glands. .... 3. *L. debilis*
BB. Receptacle conic to subglobose; phyllaries usually more than 6; anther tips not as above.
  C. Lvs., especially the middle ones, usually pinnately lobed or cleft; corollas remaining yellow in dilute aqueous alkali.
    D. Pappus always present, monomorphic, of paleae tapering to an awn; pubescence eglandular; invol. turbinate; phyllaries persistent after ripening of aks.; anther tips deltoid. .... 6. *L. platycarpha*
    DD. Pappus present or absent, monomorphic or dimorphic; invol. ± hemispheric; phyllaries deciduous upon ripening of aks.; anther tips linear to ovate.
      E. Pappus, when present, strongly dimorphic (except in rare forms of *L. Fremontii*), the longer member awns; herbage eglandular.
        F. Ak. bodies over 1.5 mm. long. .... 15. *L. minor*
        FF. Ak bodies under 1.5 mm. long.
          G. Pappus usually of 2 or more long awns alternating with very short scales (rarely of long awns only or missing).
          11. *L. Fremontii*
          GG. Pappus usually of 1 long awn and several very short scales. .... 13. *L. Burkei*
      EE. Pappus, when present, ± monomorphic, or if dimorphic the longer members not awns; herbage usually glandular. .. 14. *L. coronaria*
  CC. Lvs. all essentially entire; corollas turning deep red in dilute aequous alkali.
    D. Plants biennial or short-lived perennials; coastal .... 2. *L. macrantha*
    DD. Plants annual; coastal or inland. .... 1. *L. chrysostoma*
AA. Phyllaries united into a partial cup, the tips free.
  B. Phyllaries united into a cup over ⅔ their length; aks., if epappose, over 1.8 mm. long.
    C. Aks. epappose.
      D. Aks. obovate to oblong, strongly flattened, with a conspicuous marginal fringe of stiff blunt hairs. .... 8. *L. chrysantha*
      DD. Aks. ± clavate, not strongly flattened; ak. pubescence, if any, not restricted to margins.
        E. Aks. glabrous or pubescent with rusty or yellowish wartlike papillae. .... 9. *L. glabrata*
        EE. Aks. pubescent with short curved hairs. .... 10. *L. Ferrisiae*
    CC. Aks. pappose. .... 7. *L. glaberrima*
  BB. Phyllaries united ⅓–½ their length; epappose aks. under 1.5 mm. long.
  12. *L. conjugens*

A list of the spp. is given as recognized by Ornduff, with chromosome numbers and synonymy:

1. **L. chrysóstoma** (F. & M.) Greene. $n = 8, 16$. Equals No. 3 under *Baeria* in the FLORA with the two sspp. there recognized. [*Baeria chrysostoma* F. & M. *B. gracilis* DC. *Burrielia tenerrima* DC. *B. hirsuta* Nutt. *B. longifolia* Nutt. *B. parviflora* Nutt. *Baeria Clevelandii* Gray. *B. curta* Gray. *B. Palmeri* var. *clementina* Gray. *Lasthenia hirsutula* Greene. *Baeria h.* Greene. *B. chrysostoma* ssp. *h.* Ferris. *B. c.* var. *gracilis* formae *crassa* and *nuda* Hall.]

2. **L. macrántha** (Gray) Greene. $n = 16, 24$. Equals No. 2 under *Baeria* in the FLORA. [*Burrielia chrysostoma* var. *m.* Gray. *Baeria m.* var. *pauci-aristata* Gray. *B. m.* var. *littoralis* Jeps. *B. m.* var. *thalassophila* J. T. Howell.]

3. **L. débilis** (Greene ex Gray) Ornduff. $n = 4$. Equals No. 8 of *Baeria* in the FLORA. [*Baeria d.* Greene ex Gray.]

4. **L. leptàlea** (Gray) Ornduff. $n = 8$. Equals No. 7 under *Baeria* in the FLORA [*B. l.* (Gray) Gray. *Burrielia l.* Gray.]

5. **L. microglóssa** (DC.) Greene. $n = 12$. This is No. 9 of *Baeria* in the FLORA. [*Baeria m.* Greene.]

6. **L. platycárpha** (Gray) Greene. $n = 4$. This is No. 4 under *Baeria* in the FLORA. [*Burrielia p.* Gray. *Baeria p.* Gray. *B. carnosa* Greene. *Lasthenia c.* Greene.]

7. **L. glabérrima** DC. $n = 5$. This is No. 1 under *Lasthenia* in the FLORA. [*Rancagua g.* Endl. ex Walp.]

8. **L. chrysántha** (Greene ex Gray) Greene. $n = 7$. This is No. 1 under *Crockeria* in the FLORA. [*Crockeria* Greene ex Gray.]

9. **L. glabràta** Lindl. $n = 7$. This is No. 2 under *Lasthenia* in the FLORA. [*L. californica* DC. in part. *Hologymne c.* Bartl. *H. glabrata* Bartl. *Monolopia californica* Fisch., Mey & Avé-Lall. *M. glabrata* Fisch., Mey & Avé-Lall.]

10. **L. Ferrísiae** Ornduff. $n = 7$. Aks. intermediate between those of *L. glabrata* ssp. *Coulteri* and *L. chrysantha*; somewhat flattened, obovate to oblong, sparingly to densely clothed on faces and margins with short, whitish or straw-colored curved hairs and papillae.—Common in the San Joaquin Valley from Contra Costa Co. to n. Kern and San Luis Obispo cos.; less common in Butte and Colusa cos. Feb.–May.

11. **L. Fremóntii** (Torr. ex Gray) Greene. $n = 6$. This is No. 6 under *Baeria* in the FLORA. [*Dichaeta F.* Torr. ex Gray. *Burrielia F.* Benth. *Baeria F.* Gray. *B. F.* var. *heterochaeta* Hoov.]

12. **L. cónjugens** Greene. $n = 6$. In the FLORA this is in synonymy under *Baeria Fremontii.* [*B. F.* var. *c.* Ferris.] Description as for *L. Fremontii,* but differing by its phyllaries which are united ¼–⅓ their length; aks. always epappose, glabrous, shining; receptacle hemispheric, densely pubescent.—Vernal pools, formerly from Santa Barbara Co. to Mendocino Co. at various stations.

13. **L. Búrkei** (Greene) Greene. $n = 6$. In the FLORA this was cited in synonymy under *Baeria Fremontii.* [*B. Burkei* Greene.] Like *L. Fremontii* in most respects, but the pappus consisting of 1 long awn and many very short scales.—From vernal pools and wet meadows from s. Mendocino Co. to central Sonoma Co. and in s. Lake Co.

14. **L. coronària** (Nutt.) Ornduff. $n = 5$, or 4. This is No. 1 under *Baeria* in the FLORA as *B. californica.* [*Hymenoxys c.* Hook. *Ptilomeris anthemoides* Nutt. *Burrielia a.* Gray. *Actinolepis a.* Gray. *Baeria a.* Gray. *B. coronaria* f. *a.* Voss. *B. aristata* f. *a.* Hall. *Ptilomeris a.* Nutt. *B. a.* Cov. *P. coronaria* Nutt. *Hymenoxys californica β c.* T. & G. *Actinolepis c.* Gray. *B. c.* Gray. *Ptilomeris mutica* Nutt. *Hymenoxys m.* T. & G. *Actinolepis m.* Gray. *Baeria m.* Gray. *B. coronaria* f. *m.* Voss. *B. aristata* f. *m.* Hall. *Ptilomeris affinis* Nutt. *Actinolepis a.* Benth. & Hook. *Baeria a.* Gray. *B. aristata* var. *a.* Hall. *Ptilomeris tenella* Nutt. *Actinolepis t.* Gray. *Baeria t.* Gray. *B. aristata* var. *affinis* f. *truncata* Hall. *B. Parishii* Wats. *B. aristata* var. *P.* Hall. *B. a.* var. *P.* f. *quadrata* Hall. *B. a.* var. *P.* f. *varia* Hall.]

15. **L. mìnor** (DC.) Ornduff. $n = 4$. This is No. 5 under *Baeria* in the FLORA. [*Monolepis m.* DC. *Eriophyllum m.* Rydb. *Baeria m.* Ferris. *Dichaeta tenella* Nutt. *Baeria uliginosa* var. *t.* Gray. *B. u.* var. *tenera* Gray. *Lasthenia tenella* Greene. *Baeria tenella* Greene. *Dichaeta uliginosa* Nutt. *Baeria u.* Gray. *Lasthenia u.* Greene.]

Ssp. **marítima** (Gray) Ornduff. [*Burrielia m.* Gray. *Baeria m.* Gray. *Baeria minor* ssp. *m.* Ferris.]

p. 1145. MONOLÒPIA

3. **M. lanceolàta** Nutt. $n = 10$ (Raven & Kyhos, 1961).

p. 1146. ERIOPHÝLLUM

1. **E. lanàtum** (Pursh) Forbes. J. S. Mooring (Madroño 18: 236–239. 1966) reports the following: var. **lanàtum** $2n = 16$; var. **achillaeòìdes** $2n = 16$, 32, 48; var. **aphanáctis** $2n = 32$; var. **arachnoìdeum**, $2n = $ ca. 16; var. **crocèum**, $2n = 32$; var. **cuneàtum**, $2n = $ ca. 32; var. **grandiflorum**, $2n = 16, 32$; var. **integrifòlium**, $2n = 16$; var. **lanceolàtum**, $2n = 16$; var. **leucophýllum**, $2n = 32$.

p. 1147. 1. **E. lanàtum** (Pursh) Forbes var. **achillaeoìdes** (DC.) Jeps. occurs in Monterey Co., *Howitt & Howell* and in San Luis Obispo Co., *Hardham.*

p. 1149. 4. **E. confertiflòrum** (DC.) Gray var. **laxiflòrum** Gray seems worth recognition. The upper stems are very slender; lvs. with narrow divisions; infl. open, few-fld.; peduncles 1–3 cm. long; heads. small.—Santa Clara Co. to Tehachapi Mts., Kern Co., thence n. along Sierran foothills to Mariposa Co.

p. 1150. 8. **E. ambíguum** (Gray) Gray var. **paleàceum** (Bdg.) Ferris. Invols. 5–7 mm. high (4.5–5 in typical *ambiguum*); phyllaries broadly acute, not indurate except for carinate ridge; disk-fls. 2–3 mm. long (as against 1.3–2 mm.)—

Mono Co. to Death Valley and to Riverside Co.; Nev. *E. ambiguum* ranges
from Ft. Tejon and the Tehachapi Mts. to the Greenhorn Mts., Kern Co.

p. 1152.   RIGIOPÁPPUS
1. **R. leptoclàdus** Gray. $n = 9$, not 8 as reported in 1959 printing.

p. 1153.   TRICHOPTÍLIUM
1. **T. incìsum** (Gray) Gray. $n = 13$ (Ravens & Kyhos, 1961).

p. 1154.   CHAENÁCTIS
Spp. 1, 2 and 4 of the FLORA have $n = 6$ (Raven & Kyhos, 1961).
Abrams & Ferris (Ill. Fl. Pac. States 4: 240. 1960) recognize under
7. **C. Douglásii** (Hook.) H. & A. the following taxa in Calif.:

A. Annual to biennial, floccose-canescent, to 6 dm. high; fls. white to pinkish; phyllaries
    moderately glandular-puberulent and loosely canescent; pappus-paleae not over half
    the length of the corollas. Ne. Calif. to B.C., Mont., Ariz. . . . . Var. *achilleifolia*
AA. Perennial.
    B.   To 1 dm. high; pappus-paleae to half the corolla length; heads few. From 7000–
         9000 ft. Desert ranges and Sierra Nevada to Wash., Mont. . . . . . . Var. *montana*
    BB. From 1.5–3 dm. high; pappus-paleae more than half the corolla length. From
         3700–10,000 ft., e. side of the Sierra Nevada, and from Tulare Co. to Nevada Co.
         Var. *rubricaulis*

3. **C. suffrutéscens** Gray. $n = 6$ (Mooring, 1965).
6. **C. alpìna** (Gray) Jones. $n = 6$ (Mooring, 1965).
7. **C. Douglásii** (Hook.) H. & A. In the above treatment var. **Douglásii** is
n. of Calif. with $n = 12$ (Gillett, 1954; Raven & Kyhos, 1961); $2n = 12, 24,$
25 (Mooring, 1965).
Var. **achilleifòlia** (H. & A.) A. Nels. [*C. a.* H. & A.] Mooring (Brittonia 17:
25. 1965) suggests that Calif. plants are var. *achilleifolia* with $n = 6$ (Raven
& Kyhos, 1961).
Var. **montàna** Jones. [*C. panamintensis* Stockwell.] $n = 6$ (Raven & Kyhos,
1961).
Var. **rubricaúlis** (Rydb.) Ferris. [*C. r.* Rydb.] $n = 6$ (Raven & Kyhos,
1961).
8. **C. glabriúscula** DC. Raven & Kyhos, 1961, give $n = 6$ for vars. **lanòsa**,

p. 1156. **denudàta**, **cúrta**, **gracilénta**, **tenuifòlia**. Abrams & Ferris (Ill. Fl. Pac. States 4:
242. 1960) recognizes **C. tanacetifòlia** Gray as distinct from **C. glabriúscula** in
having 8 pappus-paleae in 2 series instead of ca. 4 in 1 series. They say that
the former is 6–15 cm. high, few- to several-stemmed and has lvs. with the
pinnate divisions crowded and has a var. **gracilénta** with plant 15–25 cm. high,
more erect; lvs. with pinnae more remote.—*C. tanacetifòlia* Gray occurs in the
inner Coast Ranges of Solano, Lake, Napa, and Yolo cos., Santa Clara Co. to
San Benito. Var. **gracilénta** (Greene) Stockwell [*C. g.* Greene. *C. g.* var. *fili-
folia* Jeps. *C. glabriuscula* var. *g.* Keck], Yolo, Lake, and Napa cos.
9. **C. macrántha** D. C. Eat. $n = 6$ (Raven & Kyhos, 1961).
10. **C. carphoclínia** Gray. $n = 8$ (Raven & Kyhos, 1961).
Var. **attenuàta** (Gray) Jones. $n = 8$ (Raven & Kyhos, 1961).
11. **C. Fremóntii** Gray. $n = 5$ (Raven & Kyhos 1961).

p. 1157. 12. **C. Xantiàna** Gray. $n = 7$ (Raven & Kyhos, 1961).
13. **C. stevioìdes** H. & A. $n = 5$ (Raven & Kyhos, 1961).
Var. **brachypáppa** (Gray) Hall. $n = 5$ (Raven & Kyhos, 1961).
14. **C. artemisiifòlia** (Harv. & Gray) Gray. $n = 8$ (Raven & Kyhos, 1961).

p. 1158. PALAFÓXIA
1. **P. lineàris** (Cav.) Lag. $n = 12$ (Raven & Kyhos, 1961); $n = 10$ (Ball,
1965).
Var. **gigantèa** Jones. $n = 12$ (Raven & Kyhos, 1961).
AMBLYOPÁPPUS
1. **A. pusíllus** H. & A. $n = 8$ (Raven & Kyhos, 1961).

p. 1159. BLENNOSPÉRMA
1. **B. nànum** (Hook.) Blake var. **robústum** J. T. Howell. $n = 7$ (Ornduff,
1960).

2. **B. Bàkeri** Heiser. Reported from 4 mi. s. of El Verano, s. of Sonoma, W. *Roderick*.

PÉCTIS

1. **P. pappòsa** Harv. & Gray ex Gray. $n = 12$ (Raven & Kyhos, 1961).

p. 1160. NICOLLÈTIA

1. **N. occidentális** Gray. $n = 10$ (Raven & Kyhos, 1961).

TAGÈTES

1. **T. minúta** L. Reported from 8 mi. n. of Visalia, Tulare Co., *Fuller*; Exeter, Tulare Co., *Haworth*.

p. 1161. DYSSÒDIA

1. **D. porophylloìdes** Gray. $n = 13$ (Raven & Kyhos, 1961).

2. **D. Coóperi** Gray. $n = 13$ (Raven & Kyhos, 1961).

4. **D. Thúrberi** (Gray) Rob. Hitherto known from mts. of e. Mojave Desert, San Bernardino Co. Taken by *L. B. Ziegler* at Pinyon Flats, San Jacinto Mts., Riverside Co. in a spot ca. 175 ft. in diam. and containing several hundred plants.

POROPHÝLLUM

1. **P. grácile** Benth. $n = 24$ (Raven & Kyhos, 1961).

p. 1163. ASTERÈAE

In Key to Genera, under A, B, CC, DD, E, change F to:

> F. Phyllaries in ± distinct vertical ranks.
> G. Upright stems annual; lvs. rigid, ± persistent.
> 81. *Petradoria*
> GG. Upright stems perennial; lvs. not rigid or persistent.
> 82. *Chrysothamnus*

p. 1164. GRINDÈLIA

1. **G. hùmilis** H. & A. $n = 6$ (Raven et al., 1960).

2. **G. hirsùtula** H. & A. $n = 12$ (Raven et al., 1960).

p. 1165. 3. **G. prócera** Greene. $n = 12$ (Dunford, 1964). Delete *G. camporum* var. *parviflora* as a synonym. The two above taxa can apparently be distinguished:

> A. Rays mostly 32–44, the laminae 8–10 mm. long; aks. 2–4 mm. long, usually dull to fuscous-brown.—San Joaquin V. from Sacramento Co. to Kern Co. and to n. base of San Gabriel Mts. . . . . *G. procera*
> AA. Rays 16–18, the laminae 7–8 mm. long; aks. 4–5.2 mm. long, strawcolor to light brown. About San Francisco Bay. . . . . *G. camporum* var. *parviflora*

4. **G. marítima** (Greene) Steyerm. $n = 12$ (Raven et al., 1960).

5. **G. strícta** DC. ssp. **venulósa** (Jeps.) Keck. $2n = 24$ (De Jong & Montgomery, 1963). Reported from Monterey Co., *Howitt & Howell*. *G. arenicola* Steyerm.; $n = 12$ (Raven et al., 1960).

6. **G. latifòlia** Kell.; $2n = 24$ (De Jong & Montgomery, 1963); $n = 12$ (Raven et al., 1960).

Ssp. **platyphýlla** (Greene) Keck. [*G. rubricaulis* var. *permixta* Steyerm.; $n = 12$ (Raven et al., 1964).]

7. **G. squarròsa** (Pursh) Dunal; $n = 6$ (Raven et al., 1960).

p. 1166. 8. **G. Hállii** Steyerm.; $n = 6$ (Raven et al., 1960).

9. **G. campòrum** Greene; $n = 12$ (Raven et al., 1960). [*G. robusta* var. *Davyi* Jeps.; $n = 6$ (Raven et al., 1960).] Insert:

Var. **parviflòra** Steyerm. Rays 16–18, the laminae 7–8 mm. long; aks. 4–5.2 mm. long, stramineous or light brown.—About San Francisco Bay.

11. **G. robústa** Nutt.; $n = 12$ (Raven et al., 1960). [*G. rubricaulis* var. *elata* Steyerm., $n = 6$ (Raven et al., 1960).]

GUTIERRÈZIA

Solbrig, O. T. Cytotaxonomic and evolutionary studies in the N. Am. spp. of Gutierrezia. Contr. Gray Herb. 188: 1–63. 1960. The Calif. spp. of Gutierrezia. Madroño 18: 75–84. 1965.

> A. Heads with only 2–3 fls.; invol. very narrow, to 1.5 mm. wide; aks. of disk fls. aborted. From desert fringes. . . . . 4. *G. microcephala*
> AA. Heads with more than 4 fls.; invol. turbinate, 1.5 or more mm. wide; aks. of disk fls. fertile.

B. The heads clustered at ends of branchlets; fls. 5–10; invol. less than 5 mm. wide.
S. Calif. . . . . 3. *G. Sarothrae*
BB. The heads mostly solitary at the ends of branchlets; fls. usually more than 10;
invol. sometimes more than 5 mm. wide.
C. Infl. loosely corymbose; heads 6–10 mm. high, 4–6 mm. wide; open, little-
branched shrub. San Francisco Bay area. . . . . 1. *G. californica*
CC. Infl. paniculate; heads 4–7 mm. high, 2–5 mm. wide; a globose, much-
branched shrub. Coast Ranges and S. Calif. . . . . 2. *G. bracteata*

p. 1167.   1. **G. califórnica** (DC.) T. & G. [*Brachyris c.* DC. *Xanthocephalum c.*
Greene.] Invol. 6–10 mm. high, 4–6 mm. broad, turbinate to campanulate,
the phyllaries ca. 20, in 3 overlapping series, lanceolate to ovate; ligulate fls.
ca. 9, the ligules narrowly lanceolate, 3–4 mm. long; tubular fls. ca. 11, glabrous, 3–4 mm. high. On serpentine, about San Francisco Bay (Angel Id.,
Oakland, Point Bonita).

           2. **G. bracteàta** Abrams. [*G. californica* var. *b.* Hall.] Invol. 5–6.5 mm. high,
conical to turbinate, the phyllaries in ca. 3 rows, narrow, elongate, carinate or
strongly convex, to 4 mm. long and 2 mm. wide; ligulate fls. usually 5 (3–6),
6–8 mm. long; tubular fls. usually 4 (2–6), 4–6 mm. long. $n = 8$ (Solbrig et
al., 1964).—Inner Coast Ranges, Yolo Co. to Riverside Co. and L. Calif.

           3. **G. Saròthrae** (Pursh) Britt. & Rusby. As in the FLORA. $n = 12$ (Solbrig
et al., 1964).

           4. **G. microcéphala** (DC.) Gray. As in the FLORA.

AMPHIPÁPPUS
           10. **A. Fremóntii** T. & G.; $n = 9$ (Raven et al., 1960).

p. 1168.   ACAMPTOPÁPPUS
           1. **A. sphaerocéphalus** (Harv. & Gray) Gray; $n = 9$ (Raven et al., 1960).
           2. **A. Shóckleyi** Gray; $n = 9$ (Raven et al., 1960).

CHRYSÓPSIS
           1. **C. villòsa** (Pursh) Nutt. var. **Bolánderi** (Gray) Gray ex Jeps. $n = 9$
(Raven et al., 1960).

p. 1169.   Var. **fastigiàta** (Greene) Hall; $n = 9$ (Raven et al., 1960).
           Var. **híspida** (Hook.) Gray ex D. C. Eat. $n = 9$ (Raven et al.)

p. 1170.   2. **C. oregòna** (Nutt.) Gray var. **scabérrima** Gray; occurs in the Greenhorn
Mts., Kern Co., *Twisselmann.*
           3. **C. Brèweri** Gray also in the Greenhorn Mts.

HETEROTHÈCA
           Shinners in 1951, Wagenknecht in 1960, and Harms in 1965 agree that
Chrysopsis and *Heterotheca* should be combined under *Heterotheca*, but the
taxa in *Chrysopsis* are still so imperfectly understood that not all the necessary combinations have been made.

p. 1171.   1. **H. grandiflòra** Nutt.; $n = 9$ (Raven et al., 1960).
           2. **H. subaxillàris** (Lam.) Britt. & Rusby was found in Ventura Co., *Pollard.*
$n = 9$ (Smith, 1965).

p. 1172.   CHAETOPÁPPA
           2. **C. aúrea** (Nutt.) Keck; $n = 9$ (Solbrig et al., 1964).
           3. **C. frágilis** (Bdg.) Keck; $n = 9$ (Solbrig et al., 1964).
           4. **C. bellidiflòra** (Greene) Keck; $n = 9$ (Solbrig et al., 1964). Occurs in
the Santa Lucia Mts., Monterey Co., *Howitt & Howell.*
           5. **C. éxilis** (Gray) Keck; $n = 9$ (Solbrig et al., 1964).
           6. **C. alsinoìdes** (Greene) Keck; $n = 9$ (Solbrig et al., 1964).

p. 1173.   HAPLOPÁPPUS
           In Key under AA and before B insert:

A′. Pappus deciduous, ± in a ring; tall annual or biennial herbs with spiny-dentate lvs.
(Section Prionopsis). . . . . 4a. *H. ciliatus*
A′A′. Pappus persistent, if plant herbaceous (Section Blepharodon).

p. 1175.   1. **H. grácilis** (Nutt.) Gray. $n = 2, 3$ (Jackson, 1965).
           1a. **H. Ravènii** Jackson near to *H. gracilis* (Nutt.) Gray, but with shorter
pappus bristles and shorter aks. and with the bases of the larger bristles ca.

twice as wide as in *H. gracilis*. In *H. Ravenii* the invol. is always hirsute, in *H. gracilis* usually strigose. In **H. R.** *n* = 4; in *H. g. n* = 2 or 3. Some plants previously referred to *H. gracilis* belong to *H. Ravenii*.

4a. **H. ciliàtus** (Nutt.) DC. [*Donia c.* Nutt. *Aster c.* O. Kuntze.] Erect, annual or biennial, 5–15 dm. high; stems very leafy to top, glabrous; lvs. oval to oblong, dentate with spine-tipped teeth, very obtuse, 3–8 cm. long; heads few, in open cymes; invol. 12–18 mm. high, the phyllaries in several series, the outer ± squarrose; rays many, the ligules 12–18 mm. long.—Mo. to Tex., Okla., New Mex. Introd. in Ventura and San Francisco cos., *Howell.*

5. **H. carthamoìdes ssp. Cusíckii** (Gray) Hall has been found in Plumas Co., *Howell.*

p. 1176.   8. **H. apargioìdes** Gray; *n* = 6 (Solbrig et al., 1964).

p. 1178.   12. **H. Whítneyi** Gray. Occurs in the Greenhorn Mts., Kern Co., *Twisselmann.*

17. **H. Macronèma** Gray. *n* = 9 (Solbrig et al., 1964). Reported from the White Mts., *Howell.*

p. 1180.   24. **H. linearifòlius** DC.; *n* = 9 (Raven et al., 1960).
Var. *intèrior* Jones; *n* = 9 (Solbrig et al., 1964).
25. **H venètus** (HBK.) Blake ssp. **vernonioìdes** (Nutt.) Hall; *n* = 6 (Raven et al., 1960).

p. 1181.   26. **H. acradènius** (Greene) Blake; *n* = 12 (Raven et al., 1960).
Ssp. **eremóphilus** (Greene) Hall; 2*n* = 12 (Raven et al., 1960).
27. **H. cànus** (Gray) Blake. *n* = 5 (Raven et al., 1960).
28. **H. squarròsus** H. & A.; *n* = 5 (Raven et al., 1960).

p. 1182.   29. **H. pinifòlius** Gray. Sends out long underground shoots to form new plants. Occurs in Monterey Co., *Howitt & Howell.*
30. **H. ericoìdes** (Less.) H. & A. 2*n* = 18 (De Jong & Montgomery, 1963).

p. 1183.   32. **H. Pálmeri** Gray ssp. **pachylèpis** Hall; *n* = 9 (Raven et al., 1960). Reported from San Emigdio Range, Kern Co., *Twisselmann.*
35. **H. Coóperi** (Gray); *n* = 9 (Raven et al., 1960).
36. **H. arboréscens** (Gray) Hall; *n* = 9 (Raven et al., 1960). Reported from the Greenhorn and Piute ranges, Kern Co., *Twisselmann.*
37. **H. Paríshii** (Greene) Blake; 2*n* = 18 (DeJong & Montgomery, 1963).

p. 1184.   38. **H. cuneàtus** Gray; *n* = 9 (Solbrig et al., 1964). Occurs in Monterey Co., *Howitt & Howell.*

p. 1185.   SOLIDÀGO

1. **S. occidentàlis** (Nutt.) T. & G.; *n* = 9 (Raven et al., 1960).
2. **S. califórnica** Nutt; *n* = 9 (Raven et al., 1960).

p. 1186.   6. **S. confinis** Gray; *n* = 9 (Raven et al., 1960; Solbrig et al., 1964).
7. **S. spectábilis** (D. C. Eat.) Gray. At Kernville, Kern Co., *Twisselmann.*
8. **S. spathulàta** DC.; *n* = 9 (Raven et al., 1960).

PETRADÒRIA
Change generic description to:
Suffrutescent herbs with woody caudex; stems several, annual, leafy to the infl., resinous, prominently striate; lvs. linear to lanceolate or oblanceolate, 3–5-parallel-veined, coriaceous, entire; infl. open, racemose to corymbose; invol. cylindric, the phyllaries in ± vertical ranks, keelless or nearly so, ovate-oblong; fls. 4–7, yellow, the rays present or absent; aks. somewhat compressed, glabrous; pappus brownish, the bristles somewhat unequal, capillary, finely twisted.

A.   Ray-fls. present; invol. 5–9 mm. high. . . . . 1. *P. pumila*
AA. Ray-fls. absent; invol. 11 or more mm. high. 2. *P. discoidea*

p. 1187.   2. **P. discoìdea** L. C. Anderson. [*Chrysothamnus gramineus* Hall.] See description of sp. no. 7 on p. 1189. Cf. Anderson, L. R. Studies on Petradoria. Trans. Kans. Acad. Sci. 66: 632–684. 1964.
CHRYSOTHÁMNUS
1. **C. panículàtus** (Gray) Hall. 2*n* = 18 (De Jong & Montgomery, 1963).

p. 1188.   4. **C. viscidiflòrus** (Hook.) Nutt. ssp. **pùmilus** (Nutt.) Hall & Clem. occurs in the Piute Mts. and on Mt. Pinos, Kern Co., *Twisselmann*. L. C. Anderson (Madroño 17: 223–4. 1964) recognizes ssp. **hùmilis** (Greene) Hall & Clem. on the basis of long narrow invols., few fls. in a head; style branches sparsely or not exserted; stigmatic appendages long. Hence separate from ssp. **pubérulus** (D. C. Eat.) Hall & Clem.

    5. **C. axillàris** Keck. L. C. Anderson makes this a ssp. of *C. viscidiflorus*.

p. 1189.   7. **C. gramíneus** Hall. See **Petradoria discoidea** L. C. Anderson.

    8. **C.** × **Bolánderi** (Gray) Greene. Considered to be a hybrid between *C. nauseosus* and *Haplopappus Macronema* by Anderson & Reveal, Madroño 18: 225–232. 1966.

p. 1190.   8. **C. Párryi** (Gray) Greene ssp. **vulcánicus** (Greene) Hall & Clem. is found in the Greenhorn Mts., Kern Co., *Twisselmann*.

p. 1191.   9. **C. nauseòsus** (Pall.) Britton ssp. **consímilis** (Greene) Hall & Clem.; $n = 9$ (Raven et al., 1960).

    Ssp. **mohavénsis** (Greene) Hall & Clem.; $n = 9$ (Raven et al., 1960).

p. 1192.   MONÓPTILON
    2. **M. bellioìdes** (Gray) Hall; $2n = 8$ (Raven et al., 1960).

p. 1194.   PSILÁCTIS
    1. **P. Còulteri** Gray. $n = 5$ (Solbrig et al., 1964).—Turner and Horne (Brittonia 16: 316–331. 1964) include *Psilactis* in *Machaeranthera* and have the combination *M. Coulteri* (Gray) Turner & Horne.

p. 1196.   ÁSTER
    2. **A. oregonénsis** (Nutt.) Cronq. ssp. **califórnicus** (Durand) Keck.
    Add to the synonymy *Sericocarpus o.* ssp. *c.* Ferris.

p. 1197.   9. **A. subspicàtus** Nees; $n = 25$ (Raven et al., 1960).
p. 1198.   10. **A. Eatònii** (Gray) Howell occurs in the Piute Mts., Kern Co., *Twisselmann*.

    13. **A. occidentàlis** (Nutt.) T. & G. Ferris (Madroño 15: 128. 1959) recognizes under *A. occidentalis* (which she restricts to the Sierra Nevada and n.):
    Var. **Paríshii** (Gray) Ferris. [*A. Fremontii* var. *P.* Gray.] Ca. 3 dm. tall; lvs. slightly clasping, linear-lanceolate, the basal oblanceolate; heads in a short cymose panicle (instead of 1 to few); invol. 5–8 mm. high (instead of 6 mm.)—Mts. of s. Calif. to L. Calif.
    Var. **delectábilis** (Hall) Ferris. [*A. d.* Hall.] Lvs. definitely clasping; heads 1–few; invol. 8–10 mm. high. $n = 16$ (Raven et al., 1960). Fresno and Tulare cos. in the Sierra Nevada.

p. 1199.   16. **A. adscéndens** Lindl. in Hook. Found in Piute Mts., Kern Co., *Twisselmann*.

p. 1200.   17. **A. pauciflòrus** Nutt. occurs at Isabella, Kern Co., *Twisselmann*.

    18. **A. alpígenus** ssp. **Andersònii** (Gray) Onno; $n = 18$ (Raven et al., 1960).

    21. **A. spinòsus** Benth; $n = 9$ (Raven et al,. 1960).

p. 1201.   23. **A. éxilis** Ell.; $2n = 10$ (Huziwara, 1958); $n = 5$ (Solbrig et al., 1964).
p. 1202.   MACHAERÁNTHERA
    2. **M. leucanthemifòlia** (Greene) Greene; $n = 5$ (Raven et al., 1960).

p. 1203.   4. **M. shasténsis** Gray var. **glossophýlla** (Piper) Cronq. & Keck. Next to last word in paragraph should be "*M.*" not "*A.*" *canescens*.

p. 1204.   5. **M. canéscens** (Pursh) Gray; $n = 4$ (Raven et al., 1960; Solbrig et al., 1964).

    6. **M. tortifòlia** (Gray) Cronq. & Keck; $n = 6$ (Raven et al., 1960).

p. 1205.   CORETHRÓGYNE
    1. **C. califórnica** var. **obovàta** (Benth.) Kuntze; $n = 5$ (Raven et al., 1960).
    3. **C. filaginifòlia** (H. & A.) Nutt.; $2n = 10$ (De Jong & Montgomery, 1963).

p. 1206.   Var. **pinetòrum** Jtn.; $n = 5$ (Raven et al., 1960).
    Var. **brevícula** (Greene) Canby; $n = 5$ (Raven et al., 1960).
    Var. **bernardìna** (Abrams) Hall; $n = 5$ (Raven et al., 1960).
    Var. **virgàta** (Benth.) Gray; $n = 5$ (Raven et al., 1960).

p. 1207.   Var. **linifòlia** Hall is treated as a sp. *C. linifolia* (Hall) Ferris in Abrams and Ferris, Ill. Fl. Pac. States 4: 238. 1960.

p. 1210.   ERÍGERON

In Key after CC, D insert:

> D′.   Lvs. to 2.5 cm. long, in part 3-toothed or -lobed at apex; heads on solitary peduncles, to 2 cm. across; rays many, pink or whitish or purplish. Garden escape. . . . . 39a. *E. Karwinskianus*
> D′D′. Lvs. not much toothed or lobed at apex. Native.
>   E.   Root-crown, etc. as in the FLORA.

p. 1211.   4. **E. philadélphicus** L.; $2n = 18$ (Mulligan, 1957).

5. **E. glaùcus** Ker. $n = 9$ (Pagni, 1954; Raven et al., 1960).

p. 1214.   21. **E. aphanáctis** (Gray) Greene; $n = 9$ (Solbrig, et al., 1964).

23. **E. Bloòmeri** Gray; $n = 9$ (Solbrig et al., 1964).

p. 1217.   38. **E. Brèweri** var. **porphyreticus** (Jones) Cronq.; $2n = 18$ (Montgomery & Yang, 1960).

p. 1218.   39. **E. foliòsus** Nutt. in Tehachapi Mts., Kern Co., *Twisselmann.*

Var. **Hartwégii** (Greene) Jeps. at Tejon Pass, Kern Co., *Twisselmann.*

Var. **stenophýllus** (Nutt.) Gray; $n = 9$ (Raven et al., 1960). Reported from Monterey Co., *Howitt & Howell.*

p. 1220.   44. **E. strigòsus** Muhl. $n = 35$–36 (Taylor, 1967).

p. 1221.   LESSÍNGIA

1. Ferris (Contr. Dudley Herb. 5: 102. 1959) transferred L. **germanòrum** Cham. var. **Peirsònii** J. T. Howell to *L. Lemmonii* Gray var. *Peirsonii.* She recognized

p. 1222.   *L. ramulosíssima* A. Nels as *L. Lemmonii* var. *r.* (A. Nels.) Ferris, with narrower invols. than in *L. Lemmonii.* She had *L. glandulifera* Gray $n = 5$ (Raven et al., 1960) as a sp. with var. *tomentosa* (Greene) Ferris and var. *pectinata* (Greene) Jeps.

3. **L. nemáclada** Greene; $n = 5$ (Solbrig et al., 1964) [*L. mendocina* Greene; $n = 5, 6$ (Raven et al., 1960).]

p. 1223.   6. **L. ramulòsa** Gray in Benth.; $n = 5$ (Raven et al., 1960).

Ferris had *L. micradenia* Greene as a sp. with var. *glabrata* (Keck) Ferris. and var. *arachnoidea* (Greene) Ferris.

7. **L. hololeùca** Greene; $n = 5$ (Solbrig et al., 1964).

p. 1224.   CONÝZA

The authority for the genus should be Less., not L., for the 1959 printing.

1a. After *C. canadensis* insert **C. Bilboàna** Remy. Like *C. canadensis* in appearance, but the corollas of the outer fls. obliquely tubular, not ligulate.— A weed in the San Francisco region; native of S. Am.

p. 1226.   BÁCCHARIS

3. **B. Douglásii** DC.; $n = 9$ (Solbrig et al., 1964).

4. **B. glutinòsa** Pers.; $n = 9$ (Turner et al., 1961).

5. **B. vimínea** DC.; $n = 9$ (Solbrig et al., 1964).

6. **B. Emòryi** Gray; $2n = 18$ (De Jong & Montgomery, 1963).

p. 1227.   8. **B. sergiloìdes** Gray. $2n = 18$ (De Jong & Montgomery, 1963).

9. **B. sarothroìdes** Gray; $2n = 18$ (De Jong & Montgomery, 1963).

p. 1228.   ÁNTHEMIS

Key out *Anthemis* as follows:

> A.   Plants annual; rays white.
>   B.   Phyllaries brown, the summit largely membranaceous, dark; stems very slender, ± reddish. Sonoma Co. . . . . 1. *A. fuscata*
>   BB. Phyllaries not brown, scarious-tipped or -margined.
>   C.   Plant glabrous or slightly hairy, foetid; aks. tubercled; receptacle-scales linear-acute. . . . . 2. *A. Cotula*
>   CC. Plant pubescent or woolly, aromatic; aks. ribbed, not tubercled; receptacle-scales lanceolate-cuspidate. . . . . 3. *A. arvensis*
>   BB. Plant perennial; rays yellow. . . . . 4. *A. tinctoria*

3. **A. arvénsis** L. One–6 dm. high; lvs. 3–5 cm. long, bipinnatifid; phyllaries viscid-tomentose, narrowly hyaline-margined; rays 15–20; pappus a minute crown or none.—Garberville, Humboldt Co.; native of Eu.

4. **A. tinctòria** L. Perennial, 3–9 dm. high, whitish-villous; lvs. evenly pinnate, the pinnae incised; rays 20–30, yellow; pappus a short crown.—Escape in Plumas and Alameda cos.; from Eu.

ACHILLÈA

1. **A. Millefòlium** L. reported from 2 mi. out of Magalia along Pentz road, Butte Co., *Howell.*

p. 1230.   HYMENÒTHRIX
Cite as reference: Turner, B. L. Taxonomy of Hymenothrix. Brittonia 14: 101–119. 1962.

2. **H. Loomísii** Blake. Recorded as e. of Weimar, Placer Co., *Fuller.*

p. 1231.   CHRYSÁNTHEMUM
1. **C. carinàtum** L. $n = 9$ (Rana, 1965). Reported from Oceano. San Luis Obispo Co., *Fuller.*

4. **C. Leucánthemum** L. $2n = 18, 36$ (Böcher & Larsen, 1957).

5. **C. anethifòlium** Webb. & Barth. $n = 9$ (Linder & Lambert, 1965).

6. **C. Parthènium** (L.) Bernh. Delete "Pers."

p. 1232.   TANACETUM
2. **T. Douglásii** DC. $n = 27$ (Raven). Raven calls attention to the fact that this sp. forms large mats, while *T. camphoràtum* Less., $n = 27$ (Raven) has more individual plants.

3. **T. camphoràtum** Less. is recorded by *Raven* as from Samoa, Humboldt Co.

p. 1233.   MATRICÀRIA
Ferris in Abrams Ill. Fl. Pac. States 4: 399. 1960 recognizes:

A. Pappus-crown minute, entire, the aks. with 2 glandular lines which extend the length of the ak. but not into the minute pappus-crown; mature heads usually 6–9 mm. high. . . . . 1. *M. matricarioides*
AA. Pappus-crown evident, with 2 short lobes or teeth, these bearing oblanceolate or elliptic glands which scarcely extend onto the body of the ak.; mature heads usually 10–11 mm. high. . . . . 2. *M. occidentalis*

1. **M. matricarioìdes** (Less.) Porter.
2. **M. occidentàlis** Greene. [*Chamomilla o.* Rydb.] Much like the preceding in its general appearance, but differing in the above technical characters. Apparently quite widely distributed in Calif.

p. 1234.   ARTEMÍSIA
To be added to literature citations: Beetle, A. A. New names within the section Tridentatae. Rhodora 61: 82–85. 1959; and A study of Sagebrush. Univ. Wyo. Bull. 368. 1960:
In Key, change DD to:

DD. Fls. of center of disk sterile, the outer ♀ and fertile.
  D′.   Plants from a taproot; lvs. largely basal, the divisions ca. 1 mm. wide. Marble Mts. . . . . 9a. *A. campestris*
  D′D′. Plants from horizontal rhizomes; lvs. well distributed, they or their divisions mostly more than 3 mm. wide.
      E.   Principal lvs. narrow, 1 cm. or less wide exclusive of lobes when present, tomentose on both sides or green above; stems rarely more than 1 m. tall.
        E′.   Lvs. entire to bipinnatifid with entire lobes, these usually rather broad. . . . . 10. *A. ludoviciana*
        E′E′. Lvs. finely divided, at least some of them bipinnatifid, some of the segms. again toothed.
                                          10a. *A. Michauxiana*
      EE.   Principal lvs. 1–5 cm. wide, etc. as in FLORA.

2. **A. tridentàta** Nutt. should be reported from the inner S. Coast Ranges: on San Carlos Creek 1 mi. n. of New Idria, San Benito Creek at 2400 ft. and 0.5 mi. below New Idria at 3700 ft., *Howbecker & Quibell*; and from 12 mi. nw. of Coalinga, Fresno Co., in the n. half Sect. 1, Township 19S, Range 14E, Mt. Diablo Base and Meridian, *H. W. Wolfram.* Mr. Wolfram reports the latter station as covering over 400 acres.

3. **A. arbúscula** Nutt. ssp. **nòva** (A. Nels.) Ward occurs n. of Kenworthy Ranger Station, San Jacinto Mts., *L. B. Ziegler.* This material frequently layers.

p. 1236.   7. **A. califórnica** Less. var. **insulàris** (Rydb.) Munz. Raven (Aliso 5: 341. 1963) proposes a new name *A. nesiótica* Raven. It differs from *A. californica* in the lvs. not or little revolute, less lobed, the segms. 1–3 dm. wide; ray-fls. to 15; disk-fls. to 40 (as opposed to 6–10 and 15–30 respectively in *A. californica*). San Clemente, Santa Barbara and San Nicolas ids.

9a. **A. campéstris** L. ssp. **boreàlis** (Pallas) Hall & Clem. var. **Wormskióldii** (Besser) Cronq. A perennial 1.5–3 dm. high, with a reddish, ± canescent stem and crowded rather narrow panicle; lvs. minutely gray-silky, mostly basal, the blades 1.5–2 cm. long, the divisions linear, scarcely 1 mm. wide; heads with invols. ca. 4 mm. high, ± villous.—On dry wind-swept bluff at 7200 ft., Marble Rim, Marble Mts., Siskiyou Co., July 22, 1966, *Gilbert Muth*. Heretofore reported from n. Ore. n. and e. The specimen seen is the basis of the above description and, so far as I can determine, falls into the above classification.

p. 1237.   10a. **A. Michauxiàna** Bess. Perennial herb 2–4 dm. high; lvs. bipinnatifid with the secondary lobes again toothed, the lobes linear, widely spreading and acute; infl. narrowly paniculiform, with heads nodding, at least at first; invol. 3.5–4 mm. high, glabrous or sparingly tomentose.—Occasional in n. Calif.; to B.C., Alta., Utah. May–Aug.

13. **A. Dracúnculus** L. ascends to 10,300 ft. in White Mts.

p. 1238.   SENECIÒNEAE

In Key, line 5 from bottom of page, after "perennial" add "or annual."

p. 1239.   ADENOCÁULON

1. **A. bìcolor** Hook.; *n* = 23 (Ornduff et al., 1963).

DIMERÈSIA

1. **D. Howéllii** Gray; *n* = 7 (Ornduff et al., 1963).

p. 1240.   ÁRNICA

1. **A. Chamissònis** Less. ssp. **foliòsa** (Nutt.) Maguire; *n* = 53–54 (Ornduff et al., 1963).

p. 1241.   3. **A. amplexicáulis** Nutt.; *n* = 33–34 (Ornduff et al., 1963).

4. **A. móllis** Hook. is found in the White Mts.

5. **A. diversifòlia** Greene. *n* = 54–57 (Taylor, 1967).

6. **A. Párryi** Gray; *n* = ca. 36 (Ornduff et al., 1963).

p. 1242.   10. **A. latifòlia** Bong.; *n* = 19 (Ornduff et al., 1963).
p. 1243.   15. **A. discoìdea** Benth.; *n* = 38 (Ornduff et al., 1963).

p. 1244.   RAILLARDÉLLA

1. **R. Mùirii** Gray. Reported from Tulare Co., *Howell*.

p. 1245.   SENÈCIO

Add to literature citations: Barkley, T. M. A revision of Senecio aureus L. and allied spp. Trans. Kans. Acad. Sci. 65: 318–408. 1962.

In Key after A, BB, CC, DD, E, insert:

> E'.   Fls. white, blue, pink or purple-red; lvs. large, cordate-ovate to
> -triangular. Garden escape. .... 9a. *S. cruentus*
> E'E'.   Fls. yellow to cream. Native.
> F.   Herbage ± villous, etc. as in the FLORA.

p. 1246.   1. **S. Lyònii** Gray. *n* = 20 (Ornduff, et al., 1963).
p. 1247.   2. **S. Douglásii** DC. var. **tularénsis** Munz was found in the Greenhorn Range, Kern Co., *Twisselmann*.

Var. **monoénsis** (Greene) Jeps.; *n* = 20 (Ornduff et al., 1963).

3. **S. Blochmániae** Greene. *n* = 20 (Ornduff et al., 1963).

4. **S. spartioìdes** T. & G. *n* = 20 (Ornduff et al., 1963).

5. **S. Fremóntii** T. & G. and var. **occidentàlis** Gray. *n* = 20 (Ornduff et al., 1963).

7. **S. Clarkiànus** Gray occurs in Nevada Co., *True & Howell*, and in the Greenhorn Mts., Kern Co., *Twisselmann*.

p. 1248.   8. **S. triangulàris** Hook. *n* = 20, 40 (Ornduff et al., 1963).

9. **S. sérra** Hook. *n* = 20 (Ornduff et al., 1963).—Reported from the Piute Mts., Kern Co., *Twisselmann*.

9a. **S. cruéntus** DC. The cult. form (Florists' *Cineraria*) with large cordate-ovate to triangular lvs., white tomentose beneath, and with large heads to 7 cm. across and fls. in shades of blue, pink, purple to white.—An occasional escape from gardens, as in the San Francisco area. Native of Canary Ids.

    10. S. integérrimus Nutt. var. màjor (Gray) Cronq.; $n = 40$ (Ornduff et al.). Var. exaltàtus (Nutt.) Cronq.; $n = 20$, 40 (Ornduff et al., 1963).

    11. S. aronicoìdes DC. [*S. exaltatus* var. *uniflosculosus* Gray.] $n = 20$ (Ornduff et al., 1963). The sp. has been collected 10 mi. sw. of Salinas, Monterey Co., *Hardham*.

    12. S. foètidus Howell. $n = 20$ (Ornduff et al., 1963).

p. 1249.   13. S. hydróphilus Nutt. [*S. foetidus* var. *hydrophiloides* T. M. Barkley.] $n = 20$ (Ornduff et al., 1963).

    14. S. astéphanus Greene. The range extends into Monterey Co., *Howitt & Howell*.

    16. S. cànus Hook. $n = 23$, 46 (Ornduff et al., 1963). $n = 69$ (Taylor, 1967).

    18. S. bernardìnus Greene. $n = 23$ (Ornduff et al., 1963).

    19. S. ionophýllus Greene. $n = 23$ (Ornduff et al., 1963). It occurs in the Tehachapi Mts. and on Piute Creek, Kern Co., *Twisselmann*.

p. 1250.   20. S. Greènei Gray. $n = 20$–23 (Ornduff et al., 1963).

    21. S. werneriifòlius Gray. $n = 22$ (Wiens & Halleck, 1962).

    23. S. pauciflòrus Pursh. Barkley recognizes S. pseudáureus Rydb. for *S. pauciflorus* var. *fallax* Greenm. ex Jeps. and S. indécorus Greene for *S. pauciflorus* var. *jucundulus* Jeps., separating them as follows:

A. Basal lvs. subcordate to truncate at base, lanceolate; heads 5–20; florets yellow.
                                                                        S. pseudaureus
AA. Basal lvs. cuneate to rounded at base, broader.
    B. Lvs. thickish, suborbicular; heads mostly 1–6; florets orange. . . . . *S. pauciflorus*
    BB. Lvs. thin, membranaceous, elliptic-ovate to oblong or subreniform; heads usually
         8–20: florets yellow. . . . . *S. indecorus*

    24. S. *cymbalarioìdes* Nutt. Change name to S. streptanthifòlius *Greene*, since there was an earlier use of the name *S. c.* by Buck. $n = 23$ (Ornduff et al., 1963).

    25. S. Clevelándii Gray. $n = 23$ (Ornduff et al., 1963).

p. 1251.   27. S. Brèweri Davy. $n = 23$ (Ornduff et al., 1963).

    28. S. eurycéphalus T. & G. $n = 23$ (Ornduff et al., 1963).

    29. S. multilobàtus T. & G. $n = 23$ (Ornduff et al., 1963).

    31. S. Jacobaèa L. $2n = 32$, 40 (Böcher & Larsen, 1955). Reported from Humboldt and Del Norte cos., *Fuller*.

p. 1252.   34. S. aphanáctis Greene. $n = 20$ (Ornduff, 1963).

    35. S. sylváticus L. $n = 20$ (Ornduff et al., 1963).

    36. S. vulgàris L. $n = 20$ (Ornduff et al., 1963).

    37. S. mohavénsis Gray. $n = 20$ (Ornduff et al., 1963).

    38. S. mikanioìdes Otto. $n = 10$ (Ornduff et al., 1963).

CROCÍDIUM

    1. C. multicáule Hook. Found at 1600 ft., 2 mi. w. of jct. of Watts V. Road with Maxon Road, Fresno Co., *Weiler*; and 10.2 mi. e. of jct. of Pine Flat Road and Trimmer Springs Road, *Weiler*; also in Kern Co., *Twisselmann* and San Luis Obispo Co., *Hardham*. $n = 9$ (Ornduff et al., 1963).

p. 1253. PETASÌTES

    1. P. palmàtus (Ait.) Gray. $2n = 30$ pairs (D. E. Anderson, 1963).

PSATHYRÒTES

    1. P. ramosíssima (Torr.) Gray. $n = 17$ (Ornduff et al., 1963).

    2. P. ánnua (Nutt.) Gray. $n = 17$ (Ornduff et al., 1963).

p. 1254. LUÌNA

    1. L. hypoleùca Benth. $n = 30$ (Ornduff et al., 1963).

ERECHTITES

    1. E. argùta (A. Rich.) DC. Add as synonym *Senecio glomeratus* Desf. The sp. has been recorded as in San Luis Obispo Co., *Hardham*, and in Monterey

Co., *Howitt & Howell.*

2. **E. prenanthoìdes** (A. Rich.) DC. Add as synonym *Senecio minimus* (Poir.) DC. The sp. occurs in Monterey Co., *Howitt & Howell.*

PEUCEPHÝLLUM

1. **P. Schóttii** (Gray) Gray. $n = 20$ (Ornduff et al., 1963).

p. 1255.   TETRADÝMIA

1. **T. axillàris** A. Nels. $n = 30$ (Ornduff et al., 1963).

p. 1256.   5. **T. glabràta** Gray. $n = 62$ (Ornduff et al., 1963).

LEPIDOSPÁRTUM

1. **L. squamàtum** (Gray) Gray. $n = 30$, ca. 45 (Ornduff et al., 1963).

2. **L. latisquàmum** Wats. $n = 30$ (Ornduff et al., 1963).

p. 1257.   CALENDÙLEAE

Change Key to:

A.   Aks. strongly incurved; lvs. entire or nearly so. .... 121. *Calendula*
AA. Aks. straight; lvs. toothed or lobed. .... 121a. *Dimorphotheca*

121a. Dimorphothèca Vaill. CAPE-MARIGOLD

Herbs or undershrubs; lvs. alternate, entire to pinnatifid. Heads solitary on terminal peduncles; invol. broadly campanulate; phyllaries in 1 series, with scarious margins; receptacle naked. Ray-fls. ♀, fertile in 1 row, the style divided into 2 long stigmatic branches. Disk-fls. bisexual, fertile; style with 2 short branches. Aks. of ray-fls. 3-angled to subterete, usually wrinkled or tuberculate, or disk-fls. smooth and with thickened margins. Ca. 7 spp. of S. Afr.

1. **D. sinuàta** DC. Annual, 1–3 dm. high, loosely branched, glandular-pubescent; lvs. oblong-lanceolate, to 9 cm. long, coarsely sinuate-dentate; heads 3.5 cm. across, the rays orange-yellow.—Reported from San Diego, Riverside, San Bernardino, Ventura, Santa Barbara and Kern cos.

2. **D. Ecklònis** DC. Shrubby perennial with narrow toothed lvs.; peduncles bearing large solitary daisy-like heads having rays white above, purplish beneath; disk blackish-blue; head closing at night.—Occasional escape from cult., as at Santa Barbara, *Pollard.*

p. 1257.   INULÈAE

In Key at bottom of Page, after A, insert:

A.   Pappus of 5–many equally long bristles. .... 122. *Inula*
AA. Pappus of an outer row of short scales and an inner of long bristles. 122a. *Pulicaria*

p. 1258.   ### 122a. Pulicària Gaertn.

Distinguished from *Inula* by the 2-ranked pappus, the outer row with short scales, the inner with longer bristles. (Latin, *pulicarius*, flea-like.)

1. **P. hispánica** (Boiss.) Boiss. Annual to perennial herb, to ca. 1 m. tall, branched, short-villous throughout; lvs. alternate, oblong to narrow-oblanceolate, clasping at base, 1–6 cm. long, entire; heads many, 7–10 mm. diam.; phyllaries linear, attenuate, 3–4.8 mm. long, villous; rays yellow, the ligules 1.5–2 mm. long; aks. cylindrical, 1 mm. long, brownish.—Adventive along streams, etc., from San Luis Obispo, Orange, Riverside cos. From the Medit. region. (Cf. Raven, Aliso 5: 251–4. 1963).

PLÙCHEA

2. **P. serícea** (Nutt.) Cov. In Kern R. region, *Twisselmann.* $n = 10$ (Turner, Powell and King, 1962).

p. 1259.   GNAPHÀLIUM

In Key, after AA, BB, C, D, EE change to:

EE.   Infl. paniculate.
    F.   Phyllaries dingy, straw-colored to pale brownish; ♀ fls. 21–32; hermaphrodite fls. 11–14; heads campanulate-subglobose. Trinity and Plumas cos. n. .... 7a. *G. Macounii*

FF. Phyllaries pink at least when young; ♀ fls. 45–58; hermaphrodite fls. 6; heads turbinate to narrow-campanulate. Humboldt Co. to Orange Co. . . . . 7. *G. ramosissimum*

In Key, AA, BB, C, DD, *G. bicolor* should be no. 9; *G. leucocephalum* no. 8.
1. **G. purpùreum** L. 2*n* = 28 (Huynh, 1965).
3. **G. japónicum** Thunb. In Del Norte, Napa and San Joaquin cos., *Fuller*.

p. 1260.   7a. **G. Macóunii** Greene. [*G. decurrens* Ives, not L. *G. Ivesii* Nels & Macbr.]
Annual or biennial, 4–9 dm. tall, corymbose above, glandular-pilose, increasingly tomentose above; lvs. thin, lanceolate to linear, 3–10 cm. long, sessile,
shortly decurrent; panicle short, to 1.5 dm. across; heads 5–6 mm. high; phyllaries imbricate, dingy, thin-scarious and shining, woolly at base; corollas yellowish; pappus-bristles falling separately.—Yellow Pine F., Trinity and Plumas
cos.; to B.C. and Quebec. July–Oct.
9. **G. bìcolor** Bioletti. Add Sierran foothills, from Madera Co. to Tulare
Co., *Ferris*.
11. **G. beneòlens** A. Davids. Occurs in the Greenhorn Range, Kern Co.,
Twisselmann; in Monterey Co., *Howitt & Howell*.

p. 1261.   13. **G. lùteo-álbum** L. The first word in line 3 should be "cm." not "dm."
Occurs at Kernville, etc., Kern Co., *Twisselmann*; on San Clemente Id., *Raven*.

p. 1262.   ANTENNÀRIA
4. Ferris in Abrams, Ill. Fl. Pac. States 4: 476. 1960, separates **A. luzulo-
ìdes** T. & G. (with heads in a close corymbiform cyme; lvs. mostly 3-nerved,
the lower 3–10 cm. long, the cauline little reduced upward) and occurring
from Lasssen Co. n. and **A. microcéphala** Gray (heads in a loose or close
panicle; lvs. 1-nerved or the midrib obscure; lower lvs. 2–4.5 cm. long; cauline
lvs. abruptly reduced upward) and from Lassen, Glenn and Trinity cos. n.
6. **A. ròsea** Greene. Ferris recognizes also **A. marginàta** Greene [*A. dioica*
var. *m.* Jeps.] from the San Bernardino Mts., as having basal lvs. glabrate on
upper surface, 1–3 cm. long; plant cespitose, 2–20 cm. high; invols. campanulate, woolly at base, 6–8 mm. high, the phyllaries with pale green base, often
brown or purplish submedial spot.

p. 1263.   ANÁPHALIS
1. Change **A. margaritàcea** to (L.) Benth. ex C. B. Clarke.

p. 1264.   FILÀGO
F. vulgàris Lam. [*F. germanica* L.] has been reported from Mendocino Co.
It differs from the spp. enumerated in the FLORA by branching proliferately
from below the lowest capitate cluster of heads (instead of these being terminal or axillary) and by the outer receptacular bracts being cuspidate with the
receptacle subulate. A native of Eu.
Chrtek & Holub (Preslia 35: 9. 1963) place *F. gallica, F. californica, F. arizonica,* and *F. depressa* in a genus *Oglifa*.

p. 1265.   PSILOCÁRPHUS
1. **P. brevíssimus** Nutt. Small poolbeds, Greenhorn foothills, Kern Co.,
Twisselmann.
3. **P. tenéllus** Nutt. var. **ténuis** (Eastw.) Cronq. is reported in Marin Co.
and extending to the coast in Monterey Co., *Howell*.

p. 1266.   EVÁX
1. **E. cauléscens** (Benth.) Gray is reported from a vernal pool 6 mi. e. of
Paso Robles on the road to Creston, San Luis Obispo Co., *Hardham*.
Var. **hùmilis** (Greene) Jeps. in the Greenhorn Range, Kern Co., *Twisselmann*.
2. **E. sparsiflòra** (Gray) Jeps. var. **brevifòlia** (Gray) Jeps. is in the San
Marcos Pass, Santa Barbara Co., *Raven*.
3. **E. acáulis** (Kell.) Greene in the Santa Lucia Mts., Monterey Co., *Howitt
& Howell*.

p. 1267.   TRICHOCORÒNIS
1. **T. Wrìghtii** (T. & G.) Gray. *n* = 15 (Turner, Powell & King, 1962).

p. 1267.   HOFMEISTÈRIA

In Phytologia 12: 469 King & Robinson make the combination **Pleurocorònis plurisèta** (Gray) King & Robinson.

p. 1269.   BRICKÉLLIA

2. **B. multiflòra** Kell. has been found in Jawbone Canyon, w. Mojave Desert, Kern Co., *Twisselmann*.

5. **B. microphýlla** (Nutt.) Gray collected by *Hardham* at Caliente Creek, Kern Co.

p. 1271.   CYNARÈAE

In Key, under AA, B, CC insert:

> C′.   Receptacle densely pitted, the pits membranous-bordered, not densely setose. .... 139a. *Onopordum*
> C′C′. Receptacle densely setose.
>   D.   Fils. united below, as in FLORA.

p. 1272.   **139a. Onopórdum L.**

Tall herbs with erect stems and sinuate or pinnatifid spiny lvs., the cauline lvs. decurrent and the stems conspicuously spiny-winged. Heads homogamous; invol. of many rows of conspicuous spiny tegules. Receptacle naked, deeply pitted, the pits with toothed membranous borders. Florets all tubular, hermaphrodite, usually red-purple; anthers with terminal subulate appendages and short basal tails. Aks. obovoid, compressed or 4-angled; pappus of many rows of rough hairs united into a basal ring. Ca. 20 spp., Eurasian. (Greek name for Cotton Thistle.)

A.   Invol. glandular-pubescent; mature lvs. green, glabrescent. .... 1. *O. tauricum*
AA. Invol. arachnoid; lvs. gray or whitish beneath. .... 2. *O. Acanthium*

1. **O. táuricum** Willd. Biennial, 3–5 dm. tall, branched; invol. sub-globose, the phyllaries lanceolate, spine-tipped; fls. purplish, glabrous.—Medit. region. Adventive in Siskiyou Co., sw. of Dorris, *Fuller*.

2. **O. Acánthium** L. SCOTCH THISTLE. Biennial, 5 to 20 dm. tall, with a close arachnoid tomentum; invol. subglobose, 3–5 cm. diam.; phyllaries lanceolate; fls. reddish purple. $2n = 34$ (Moore & Frankton, 1962).—Reported from Siskiyou, Modoc, Lake, Lassen, Monterey, San Benito, Tulare and Sierra cos., *Fuller*.

p. 1273.   SÍLYBUM

1. **S. Mariànum** (L.) Gaertn. $2n = 34$ (Moore & Frankton, 1962).

CARTHÀMUS

1. **C. lanàtus** L. Now known from Humboldt, Napa, Sonoma and s. Mendocino cos.

2. **C. baèticus** (Boiss. & Reut.) Nym. [*C. lanatus* ssp. *creticus* (L.) Holmb.] In Calaveras Co., *Fuller*.

3. **C. tinctòrius** L. In the Temblor Range, at Arvin, etc., Kern Co., *Twisselmann*.

p. 1275.   CÍRSIUM

In Key after D, EE, FF, GG insert:

> G′.   Plants annual, sometimes biennial, glabrous to ± arachnoid. San Luis Obispo and Santa Barbara cos.
>   12a. *C. loncholepis*
> G′G′. Plants perennial, if subglabrous, then with rhizome-like roots, if arachnoid, then densely so.
>   H.   Heads solitary, etc. as in the FLORA.

p. 1276.   In Key after last HH, add:

> I.   Heads often broader than long, hemispheric; phyllaries with spines 5–10 mm. long, the outer phyllaries often reflexed.
>   29. *C. neomexicanum*
> II. Heads subglobose; phyllaries with spines mostly 3–7 mm. long, the outer phyllaries spreading or ascending. ... 29a. *C. utahense*

5. **C. remotifòlium** (Hook.) DC. From the synonymy delete *C. r.* ssp. *pseudocarlinoides* Petr.

p. 1277.   6. **C. callilèpis** (Greene) Jeps. Howell recognizes **C. c.** var. **pseudocarlinoìdes** (Petrak) J. T. Howell as having more loosely ascending, not appressed phyllaries and less graduated.—Marin Co. to Ore.

7. **C. quercetòrum** (Gray) Jeps. In Sacramento and Solano cos., *Fuller.*

10. **C. crassicáule** (Gray) Jeps. Lost Hills, Kern Co., *Twisselmann.*

12. **C. foliòsum** (Hook.) DC. $2n = 34$ (Ownbey & Hsi, 1963).

p. 1278.   12a. **C. loncholèpis** Petr. Near *C. foliosum* (Hook.) DC. Annual or biennial, with a taproot, nearly or quite glabrous; heads solitary or clustered at ends of branches; phyllaries loosely imbricate, mostly linear- or ovate-lanceolate.—San Luis Obispo and Santa Barbara cos.

13. **C. Drummóndii** T. & G. $2n = 34$ (Ownbey & Hsi, 1963).

14. **C. tiogànum** (Congd.) Petr. [*Cnicus t.* Congd.]

15. **C. undulàtum** (Nutt.) Spreng. $2n = 26$ (Frankton & Moore, 1961). Collected 3.5 mi. ne. of Livermore, at Escondido, San Diego Co. and in Lassen Co., Alameda Co., *Fuller.* Once reported also from Catalina Id.

17. **C. Brèweri** (Gray) Jeps. J. T. Howell in Abrams, Ill. Fl. Pac. States 4: 520. 1960, uses **C. Douglásii** DC. [*C. Breweri* var. *Wrangelii* Petr.] for plants to 1.8 m. tall; lvs. more spiny and with short decurrent bases; heads 2.5–3.5 cm. long, bowl-shaped.—Monterey Co. to Mendocino Co.

For **C. Brèweri** (Gray) Jeps. [*C. B.* vars. *canescens* and *lanosissimum* Petr.] Howell uses **C. Douglásii** var. **canéscens** (Petr.) J. T. Howell. To 2.5 m. tall; lvs. less spiny and with longer decurrent bases; heads 2–3 cm. long.—Lake Co. to Siskiyou Co. and in the Sierra Nevada from Lake Tahoe north.

18. **C. Vàseyi** (Gray) Jeps. is **C. hydrophìlum** (Greene) Jeps. var. **Vàseyi** (Gray) J. T. Howell.

p. 1279.   20. **C. ochrocéntrum** Gray. $2n = 30, 31, 32$ (Ownbey & Hsi, 1963). Reported from Lassen, Plumas, Los Angeles & San Diego cos.

21. **C. Andersònii** (Gray) Petr. in the Piute Mts., Kern Co., *Twisselmann.*

24. **C. cymòsum** (Greene) J. T. Howell. In Tehachapi Mts., *Twisselmann.*

25. Change *C. Còulteri* Harv. & Gray to **C. proteànum** J. T. Howell.

p. 1280.   26. **C. occidentàle** (Nutt.) Jeps. Add as synonyms *C. Coulteri* Harv. & Gray. *C. o.* var. *C.* Jeps.

30. **C. arvénse** (L.) Scop. $2n = 34$ (Moore & Frankton, 1962).

Var. **mìte** Wimmer & Grabowski. Lvs. nearly glabrous, undulate-margined or very shallowly lobed.—In Modoc Co., *Fuller.*

31. **C. utahénse** Petr. Differing from *C. neomexicanum* Gray in having subglobose (not hemispheric) heads; phyllaries with spines 3–7 mm. long, the outer phyllaries spreading or ascending (not 5–10 mm. or reflexed).—E. of the Sierra Nevada; to the Rocky Mts.

p. 1281.   CÁRDUUS

1. **C. pycnocéphalus** L. $2n = 54$ (Moore & Frankton, 1962). Known now from Butte, Mariposa, Eldorado, Nevada, and Fuller cos., *Fuller.*

2. **C. tenuiflòrus** Curt. Additional reports: Santa Barbara Co., Sierra Nevada foothills in Tulare Co., *Fuller,* Riverside Co., *Howell.*

3. **C. nùtans** L. Near Victorville, San Bernardino Co., *Fuller;* 2 mi. s. of Bordertown, Nev. in Nevada Co., and Long Valley nw. part of Sierra Co., *Fuller;* 4 mi. s. of Castella, Shasta Co.

CENTÁUREA

In Key, after AA, B, CC, change to:

D. Invol. cylindric, not more than 1 cm. long.
 E. Invol. ca. 7 mm. long; fls. usually pink or lavender; pappus bristles slender, to 2.5 mm. long. . . . . 9. *C. virgata*
 EE. Invol. ca. 1 cm. long; fls. usually white; pappus none or of scales less than 1 mm. long. . . . . 9a. *C. diffusa*

p. 1282.   2. **C. Cinerària** L. $2n = 18$ (Gori, 1954; Larsen, 1956).

3. **C. maculòsa** Lam. Now in Lassen, Nevada, Placer, Siskiyou, and Trinity cos., *Fuller.*

9. **C. virgàta** Lam. var. **squarròsa** (Willd.) Boiss. Add Shasta Co., *Fuller.*

9a. **C. diffùsa** Lam. Differing from *C. virgata* in having white rather than pink or lavender fls.; invol. longer.—Reported from Lassen, Siskiyou, and Modoc cos., *Fuller;* native of e. Medit. region.

10. **C. dilùta** Ait. Vista, San Diego Co., *Fuller.*

p. 1283.   11. **C. ibèrica** Trev. Carmel R., Monterey Co., *Howitt & Howell;* e. of Livermore, Alameda Co., *Marsh.*

13. **C. sulphùrea** Willd. Reported from Sacramento, Eldorado and San Joaquin cos., *Fuller.*

15. **C. meliténsis** L. $2n = 36$ (Chiappini, 1955).

CNÌCUS

1. **C. benedíctus** L. $n = 11$ (Moore & Frankton, 1962).

p. 1285.   TRÍXIS

1. **T. califórnica** Kell. $n = 27$ (Turner, Powell & King, 1962).

p. 1287.   CICHORIÈAE

In Key after AA, BB, CC, D, E, change to:

       F.   Plants nonscapose, usually much branched.
           F'.   Plants shrubs 1–2 m. high; lvs. 6–13 cm. long, in tufts at ends of branches, irregularly sinuate-toothed. San Clemente Id. .... 163a. *Munzothamnus*
           F'F'. Plants herbaceous, or at least lower in height.
              G.   Pappus not plumose.
                 G'.   Plants perennial or annual; heads relatively slender.
                     H.   The pappus of 5 rigid tapering awns.
                         159. *Chaetadelphia*
                     HH. The pappus of many capillary bristles.
                         160 *Lygodesmia*
                 G'G'. Plants annual; heads subglobose.
                         163. *Malacothrix*
              GG. Pappus plumose, etc. as in the FLORA.

In Key after AA, BB, CC, D, change EE to:

       EE. Aks. epappose.
           F.   Florets white; glaucous scapose native with broad spinulose-denticulate lvs. Deserts. .... 167. *Atrichoseris*
           FF. Florets yellow; stems leafy. Adventive. .. 167a. *Rhagadiolus*

In Key, after DD, EE, F, GG, change to:

       HH. Aks. beaked.
           H'.   Invol. of 1 row of 7–8 phyllaries.
                     170a. *Urospermum*
           H'H'. Invol. of 2 or more rows of phyllaries.
              I.   Stems leafy.
                 J.   Outer phyllaries broader than the inner; plants rough-bristly throughout. .... 172. *Picris*
                 JJ.   Outer and inner phyllaries equal in a single subcylindric series and with small green scales at base; plants hirsute at base only.
                       172a. *Chondrilla*
              II.   Stems scapose; outer phyllaries very small.
                     173. *Leontodon*

Toward end of Key, change H to:

       H.   Pappus present.
           H'.   Phyllaries usually 2-seriate; pappus of many bristles.
              I, II, J and JJ. as in the FLORA.
           H'H'. Phyllaries in 1–2 series; pappus of 4–10 scales. .... 180. *Tolpis*

p. 1288.   CICHÒRIUM

2. **C. Endìva** L. ENDIVE. Bracts subtending heads leafy, commonly longer than the heads; fls. purple, in heads ca. 4 cm. across.—Cult. as a salad plant and escaped in the Salinas Valley, Monterey Co., *Howell.* From Eurasia.

p. 1289.   MICRÓSERIS
In Key, AA, BB, CC, DD, E should be Alameda not Amador Co., in 1959 printing.
In Key after A, B, CC "Pappus-bristles not plumose, 6–10" insert:

> D.   Invol. 25–75-fld., 10–25 mm. high. Sonoma and Lassen cos. to Wash.
>   1. M. laciniata
> DD. Invol. 15–25-fld., 8–18 mm. high. Siskiyou Mts. .... 1a. M. Howellii

p. 1290.   1a. M. Howéllii Gray. [Scorzonella H. Greene.] Perennial with fleshy fusiform taproot; stem slender, erect, 1.5–5 dm. tall; lvs. chiefly basal, entire to
laciniate-pinnatifid with slender lobes; heads 15–25-fld.; invol. 8–18 mm. high;
florets pale yellow; pappus 6–12 mm. long, the paleae 6–10 in number, 3–6
mm. long, awned.—Siskiyou Mts.
        6. Change M. Lindleyi (DC.) Gray to M. linearifòlia (Nutt.) Sch-Bip.
p. 1291.   9. M. acumìnàta Greene. In last line change Amador to Alameda, in 1959
printing.
p. 1293.   AGOSÉRIS
        4. A. apargioìdes (Less.) Greene var. Eastwoodiae (Fedde) Munz, not Q.
Jones. [A. Eastwoodae Fedde in Just, Bot. Jahresb. 31: 808. 1904.]
p. 1294.   PHALACRÓSERIS
        1. P. Bolánderi Gray. In Nevada Co., True.
p. 1295.   STEPHANOMÈRIA
Insert paragraph after 1. S. virgàta Benth.:
        S. carotífera Hoov., a perennial from near Morro Bay, San Luis Obispo Co.
was described by Hoover for plants differing from S. virgata, an annual, which
it resembles in heads, fls., aks. The proposed sp., however, has a fleshy root and
divaricate branching.
p. 1297.   MALACÒTHRIX
        Insert literature refs.: Williams, E. W. The genus Malacothrix. Am. Midl.
Natur. 58: 494–512. 1957. Davis, Wm. S. and P. H. Raven. Three new spp.
related to M. Clevelandii, Madroño 16: 258–266. 1962.
p. 1298.   Insert in Key after FF, (lines 1 and 2 at top of page):

> G. Aks. less than 1.7 mm. long, fusiform, with 5 of the 18
>   ribs more prominent than the others; invol. less than 8
>   mm. high.
> H. Aks. brown or straw-colored; cauline lvs. often
>   toothed; plants usually unbranched below. Tehama
>   Co. and Glenn Co. to L. Calif. .. 6. M. Clevelandii
> HH. Aks. dark purplish-brown, rarely paler; cauline lvs.
>   entire; plants often well-branched from base. Santa
>   Cruz Id., Hueneme Beach, Ventura Co. 6a. M. similis
> GG. Aks. more than 1.7 mm. long, subcylindrical, gray-brown
>   to straw-colored, with 15 equally prominent ribs; invol.
>   7–10 mm. high. Deserts, Inyo Co. to e. San Diego Co.
>   6b. M. Stebbinsii

        1. M. Còulteri Harv. & Gray var. cognàta Jeps. has stem lvs. parted nearly
to the midrib into linear divisions. Santa Cruz and Santa Rosa ids. San Pedro
Hills, Los Angeles Co.
        4. M. sonchoìdes (Nutt.) T. & G. The report in the FLORA of $2n = 18$ is an
error.
        6. M. Clevelándii Gray. Stems usually 1, sometimes several from base; basal
lvs. linear to linear-lanceolate, dentate, pinnatifid or lobed; cauline lvs. often
toothed; heads cylindrical to narrow-campanulate, 4–8 mm. high, 19–67-fld.;
ligules yellow; pollen grains ca. 25μ in diam.; aks. truncate-fusiform, 1.4–1.8
mm. long, slightly curved, 5 of the 15 ribs more prominent than the others,
apex of the ak. flared, bordered by a ring of 14–17 white-scarious teeth; persistent seta on ak. 1; $n = 7$.—From Tehama and Glenn cos. to L. Calif.
        6a. M. símilis Davis & Raven. Usually branched from the base; basal lvs.
linear-lanceolate, entire to pinnatifid; cauline lvs. subentire; heads narrow-
campanulate, 6–10 mm. high, 32–73-fld.; pollen-grains ca. 30μ in diam.; aks.

truncate-fusiform, 1.4–1.7 mm. long, slightly curved, dark purplish-brown, 5 of the 15 ribs prominent; ak.-apex with ca. 18 white-scarious teeth, persistent seta 1; $n = 14$.—Santa Cruz Id.; Hueneme Beach in Ventura Co.; L. Calif.

6b. **M. Stebbínsii** Davis & Raven. Usually simple at the base; basal lvs. lanceolate to oblanceolate, dentate, rarely pinnatifid; heads campanulate, 7–10 mm. high, 19–70-fld.; aks. 1.7–2.3 mm. long, rarely curved, with 15 equally prominent ribs, apex bordered by a ring of 14–17 white-scarious teeth, persistent seta usually 1.—Deserts, Inyo Co. to e. San Diego Co.; Nev., Ariz., Son.

p. 1299.   8. **M. indécora** Greene and 9. **M. squálida** Greene are both treated as vars. of *M. foliòsa* Gray by Williams.

10. **M. incàna** (Nutt.) T. & G. Williams makes the combination **M. i.** var. **succulénta** (Elmer) Williams.

11. **M. saxátilis** (Nutt.) T. & G. Ferris recognizes var. **altíssima** (Greene) Ferris [*M. a.* Greene.] as distinct from var. **tenuifòlia** in having the stems partly subterranean, arising singly from branches of a deep-seated root, instead of at the surface of the ground; lvs. 1–2 dm. long, deeply laciniate-lobed.—Tehachapi Mts., Mt. Pinos and mts. of Santa Barbara Co. s. to Santa Monica Mts., Los Angeles Co.

p. 1300.   12. **M. Blàirii** (M. & J.) M. & J. Transfer to:

163a. Munzothámnus Raven

Shrub 1–1.5 m. tall; lvs. in tufts at ends of branches, large, coarsely sinuate or lobulate. Invols. 9–12-fld., narrow. Florets purple. Pappus setae thick, few, plumose. One sp. from San Clemente Id. (*Munz* and *shrub*).

1. **M. Blàirii** (M. & J.) Raven. [*Stephanomeria B.* M. & J. *Malacothrix B.* M. & J.] Lvs. obovate to oblong-obovate, 5–15 cm. long; infl. paniculate, leafless, 1–2 dm. long; aks. 3–3.5 mm. long; pappus-bristles many, 4 mm. long.—Rocky canyon-walls; Coastal Sage Scrub; San Clemente Id. July–Sept.

p. 1301.   ## 167a. Rhagadìolus Juss.

Annual, divergently branched above. Lvs. largely basal, much reduced upward, the lower oblanceolate or broader, petioled, toothed to pinnatifid. Heads rather small, long-peduncled; invol. double, the outer phyllaries minute, the inner 5–8, much enlarged in fr., keeled. Fls. yellow. Aks. linear-subulate, without pappus, the outer rather persistent with the invol., the inner soon deciduous. Medit.

1. **R. édulis** Willd. Low annual; lower lvs. broadly oblong-oblanceolate, dentate; heads ca. 1 cm. high; inner phyllaries linear and to 2.5 cm. in fr.—Adventive near Napa, Napa Co., *Raven*.

p. 1302.   TRAGOPÒGON

3. **T. praténsis** L. Reported from San Luis Obispo Co., *Frey*; Kern Co., *Twisselmann.*

170a. Urospérmum Scop.

Annual to biennial, few-branched plants. Heads solitary on long peduncles, medium to large; phyllaries 7–8 in 1 series, connate at base. Florets yellow. Aks. ending in a hollow beak separated from the true ovary-cavity by a septum. Pappus-bristles plumose, in 2 series hanging together at the base in a ring and falling simultaneously. Two spp. Medit. (Greek, *oura,* tail, and *sperma,* seed.)

1. **U. picroìdes** (L.) Schmidt. Three–4 dm. tall, hispid, even subspinose below; lvs. pubescent-hispid, the lower oblong-obovate, pinnatifid or dentate, the upper lanceolate, clasping; peduncles long, naked; heads medium-large; aks. flat, tuberculate.—Adventive on Univ. of Calif. campus at Berkeley, *Carter.*

HYPOCHOÈRIS
In Key, line 1, insert "more or less" after "annual."

p. 1303.   172a. **Chondrílla** L.

Caulescent, branched, hispid below. Lower lvs. sinuate or runcinate, the upper entire. Heads small, subsessile, 7–12-fld., yellow. Invol. of linear subequal phyllaries in 1 series. Aks. oblong, slender-beaked. (Greek, *chondrile*, a kind of endive or chicory.)

1. **C. juncèa** L. SKELETON WEED. Biennial, 4–10 dm. tall.—Reported as weed from San Luis Obispo, Placer, Nevada, Sacramento and Eldorado cos.; from the Medit. basin.

SÓNCHUS

1. **S. arvénsis** L. $n = 9$ (Mehra et al., 1965).—In Siskiyou Co., *Fuller*; near Guadalupe, Santa Barbara Co., *Fuller*.

p. 1304.   4. **S. ásper** (L.) Garsault. $2n = 18$ (various workers). Said to have, as a distinctive character, thin papery aks. rather than thickish ones.

p. 1305.   LACTÙCA

5. **L. salígna** L. Reported from Monterey Co., *Howitt & Howell*.

7. **L. ludoviciàna** (Nutt.) DC. [*Sonchus l.* Nutt.] Near *L. canadensis* in its beaked aks. but the fruiting invols. 15–22 mm. long (not 10–15) and pappus 7–12 mm. long (not 5–7); florets 20–56 (not 13–22).—Reported from San Bernardino, *Ferris*; native of central U.S.

HIERÀCIUM

Change line 3 of Key to:

Ligules yellow or orange; stem and invol. pubescent to hirsute.

Change line 4 to:

Heads yellow.

Add as last line of Key:

Heads orange-red. . . . . 8. *H. aurantiacum*

4. **H. argùtum** Nutt. var. **Paríshii** (Gray) Jeps. in San Luis Obispo Co., *Hardham*.

p. 1306.   6. **H. grácile** Hook. Add to synonymy *H. triste* ssp. *g.* Calder & Taylor.

8. **H. aurantiàcum** L. Long-hirsute, rank perennial with many-leaved basal rosettes and coarse rooting stolons; lvs. 5–20 cm. long; scapes 2–7 dm. tall, naked or with 1–2 lvs.; heads orange-red, ca. 2 cm. across, in corymbs.—In lawns, Grass Valley, Nevada Co., *Fuller*; native of Europe.

p. 1307.   CRÈPIS
In Key change AA to:

AA. Introduced annuals or biennials, or perennial in *C. bursifolia*.
  B.   Invols. 5–8 mm. long; aks. 2–3.5 mm. long. . . . . 10. *C. capillaris*
  BB. Invols. 8–12 mm. long; aks. 3.5–8 mm. long.
    C.   Aks. 6–8 mm. long; invols. not usually strongly setose.
      D.   Annual or biennial; beak of ak. not filiform, scarcely longer than the
           body. . . . . 11. *C. vesicaria*
      DD. Perennial; beak of the ak. filiform, ca. twice the length of the ak.-body.
                                                                           13. *C. bursifolia*
    CC. Aks. 3–5 mm. long; invols. strongly setose. . . . . 12. *C. setosa*

p. 1309.   In the 1959 printing the lines for 10, 11, 12 were badly jumbled. Change as follows:

10. **C. capillaris** (L.) Wallr. First 3 lines OK. Transpose lines 3, 4, and 5 from 12. *C. setòsa*. The last 2 lines are OK, and are followed by "June–Aug." from the end of *setosa*.

11. **C. vesicària** L. ssp. **taraxacifòlia** (Thuill.) Thell. First 4 lines OK, followed by the last 3 lines from Ssp. *Hallii* above, beginning "9–13."

12. **C. setòsa** Haller f. Combine the first 2 lines of *C. setosa* and the last 3 lines of *C. vesicaria* ssp. *taraxacifolia*. Add:

13. **C. bursifòlia** L. Perennial, 1–3.5 dm. tall, with several stems from a woody caudex, tomentulose, cymosely branched above, each with 2–14 heads; lvs. mostly basal, these 5–15 cm. long, oblanceolate in outline, lyrately pinnatifid; invols. 9–11 mm. long, cylindric, canescent, farinose, sometimes somewhat setulose; aks. 6–7.5 mm. long, 10-ribbed, the filamentous beak ca. twice as long as the body; pappus 3–4 mm. long.—Adventive in region of San Francisco Bay. Native of Italy. May–June.

p. 1310.

180. Tólpis Gaertn.

Low herbs with oblong to oblong-spathulate, entire to pinnatifid lvs. or the upper lvs. linear. Heads long-peduncled, yellow. Phyllaries in 1–2 series; receptacle naked. Aks. oblong, 6–8-costate; pappus of 4–10 seta-like scales. (Greek, *tolupe*, ball, referring to the form of the invol.)

1. **T. barbàta** Willd. Annual, 2–4 dm. tall, the stem glabrous, branched; lvs. toothed, the lower petioled; heads 1.5–3 cm. in diam.; pappus-bristles 4–5. —Escape at Pacific Grove, Monterey Co.; native of Medit. region.

2. **T. umbellàta** Bertol. Heads 1–1.5 cm. diam.—Escape nw. of Ukiah, Mendocino Co.; native of Medit. region.

p. 1311. MONOCOTYLEDÒNEAE

In Key, after AA, B, CC, D, EE, FF, add:

GGG. Lvs. clustered at the nodes or on short branches each with a sheath and a narrow blade. . . *Halodule* p. 1324

In Key, after AA, BB, change to:

C. Carpels ± free, 1-loculed.
D. Parts of perianth usually 2 (1–3), petaloid. *Aponogetonaceae* p. 1312

DD. Parts of perianth 6, in 2 series, the inner petaloid.
Alismataceae p. 1312

p. 1312. Caption for Fig. 121 should read *Echinodorus Berteroi*.
p. 1313. MACHAEROCÁRPUS

1. **M. califórnicus** (Torr.) Small. In Bear V., Kern Co., *Twisselmann*.

1a. Aponogetonàceae. APONOGETON FAMILY

Aquatic perennial herbs with tuberous rhizome and floating or submerged lvs.

1. Aponogèton L. f.

Lvs. long-petioled, linear-oblong, with many parallel and transverse veins. Infl. a simple or forked spike. Fls. mostly bisexual; perianth parts mostly 2, petaloid. Stamens 6 or more, in 2 whorls. Pistils 3–4, free. Ovules 2–8, basal. (Origin of name uncertain.)

1. **A. distàchyus** L. f. CAPE POND-WEED. Fls. white, fragrant, with purplish anthers.—Escape from cult., San Mateo Co., *Rubtzoff*. From S. Afr.

p. 1313. SAGITTÀRIA

4. **S. cuneàta** Sheld. Reported from near sea level, Marin Co., *Howell*.

p. 1314. ALÍSMA

Add as citations to literature: Hendricks, A. J. A revision of the genus Alisma. Am. Midl. Nat. 58: 470–493. 1957. Pogan, E. Taxonomic value of A. triviale Pursh and A. subcordatum Raf. Can. J. Bot. 41: 1011–1013. 1963.

1. **A. triviàle** Pursh. $2n = 28$.

2. Change A. *Geyeri* Torr. to **A. subcordàtum** Raf. with sepals in anthesis 2–2.5 mm. long; petals white, 1–2 mm. long; aks. 1.5–2 mm. long; $2n = 14$. —Yosemite Valley, Mariposa Co., Modoc Co.; to N.Y., Quebec.

3. **A. lanceolàtum** With. Lvs. narrow-lanceolate, 0.5–2 dm. long; petals

rose, ± pointed apically; $2n = 26$.—Natur. in Sonoma Co., Marin Co., Colusa Co., Placer Co.; from Eurasia.

p. 1317. POTAMOGÈTON
    4. **P. Robbínsii** Oakes. $n = 26$ (Stern, 1961).
    5. **P. críspus** L. Found in Sonoma Co., *Rubtzoff*.
    7. **P. foliòsus** Raf. $2n = 28$ (Stern, 1961).
    8. **P. pusíllus** L. $2n = 26$ (Harada, 1956).

p. 1318.   10. **P. diversifòlius** Raf. Occurs in Sonoma, Lake and Modoc cos., *Rubtzoff*.
    11. **P. epihỳdrus** ssp. **Nuttállii** (Cham. & Schlecht.) Calder & Taylor.
    13. **P. amplifòlius** Tuckerm. $n = 26$ (Stern, 1961).
    15. **P. nàtans** L. $2n = 52$ (Löve & Löve, 1956); $n = 26$ (Stern, 1961).

p. 1319.   16. **P. gramíneus** L. $n = 26$ (Stern, 1961).
    17. **P. illinoénsis** Morong. $n = 52$ (Stern, 1961).
    18. **P. praelóngus** Wulf. $2n = 52$ (Löve & Löve, 1956).
    19. **P. Richardsònii** (Benn.) Rydb. $n = 26$ (Stern, 1961). Reported from Lake Co., *Rubtzoff*.

RÙPPIA
In Key, "Lvs. obtusish" goes with **R. spiràlis** ($2n = 10$) and "lvs. acute" goes with **R. marítima** ($2n = 20$).

p. 1320. TRIGLÓCHIN
Used by Linnaeus as a neuter noun. Our species should be:
    1. **T. striàtum** R. & P.

p. 1321.   2. **T. palústre** L. $2n = 24$ (Larsen, K., 1966).
    3. **T. marítimum** L. $2n = 12$ to 144 (Löve & Löve, 1958). Found in Monterey Co., *Howitt & Howell*.
    4. **T. concínnum** Davy. $2n = 24$ (Larsen, 1966); 48 (Löve & Löve, 1958). Löve & Löve recognize **T. débile** (Jones) Löve & Löve, with $2n = 96$.

LILAÈA
    1. **L. scilloìdes** (Poir.) Haum. $2n = 12$ (Larsen, 1966).

p. 1324. ZANNICHÉLLIA
    1. **Z. palústris** L. $2n = 12$ (Reese, 1957).

HALÓDULE
Under Zannichelliaceae add 2. **Halódule** Endl.
Dioecious; style shorter than the stigma (instead of longer); pollen filiform (not globose); carpels 2 and united, or 1. Fr. a nutlet.
    1. **H. Wrìghtii** Aschers. [*Diplanthera* W. Aschers.] Lvs. bicuspidate at the semilunate apex; anthers ca. 6 mm. long; mature fr. black.—Introd. intentionally into the Salton Sea from Texas and now well established. Native in se. states and W. Indies.

NÀJAS
    2. **N. flexilis** (Willd.) Rostk. & Schmidt is apparently not in the California flora and plants so identified in the past are largely *N. guadalupensis fide Thorne*.

p. 1325. ELODÈA
Cite as a reference: St. John, H. Monograph of the genus Elodea. Part 1. Research studies Wash. State Univ. 30: 19–44. 1962.

p. 1326.   1. **E. dénsa** Plancha. Add as a synonym *Egeria densa* St. John.
    2. **E. canadénsis** Michx. $n = 24$ (Harada, 1956).
    2a. **E. Brandègeae** St. John. Differing from *E. canadensis* by having upper and middle lvs. 5–8 mm. long, rather than 6–13; fls. perfect, not dioecious; sepals 3.8 mm. long, as against 2.2 mm.; stigmas 0.3 mm. long, entire, as opposed to 4 mm., bifid.—Truckee, Sierra Nevada.

p. 1327. In Key AA, B, CC, DD, EE, change to "Anthers often seemingly basifixed." In Key, under A, BB, C, D, change to:

    E. Lvs. not equitant.
        F. The lvs. 5–10 dm. long, dry; pedicels 2–5 cm. long.
                             1. *Xerophyllum*

FF. The lvs. shorter, fleshy; pedicels ca. 1 cm. long.

1a. *Asphodelus*

EE. Lvs. equitant.
F. and FF. as in the FLORA.

p. 1328.   1a. **Asphodèlus** L. ASPHODEL

Near to *Narthecium*, but lvs. spirally arranged, not equitant. Fls. white to pinkish, with jointed pedicels; perianth-segms. with a single colored midvein; stamens dilated at base and covering the ovary. Several spp. Old World.

1. **A. fistulòsus** L. Root system of several tubers; stems 2–6 dm. high, glabrous; lvs. straight, semiterete; fls. in open panicles; perianth 8–12 mm. long; caps. 4–6 mm. long, subglobose.—Adventive in San Diego and Santa Barbara cos. Native of Medit. region.

NARTHÈCIUM
1. **N. califórnicum** Baker. $n = 13$ (Cave, 1966). Howell reports this as far s. as Tulare Co.

TOFIÈLDIA
1. **T. glutinòsa** Pers. ssp. **occidentàlis** (Wats.) C. L. Hitchc. $n = 15$ (Cave, 1966).

p. 1329.   SCHOENOLÍRION
1. **S. álbum** Durand. $n = 26$ (Cave, 1966).

CHLORÓGALUM
1. **C. pomeridiànum** (DC.) Kunth $n = 15$ (Cave, 1966).
Var. **divaricàtum** (Lindl.) Hoov. extends as far s. as Santa Barbara Co.

p. 1330.   5. **C. purpùreum** Bdg. var. **redúctum** Hoov. Described as 1–2 dm. tall.—La Panza road, San Luis Obispo Co., apparently on serpentine soil.

p. 1331.   SMILACÌNA
1. **S. racemòsa** (L.) Desf. $2n = 36$ (Therman, 1956).

MAIÁNTHEMUM
1. **M. dilatàtum** (Wood) Nels. & Macbr. $n = 18$ (Therman, 1956). Occurs in San Mateo Co., *Howell*.

p. 1332.   DÍSPORUM
3. **D. Hoòkeri** (Torr.) Nichols. In San Luis Obispo Co., *Hardham*.

p. 1333.   STENÁNTHIUM
1. **S. occidentàle** Gray. $n = 8$ (Cave, 1966).

p. 1335.   ZIGADÈNUS
6. **Z. exaltàtus** Eastw. In Piute and Greenhorn mts., Kern Co., *Twisselmann*.

VERÀTRUM
1, 2, 3. **V. insolìtum** Jeps., **V. fimbriàtum** Gray, **V. califórnicum** Durand. $n = 16$ (Cave, 1966).

p. 1336.   ASPÁRAGUS
1. **A. officinàlis** L. is largely dioecious.

p. 1337.   ERYTHRÒNIUM
3. **E. tuolumnénse** Appleg. $n = 12$ (Cave, 1966).
4. **E. grandiflòrum** Pursh. Add ssp. **Pusatèrii** Munz & Howell. Lvs. green, not mottled, ± crisped-undulate, 2–5 dm. long, the blade 1.5–2.5 dm. long; infl. 1–3 dm. tall, 1–3-fld.; perianth-segms. 2–3 cm. long, yellowish orange on lower half or third, cream color in distal part; anthers yellow.—Rocky soil below Hockett Lakes, at ca. 8000 ft., Tulare Co.

p. 1340.   FRITILLÀRIA
6. **F. agréstis** Greene. Temblor Range, Kern Co., *Twisselmann*.
8a. **F. Roderíckii** Knight. Proposed as a new sp. near to *B. biflora* in having the lvs. mostly near the ground, but differing in the possession of some rice-grain bulblets; perianth-segms. creamy-greenish on lower third and the inner surface with raised veins; fils. in 1, not 2 ranks, equal in length; $n = 12$.—On clay, Mendocino Co.

p. 1341.   15. **F. atropurpùrea** Nutt. $n = 12$ (Bottino, 1965).

p. 1347.   CALOCHÓRTUS

3. **C. pulchéllus** Dougl. reported from Upper Cache Creek, w. Colusa Co., *Holt.*

p. 1351.   23a. **C. símulans** (Hoov.) Munz. comb. nov. [*Mariposa simulans,* Hoov. Leafl. W. Bot. 4: 4. 1944.] Differs from *V. venustus* Dougl. ex Benth. in petals not having margins above lower third, and with a red spot surrounding the glandular area and frequently a small red spot immediately above it; petals cuneate, with straight sides.—Central San Luis Obispo Co. In *C. venustus* the petals have a conspicuous dark spot and frequently also a lighter spot near the apex, petals inwardly curved so as to be clawlike near the base.

25. **C. Véstae** Purdy. Reported from Greenhorn Range, Kern Co., *Twisselmann.*

p. 1352.   30. **C. invenústus** Greene. $2n = 7$ pairs (Raven, Kyhos & Hill, 1965). Found in Kern Co., *Twisselmann.*

p. 1353.   34. **C. clavátus** Wats. Insert: *C. clavatus* in its typical form is largely on soil of serpentine origin, has deep yellow petals and uniformly deep purple anthers.—From San Luis Obispo Co. to Santa Barbara Co.

Ssp. **pállidus** (Hoov.) Munz, comb. nov. [*Mariposa clavata* (Wats.) Hoov. var. *pallida* Hoov. Leafl. W. Bot. 10: 126. 1964.] Differs from var. *clavatus* by having petals light yellow, the hairs gradually enlarged toward the apex, distinctly less than 0.1 mm. in dried specimens, fungoid processes of gland smaller and less branched; anthers yellow to pale or medium purple.—S. Coast Ranges from San Joaquin and Stanislaus cos. to n. Los Angeles Co. and Kern Co.

Ssp. **recurvifólius** (Hoov.) Munz, comb. nov. [*Mariposa clavata* var. *recurvifolia* Hoov. Leafl. W. Bot. 10: 126–127. 1964.] Plants dwarf, 9–12 cm. tall, the internodes to 2 cm. long; lvs. strongly recurved; fls. of typical *clavata.*—N. of Arroyo de la Cruz, San Luis Obispo Co., on ocean bluff.

Var. **àvius** Jeps. Sepals equaling or exceeding petals; gland in a deeper pocket.—Base of Sierra Nevada, Eldorado Co. to Mariposa Co.

36. **C. Weèdii** Wood extends s. into L. Calif.

p. 1357.   EICHHORNIA

1. **E. crássipes** (Mart.) Solms. The first word in the last line of the description should be "serious" not "series" in the 1959 printing.—Reported from a pond, San Ysidro, San Diego Co., *Fuller.*

ARÀCEAE

Add to the Key:

Spathe greenish without, whitish within; lvs. sagittate. .... 4. *Arum*

p. 1358.   4. Árum L.

Low simple herbs with underground tubers, hastate or sagittate lvs. and scape bearing a spathe, that withers after anthesis, and a spadix of minute naked fls. Several spp. (Greek, *aron,* ancient name.)

1. **A. itálicum** Mill. To 1 m. high; lvs. surpassing the spathe which is long-pointed, green without, whitish within.—Established on Mendocino Prairie and Albion River, Mendocino Co., *Marie Kelley.* From the Medit. region.

LYSICHÌTON

1. **L. americànum** Hult. & St. John. $2n = 28$ (Löve & Kawano, 1961).

p. 1358.   LEMNÀCEAE

At end of family description insert: Daubs, E. H. A monograph of Lemnaceae. Ill. Biol. Mon. 34: 1–118. 1965.

SPIRODÈLA

2. **S. oligorhìza** (Kurz) Hegelm. A definite collection cited from Calif. is *Heckard & Bacigalupi 7693.*

LÉMNA

Use the following key:

A. Fronds usually submerged, long-stipitate, many remaining attached, forming long chains. . . . . 1. *L. trisulca*
AA. Fronds usually floating, short-stipitate or sessile, mostly 2–5 attached.
   B. Dorsal surface flat, smooth, with no prominent protuberances, 1-veined or veinless.
      C. Plants narrow-elliptical, often 8–10 attached; base asymmetrical.
                                                 6. *L. valdiviana*
      CC. Plants oval, symmetrical, seldom more than 2 remaining attached.
                                                   2. *L. minima*
   BB. Dorsal surface with ± prominent protuberances, indistinctly to prominently 3-veined.
      C. Root sheath with definite wings or appendages. . . . . 4. *L. perpusilla*
      CC. Root sheath without definite wings or appendages.
         D. Ventral surface of frond flat to slightly convex, but not inflated.
            E. Dorsal surface dark green, apex symmetrical; air spaces not prominent. . . . . 3. *L. minor*
            EE. Dorsal surface mottled yellow-green, apex asymmetrical; air spaces not prominent. . . . . 5. *L. gibba*
        DD. Ventral surface of frond noticeably convex, the air spaces inflated; both surfaces showing red-purple coloring.
            E. Air spaces strongly inflated, gibbous; apex asymmetrical.
                                                  5. *L. gibba*
            EE. Air spaces slightly inflated, the apex symmetrical. . . 7. *L. obscura*

p. 1359.   7. **L. obscùra** (Austin) Daubs. [*L. minor* var. *o.* Austin.] Plants solitary or 2–3 attached, elliptic-orbicular to obovate, slightly asymmetrical; ventral surface strongly red-purple, slightly inflated.—Occasional in Calif.; e. and s. U.S.; Mex.

WOLFFIÉLLA
    1. **W. oblónga** (Phil.) Hegelm. Daubs does not have this sp. as occurring in Calif.
    2. **W. lingulàta** (Hegelm.) Hegelm. Reported now as from Marin, Sonoma and Butte cos.

WÓLFFIA
    1. **W. columbiàna** Karst. according to Daubs does not have brown pigment. He reports as from Calif. a plant that does have brown pigment cells making it punctate, namely **W. punctàta** Griseb.

p. 1362.   YÚCCA
    4. **Y. Whípplei** Torr. ssp. **caespitòsa** (Jones) Haines ranges n. to Tehipite Valley, Fresno Co.

NOLÌNA
    1. **N. interràta** Gentry. In the first line of the description it should read "2–3 m. long" not "mm."; in the 1959 printing.
    2. **N. Párryi** ssp. **Wólfii** Munz. Kern Plateau, Kern Co., *Twisselmann.*

p. 1363.   3. **N. Bigelòvii** (Torr.) Wats. $n = 19$ (Cave, 1964).
p. 1364.   WASHINGTÒNIA
    1. **W. filífera** (Lindl.) Wendl. is natur. in Kern Co., *Twisselmann.*

p. 1365.   SPARGÀNIUM
    4. **S. multipedunculàtum** (Morong) Rydb. reported as in Sonoma Co., *Rubtzoff.*

p. 1366.   TÝPHA
    S. Galen Smith (Am. Midl. Nat. 78: 257–287. 1967) recognizes three species: **T. latifòlia** L., **T. angustifòlia** L. and **T. domingénsis** Pers. **T. ✕ glaùca** Godron represents hybrids between *T. angustifolia* and *T. latifolia*, *T. domingensis* and *T. latifolia*, and trihybrids. It occurs rather widely in central California.

p. 1367.   AMARYLLIDÀCEAE
    In Key at bottom of page, after line 2 "Fils. not appendaged" etc., insert:

Perianth-segms. connate at base or to the middle. . . . . 1a. *Nothoscordum*
Perianth-segms. distinct or barely united at the base into a ring.
    Pedicels not subtended etc. as in the FLORA.

p. 1369.   ÁLLIUM
    In Key, A, B, CC, DD, E, change F:

F.   Perianth-segms. 8–12 mm. long; bracts 15–20 mm. long.
  G.   Perianth-segms. lanceolate, bright rose, the inner serru-
          late at tip. Native in n. Calif. . . . . 36. *A. acuminatum*
  GG. Perianth-segms. rounded at apex, white, not serrulate.
          Garden escape. . . . . 36a. *A. neapolitanum*
FF. Perianth-segms. 5–8 mm. long, not serrulate; bracts 8–12 mm.
          long. Middle and s. Calif.
  G. and GG. as in the FLORA.

p. 1373.   16. **A. unifòlium** Kell. s. into San Luis Obispo Co., *Hardham.*
              18. **A. praècox** Bdg. $n = 14$ (Lenz, 1966).

p. 1378.   36a. **A. neapolitànum** Cyr. Bulb coats with quadrate reticulations having
very heavy thick walls; scape 3–6 dm. high, subterete; lvs. 2–3 or more, lance-
linear, loose-spreading, shorter than the scape, 1–3 cm. broad; pedicels 3–4
cm. long; fls. pure white, the perianth-segms. ovate, obtuse, 10–12 mm. long;
stamens included; ovary not crested; stigma subentire.—Garden escape reported from Butte, Yolo, Sacramento, Napa, Sonoma, Marin, San Francisco,
and Orange cos. From the Medit. region.
              36b. **A. triquètrum** L. Near *A. neapolitanum,* but stem of the scape sharply
3-angled; lvs. 4–10 mm. broad; perianth-segms. oblong-lanceolate, 12–18 mm.
long; stigma trifid.—Said by *Howell* to be a garden escape in Calif. Also from
the Medit. region.
              38. **A. Davísiae** Jones can be reported from above Kenworthy Ranger Sta-
tion, San Jacinto Mts., Riverside Co. at 5300 ft., *L. B. Ziegler.*

1a. **Nothoscórdum** Kunth.

              Stock a tunicated bulb. Plant without onion smell. Perianth campanulate,
the segms. joined at the base into a short tube. Ovules 4–12 for each locule.
              1. **N. inòdorum** (Ait.) Nichols. Lvs. basal, 2.5–3 dm. long; scape 2–4 dm.
long; spathe 2-valved; fls. many, scented; perianth-segms. 8–14 mm. long, dull
white, with greenish base and reddish midrib outside.—Reported as adventive
in Marin and Fresno cos., *Fuller.* From se. U.S.

p. 1378.   MUÍLLA
              1. **M. marítima** (Torr.) Wats. $2n = 20$ (Lenz, 1966).

p. 1379.   BLOOMÈRIA
              Hoover (Herbertia 11: 21. 1955) described *B. humilis* from San Luis
Obispo Co., which he separated from *B. crocea:*

Corm never with offsets; scape rarely less than 15 cm. tall; basal lf. always solitary; perianth-segms. abruptly spreading from base; lower portion of fls. papillose. . . 1. *B. crocea*
Corm often with offsets; scape rarely more than 8 cm. tall; basal lvs. 1 or 2; perianth-
segms. approximate toward base, gradually curving outward; lower portion of fls. often
smooth. . . . . 1a. *B. humilis*

              1. **B. cròcea** (Torr.) Cov. $2n = 18$ (Lenz, 1966).
              2. **B. Clevelándii** Wats. is transferred to *Muilla Clevelandii* (Wats.) Hoov.
because of having more lvs., which are not keeled or channeled and in not
having the lower portion of the fls. terminate in a cuplike insertion for the
upper portion.

p. 1380.   BRODIAÈA
              In Key insert after A and B:

      B′.   Spathe-valves 2; fls. solitary. . . . . 1a. *B. uniflora*
      B′B′. Spathe-valves 3 or more; fls. several.
          C.   Perianth-tube obtuse, etc. as in the FLORA.

p. 1381.   In Key, AA, B, CC, DD, E, FF, GG, change HH to:

      HH. The fils. 1 mm. long.
          I.   Fils. broadly triangular; staminodia with in-
                  curved apex. Monterey Co. to San Diego Co.,
                  Santa Cruz Id. . . . . 16. *B. jolonensis*
          II. Fils. linear; staminodia erect. San Clement Id.
                  22a. *B. kinkiensis*

1a. **B. uniflòra** (Lindl.) Engler. [*Triteleia u.* Lindl. *Ipheion u.* Raf.] Spring bloomer with onionlike odor; from small deep-seated bulbs; lvs. nearly flat; scape 1.5–2 dm. high, bracted about midway; fl. white with bluish tinge, 3–3.5 cm. across.—Escape from cult., as at Santa Barbara, *Pollard.* Originally from Argentina. Work now being done on what the FLORA has as one genus, *Brodiaea,* indicates that there should be a number of genera recognized.

3. **B. clementìna** (Hoov.) Munz. 2n = 16 (Niehaus, 1965).

4. **B. láxa** (Benth.) Wats. 2n = 16, 32, 48 (Lenz, 1966).

p. 1382.   6. **B. Dúdleyi** (Hoov.) Munz. n = 8 (Niehaus, 1965).

7. **B. lùgens** (Greene) Baker. Reported from Pinnacles, San Benito Co., *Hoover.*

8. **B. lùtea** (Lindl.) Mort. var. **Coòkii** (Hoov.) Munz, comb. nov. [*Triteleia ixiodes* var. *Cookii* Hoov., Plant Life 11: 19. 1955.] Described from the Santa Lucia Mts., above San Simeon, San Luis Obispo Co. for plant with perianth white, purple-tinged without, the segms. reflexed.

[*B. ixioides* 2n = 14 (Lenz, 1966).]

Var. **scàbra** (Greene) Munz. Add *Triteleia scabra* Hoov. as syn.

Var. **analìna** (Greene) Munz. Add as synonym *Triteleia l.* var. *a.* Hoov. n = 20 (Niehaus, 1965); 2n = 10 (Lenz, 1966). Occurs in Piute Mts., Kern Co., *Twisselmann.*

p. 1383.   10. **B. hyacinthìna** (Lindl.) Baker. The word in synonymy should be spelled *Hesperoscordum.* The sp. *hyacinthina* is reported from San Luis Obispo Co., *Hardham.* n = 28, 35 (Niehaus, 1965); 2n = 28 (Lenz, 1966).

Var. **Greènei** (Hoov.) Munz. 2n = 16 (Niehaus, 1965).

11. **B. gracilis** Wats. n = 8 (Niehaus, 1965).

14. **B. élegans** Hoov. n = 8 (Niehaus, 1965). Add:

Var. **austràlis** Hoov. Staminodia longer than the stamens, purple-tinged, obtuse, with slightly involute margin.—Tulare Co.

p. 1384.   15. **B. coronària** (Salisb.) Engler. 2n = 24 (Niehaus, 1965).

Var. **macropòda** (Torr.) Hoov. 2n = 36 (Niehaus, 1965).

16. **B. jolonénsis** Eastw. 2n = 12 (Niehaus, 1965).

18. **B. pállida** Hoov. n = 6 (Niehaus, 1965).

p. 1385.   20. **B. califórnica** Lindl. var. **leptándra** (Greene) Hoov. 2n = 12 (Niehaus, 1965).

21. **B. appendiculàta** Hoov. n = 6 (Niehaus, 1965).

22. **B. filifòlia** Wats. 2n = 32 (Niehaus, 1965).

22a. **B. kinkiénsis** Niehaus. Corm with heavy fibrous outer coat; lvs. linear, 2–4 dm. long; scape 2–3 dm. tall; pedicels 3–8 cm. long; perianth-tube whitish with brown-purple midribs, rounded at base, 12 mm. long, 4–5 mm. wide, not splitting as caps. matures; perianth-segms. violet, 13–17 mm. long, spreading, the outer oblong, the inner obovate; staminodia erect, 7 mm. long, 3 mm. wide, cuspidate; fils. 1 mm. long; anthers 4–5 mm. long, retuse; 2n = 32 (Niehaus).—San Clemente Id.

23. **B. Orcúttii** (Greene) Baker. 2n = 24 (Lenz, 1966).

24. **B. pulchélla** (Salisb.) Greene. 2n = 18 pairs (Raven, Kyhos & Hill, 1965); 2n = 18, 36, 45, 54, 72 (Lenz, 1966).

Var. **pauciflòra** (Torr.) Mort. 2n = 36 (Lenz, 1966).

25. **B. multiflòra** Benth. 2n = 18, 45 (Lenz, 1966).

p. 1386.   27. **B. volùbilis** (Morière) Baker. 2n = 18 (Lenz, 1966).

p. 1387.   IRIDÀCEAE

Change the Key to:

A. Spathes more than 1-fld.
  B. Infl. umbellate; the perianth not more than 2 cm. long.
    C. Perianth-segms. all alike. .... 2. *Sisyrinchium*
    CC. Perianth-segms. not alike, the 3 inner longer than the 3 outer. 2a. *Libertia*
  BB. Infl. not umbellate; perianth-segms. not all alike, or, if so, more than 2 cm. long.
    C. Perianth with 3 erect and 3 spreading or drooping segms.; fls. not in an elongate spikelike infl. .... 1. *Iris*
    CC. Perianth not as above; infl. spikelike.

D. The perianth irregular, the 3 upper segms. larger than the 3 lower.
  E. Style branches simple, not bifid.; fls. 3–7 cm. long.
    F. Perianth tube constricted near or below the middle into a
        narrow cylindrical or filiform basal part. ... 5. *Chasmanthe*
    FF. Perianth tube tapering gradually from base to throat, curved.
                                                                3. *Gladiolus*
    EE. Style branches bifid; fls. mostly less than 3.5 cm. long. 6. *Freesia*
  DD. The perianth regular or essentially so.
    E. Lvs. 2.5–6 cm. wide. .... 4. *Watsonia*
    EE. Lvs. setaceous. .... 7. *Romulea*
AA. Spathes 1–3-fld., often appearing calyx-like.
  B. Lvs. setaceous; infl. 1–3-fld.; perianth with red-lilac limb. .... 7. *Romulea*
  BB. Lvs. 1 cm. or more broad; infl. a lax panicle of several many-fld. spikes; perianth
      with orange-red limb. .... 8. *Crocosmia*

p. 1388.   ÌRIS
           Line 1 at top of page. Change "Studies" to "Revision" in 1959 printing.
           In Key, change to:

           AA. Rhizome 20–40 mm. thick.
             B. Lvs. linear, generally less than 10 mm. wide.
               C. Lvs. light green, mostly 3–6 mm. wide; spathes largely scarious; fls. usually
                   2–3 on a stem. Mostly in Montane Coniferous F. ..... 12. *I. missouriensis*
               CC. Lvs. dark green, ca. 6–10 mm. wide; spathe largely herbaceous; fls. up to 8
                   on a stem. Plants from near the coast. .... 13. *I. longipetala*
             BB. Lvs. ensiform, 15–25 mm. wide; fls. 2–3 on a stem, yellow. Escape from cult.
                                                                14. *I. Pseudoacorus*

p. 1390.   4. **I. chrysophýlla** Howell. Add as synonym *I. tenax* ssp. *c.* Clarkson.
           8. **I. bracteàta** Wats. Insert as a synonym *I. tenax* ssp. *b.* Clarkson.
p. 1391.   10. **I. innominàta** Henders. Add as synonym *I. tenax* ssp. *i.* Clarkson.
           11. **I. Douglasiàna** Herb. Insert as synonyms *I. tenax* ssp. *D.* Clarkson and
           I. tenax ssp. *Thompsonii* Clarkson.

p. 1392.   14. **I. Pseudàcorus** L. Erect, glabrous, rather glaucous, 4–15 dm. high;
           rhizome often 3–4 cm. diam.; lvs. 15–25 mm. wide, ca. as long as the com-
           pressed terete scape; fls. 8–10 cm. diam., yellow, the outer segms. often
           purple-veined with an orange spot near the base; caps. elliptic, apiculate.—
           Garden-escape in wet places, Sonoma Co., *Rubtzoff* and near Mettler, Kern
           Co., *Twisselmann*.

           SISYRÍNCHIUM
           Change description of genus to "Tufted annuals or usually perennials from a
           short rootstock."
           Insert before the present Key:

           Plants annual. .... 7. *S. minus*
           Plants perennial.
             Fls. mostly blue, etc. as in present Key.

p. 1393.   4. **S. halóphilum** Greene. In Piute and Tehachapi mts., Kern Co., *Twissel-
           mann*.
           7. **S. mìnus** Engelm. & Gray. Small annual, the fls. lavender-pink to purple-
           rose, white with yellow eye, or all yellow.—Collected in grassy field on Sepul-
           veda Blvd., Los Angeles, *F. W. Gould in 1944*; native of Tex., La. Apr.–May.

                                        2a. **Libértia** Spreng.

           Perennial herbs with short creeping rhizome; lvs. linear, equitant; perianth
           without any tube above the ovary, the segms. obovate, the 3 outer shorter
           than the 3 inner. Several spp. in the S. Hemis. (Marie *Libert*, 1782–1865,
           Belgian student of liverworts.)
           1. **L. formòsa** Grah. Lvs. 3–4.5 dm. long, rigid; outer perianth-segms.
           brown, the inner white.—Natur. in San Francisco. Native of Chile.
p. 1394.   WATSÒNIA
           1. Change to **W. bulbillífera** Matthews & L. Bolus. [*W. angusta* Calif. auth.,
           not Ker.] With clusters of bulbils at lower nodes of infl.—Known from Mendo-
           cino and Sonoma cos.

p. 1394.   **5. Chasmánthe N. E. Br.**

Differing from *Gladiolus* by having the perianth tube constricted near or below the middle into a narrow or basal part. Ca. 9 spp.; African. (Greek, *chasme*, gaping, and *anthe*, flower.)

    1. **C. aethiòpica** (L.) N. E. Br. [*Antholyza a.* L.] Stems ca. 1 m. high; fls. red-yellow, 3–6 cm. long, the cylindrical part ca. ½ the whole.—Cult. and escaped, as in Santa Barbara, *Pollard.* Point Lobos State Reserve, Monterey Co., *Fuller.* Native of S. Afr.

6. Freèsia Klatt

Cormous plants with plane narrow lvs. below and showy fls. in loose secund spikes at top of the slender stem; perianth tubular, funnel-shaped, the segms. ± unequal. One or more spp. S. Afr. (E. M. *Fries,* 1795?–1876, Swedish botanist.)

    1. **F. refrácta** Klatt. Two–4 dm. tall; basal lvs. 1–1.5 dm. long; fls. solitary in the short spathes, usually ± yellow, to 3.5 cm. long, fragrant.—Common garden plant occasionally becoming established as at San Luis Obispo and San Francisco. Native of Afr.

7. Romulèa Maratti

Corm tunicated. Foliage lvs. tufted, slender, linear. Scape simple or branched. Fls. 1–3 in a spathe, long-peduncled. Perianth-segms. in 2 similar series; tube short. Style-branches linear, bifid. Caps. 3-lobed. Ca. 70 spp. of Medit. region and S. Afr. (*Romulus,* one of the founders of Rome.)

    1. **R. ròsea** Eckl. Corm globose, 8–12 mm. thick; lvs. 1.5–3 dm. long, setaceous; peduncle to 1.5 dm. long, 1–3-fld.; outer spathe 2 cm. long; perianth with yellow throat and red-lilac limb.—Adventive at Carmel Highlands, Monterey Co., *Fuller*; native of S. Afr.

8. Crocósmia Planch.

Corm with reticulated tunics; lvs. many, equitant; infl. a panicle of several spikes; spathe-valves calyxlike, notched or cut; fl. 1 in each spathe; perianth with tube somewhat dilated above; segms. subequal, oblong to obovate; stamens 3, inserted at base of funnel. S. Afr. (Greek, *crocus,* saffron, and *osme,* smell, because of odor of dried fls. immersed in water.)

    1. **C. crocosmiflòra** N. E. Br. MONTBRETIA. Sts. to 1 m., branching; lvs. 2–4 dm. long; fls. orange-crimson, 3–5 cm. diam.—Garden hybrid, widely cult., sometimes establishing itself as a wild plant.

p. 1396.   CYPRIPÈDIUM

    3. **C. califórnicum** Gray. Reported from Belden, Plumas Co.

HABENÀRIA

    2. **H. élegans** (Lindl.) Boland. $2n = 21$ pairs (Raven, Kyhos & Hill, 1965). Calder & Taylor have as new combs.: *H. unalascensis* ssp. *maritima* and *elata.*

    3. **H. dilatàta** var. **leucostàchys** (Lindl.) Ames. $n = 21$ (Raven, Kyhos and Hill, 1965).

p. 1397.   SPIRÁNTHES

    2. **S. porrifòlia** Lindl. Reported from Monterey Co., *Howitt & Howell.*

p. 1398.   LÍSTERA

    1. **L. cordàta** (L.) R. Br. in Ait. has greenish or purplish fls., the 2 forms usually growing intermingled. $2n = 36$–38 (Löve & Löve, 1956). $n = 19$ (Taylor, 1967).—Collected in Del Norte Co., *Munz.* The greenish form has been called *L. nephrophylla* Rydb., [*L. c.* var. *n* Hult., *L. c.* ssp. *n.* Löve & Löve.]

EPIPÁCTIS

Insert after generic description

> The lip distinctly 3-lobed; lateral lobes erect and forming a sac which is papillose within; mid-lobe usually linear-oblanceolate; sepals 1.2–1.3 cm. long. .... 1. *E. gigantea*
> The lip not 3-lobed; sac not papillose within; the apical part of the lip usually triangular-ovate; sepals 1–1.2 cm. long. .... 2. *E. Helleborine*

p. 1399   1. **E. gigantèa** Dougl. ex Hook. $n = 20$ (Raven, Kyhos & Hill, 1965).
2. **E. Helleborìne** (L.) Crantz. [*Serapias H.* L.] Differing from *E. gigantea* particularly in its smaller fls. and non-lobed lip.—Reported from the counties about San Francisco Bay, *Howell*; found also in the e. U.S.; native of Old World.
GOODYÈRA
1. **G. oblongifòlia** Raf. reported from Santa Cruz Mts., *Howell*.
CALÝPSO
1. **C. bulbòsa** (L.) Oakes was found in the Santa Cruz Mts., *Crandall*. Calder & Taylor distinguish western plants as **C. bulbòsa** ssp. **occidentàlis** (Holz) Calder & Taylor.

p. 1400.   CORALLORHÌZA
1. **C. striàta** Lindl. reported from Fresno Co., *Collett*.
3. Calder & Taylor use the comb. *C. maculàta* Raf. ssp. *Mertensiàna* (Dougl.) Calder & Taylor.

p. 1402.   JÚNCUS
In Key, AA, B, CC, change D to:

> D. Perennials, usually with flat lf.-blades.
> D′. Anthers 3, red to dark purple; perianth 2–3.5 mm. long. Nevada Co. .... 21a. *J. marginatus*
> D′D′. Anthers 6.
> E. Lf.-sheath passing gradually, etc. as in the FLORA.

p. 1403.   In Key change the last DD to:

> DD. Anthers usually shorter than fils.; style short.

p. 1404.   2. **J. Párryi** Engelm. Found in the White Mts. at 11,800 ft.
5. **J. mexicànus** Willd. In the White Mts. at 11,900 ft.
p. 1405.   6. **J. bálticus** Willd. $2n = 40$ (Löve & Löve, 1956).
11. **J. bufònis** L. var. **Congdònii** (Wats.) J. T. Howell. [*J. C.* Wats.] Seeds nearly smooth, shining, translucent.—Merced Co.
p. 1406.   12. **J. sphaerocárpus** Nees. $2n = 36$ (Snogerup, 1958).—Rare in the S. Coast Ranges.
p. 1407.   17. **J. Covíllei** Piper. Ranges s. to Marin Co., *Howell*.
18. **J. orthophýllus** Cov. Found in Kern Co., *Twisselmann*.
20. **J. macrophýllus** Cov. occurs in the Greenhorn Range, Kern Co., *Twisselmann* and in Monterey Co., *Howell*.
21a. **J. marginàtus** Rostk. Cespitose from a short thick and often knotty rhizome; stems slender, 2–8 dm. high; lvs. green, flat, soft, the basal 4–20 cm. long, 1–4 mm. broad; infl. 1–10 cm. long, with ca. 2–30 heads of 2–12 fls. each; perianth 3–3.5 mm. long, reddish brown; stamens 3, with reddish anthers; caps. rounded, beakless; seeds brown, many-ribbed, 0.5 mm. long.— Ca. 7 mi. e. of Nevada City, Nevada Co., at 3100 ft.; Ariz. and Rocky Mts. to New England.
p. 1408.   26. **J. Kellóggii** Engelm. in Monterey Co., *Howitt & Howell*.
27. **J. capillàris** F. J. Herm. Report for Monterey Co. erroneous.
28. **J. bryoìdes** F. J. Herm. is in Monterey Co. at The Indians, having 2 bracts instead of the usual 1.
p. 1409.   30. **J. unciàlis** Greene. is in Monterey Co.
34. **J. acuminàtus** Michx. F. J. Hermann uses f. **sphaerocéphalus** Herm. for the Calif. plant.
35. **J. rugulòsus** Engelm. has been found n. into Monterey Co., *Howitt & Howell*; Kern Co., *Twisselmann*.
p. 1410.   37. **J. articulàtus** L. $2n = 80$ (Löve & Löve, 1956).

41. **J. Mertensiànus** Bong. F. J. Hermann (Leafl. W. Bot. 10: 81–86. 1964) revises this complex as follows: (combining spp. 41, 42, 43 of the FLORA)

Heads usually solitary, sometimes 2, many-fld. (12- or more-).
Perianth-segms. purplish-black, flaccid, narrow and exposing much of the mature caps.; bracts spathaceous; anthers usually much shorter than the fils.; auricles rounded, opaque, 1–2 mm. long. Calif. to Rocky Mts. .... *J. Mertensianus*
Perianth-segms. brown, stiffish; bract narrow; anthers and fils. usually subequal; auricles rounded to acute, translucent. Mts. of s. Calif. .... Var. *Duranii*
(*J.M.* ssp. *M.* var. *Duranii* F. J. Herm.)
Heads usually several to many, few-fld. (12- or fewer-), usually dark brown; perianth-segms. usually stiffish; bracts not spathaceous; anthers longer than the fils. Mts., Calif. to Wash., Wyo. .... Ssp. *gracilis*
(*J.M.* ssp. *gracilis* (Engelm.) F. J. Herm. *J. phaeocephalus* var. *gracilis* Engelm. *J. nevadensis* Wats.)

Rubtzoff (Leafl. W. Bot. 10: 168. 1965) reports **J. Mertensiànus** ssp. **grácilis** from Boggs Lake, s. Lake Co. The nearest previously known station was Trinity Co., *Mason.*

49. **J. ensifòlius** Wikstr. Greenhorn Mts., Kern Co., *Twisselmann.*

p. 1412. LÚZULA

3. **L. subcongésta** (Wats.) Jeps. not Buch.

p. 1413. 5. **L. spicàta** (L.) DC. occurs in the White Mts. Add to synonymy *L. s.* ssp. *saximontana* Löve & Löve.

6. **L. comòsa** E. Mey. Add to the synonyms *L. multiflora* (Retz.) Lejeune var. *comosa* (E. Mey.) St. John. Change "anthers" etc. to "anthers equal to or longer than fils."

p. 1414. CYPERÀCEAE

In legend under Fig. 133, the next to the last word in line 2 should be "spikelets" not "spikes."

p. 1415. At end of Key to Genera, change to:

AA. Fls. all unisexual, ♂ and ♀ in separate spikes or separate parts of the same spike.
   B. Female fls. enclosed in perigynia, which often end in a beak. Many spp. Common.
                          12. *Carex*
   BB. Female fls. without perigynia, but closely enfolded by an inner glume. One sp., Convict Lake Basin, Sierra Nevada. .... 13. *Kobresia*

SCÍRPUS

Following in part changes suggested by T. Koyama (Can. J. Bot. 40: 913–937. 1962 and 41: 1117–1122. 1963) and by others, I submit the following key for California species:

A. Bristles much exserted, upwardly barbed. .... 1. *S. criniger*
AA. Bristles, where present, included within scales and usually downwardly barbed.
   B. Infl. subtended by involucral lvs.
      C. Involucral lvs. 2–5, usually exceeding the infl.
         D. Spikelets small, 0.3–0.6 cm. long.
           E. Aks. lenticular; style 2-fid; stamens 2. .... 2. *S. microcarpus*
           EE. Aks. triangular; style 3-fid; stamens 3.
              F. Perianth bristles 2–4 mm. long, the teeth antrorse, rather scattered; infl. mostly with primary rays and less diffuse branching.
                          3. *S. Congdonii*
              FF. Perianth bristles 1–2.5 mm. long, the teeth retrorse, close together; infl. open, diffuse. .... 3a. *S. diffusus*
        DD. Spikelets larger, 1–4 cm. long.
           E. Aks. rhomboid-obovoid, 3-angled with pale, slightly concave sides; perianth bristles 6, strongly scabrous with spinules, persistent on mature aks.; lvs. evenly distributed the full length of the culms.
                          4. *S. fluviatilis*
           EE. Aks. obovate to broadly so, lenticular or compressed-triangular with convex sides; perianth bristles fewer than 5, scaberulous with minute hairlike appressed spinules, deciduous; lvs. mostly basal but sometimes with a few on the culm.
              F. Floral scales rufescent, chartaceous, not translucent, very tightly appressed, the awn short and abruptly recurved.
                          5. *S. robustus*
              FF. Floral scales pale- to chestnut-brown but not rufescent, thin-membranaceous, semitranslucent particularly on the hyaline margin, ± loose, the awn long and gradually recurved.

G. Spikelets ovoid, usually more than 6 mm. thick, solitary or clustered in groups of 2 or 3 on umbel rays, sometimes all congested in a large head; aks. broadly ovate, more frequently digynous. 6. *S. maritimus* var. *paludosus*
GG. Spikelets lanceolate to linear lanceolate, usually less than 6 mm. thick, clustered in groups of 2–5 on well-elongated umbel rays; aks. oblong-obovate, more frequently trigynous. .... 6. *S. maritimus* var. *tuberosus*
CC. Involucral lf. solitary, often appearing as a continuation of the culm.
  D. Culm leafy, triangular or subterete; spikelets few, 1–12.
    E. Perennials with rhizomes; culms not filiform; bristles present.
      F. Culm subterete; scales not awned.
        G. Spikelets 2–8; style 2-cleft; lvs. ca. 2 mm. wide. Mono Co. to Modoc Co. .... 8. *S. nevadensis*
        GG. Spikelet 1; style 3-cleft; lvs. 0.5–1 mm. wide. Del Norte Co., Nevada Co. .... 8a. *S. subterminalis*
      FF. Culm sharply triangular; scales short-awned.
        G. Infl. with the 2nd and 3rd bracts scalelike and to as long as the lowest spikelet; lf.-blades convolute; plant to ca. 1 m. tall.
          H. Floral scales rusty brown or yellow brown, thinly coriaceous along the midvein, the long excurrent mucro exceeding the acute teeth at the scale apex.
            7. *S. americanus* var. *longispicatus*
          HH. Floral scales purple-fuscous or purplish-sanguineous, membranaceous along the midvein, the short upright mucro shorter than or equalling the rounded small teeth at the scale apex.
            7. *S. americanus* var. *monophyllus*
        GG. Infl. without second and third bracts; lf.-blades flat.
          H. Aks. light brown or gray, the surface minutely pitted, common; native. .... 9. *S. Olneyi*
          HH. Aks. dark brown, the surface horizontally rugose; rare weed of rice fields. ...... 10. *S. mucronatus*
    EE. Annuals with fibrous roots, or rarely perennials; culms filiform; bristles absent.
      F. Annuals; aks. punctate or transversely corrugate.
        G. Scales sharply keeled, acute or acuminate; involucral lf. to 2.5 cm. long. .... 13. *S. koilepis*
        GG. Scales only slightly keeled at tip.
          H. The scales obtuse; aks. punctate. Native.
            12. *S. cernuus*
          HH. The scales acuminate; aks. transversely corrugate. Rare adventive. .... 12a. *S. saximontanus*
      FF. Perennials; aks. longitudinally ribbed. ...... 11. *S. setaceus*
  DD. Lvs. of culm reduced to basal sheaths with short blades, to 8 cm. long; culm stout and terete; spikelets numerous in umbels.
    E. Bristles filiform, barbed retrorsely.
      F. Scales well exceeding the ak., pale brown and sanguineous-tinged, with dark red gummy spots at least on the upper half; spikelets on relatively short rigid rays. .... 14. *S. acutus*
      FF. Scales equalling or only very slightly exceeding the ak., rusty brown, smooth or with a few dark red gummy spots on the upper midvein only; spikelets ± nodding on elongate slender rays. .... 15. *S. validus*
    EE. Bristles broad, plumose with dense soft hairs... 16. *S. californicus*
BB. Infl. subtended by the long-awned lowermost scale of the spikelet; true involucral lvs. absent.
  C. Plants not stoloniferous; bristles 6; ak. strongly trigonous. Tulare and Inyo cos. to Tuolumne and Mono cos. at high altitudes. ...... 17. *S. Clementis*
  CC. Plant stoloniferous, with slender scaly stolons and filiform rhizomes; bristles 0; ak. compressed. Convict Lake, Mono Co. .... 18. *S. Rollandii*

p. 1416.   1. **S. crìniger** Gray. At elevs. as low as 150 ft., Del Norte Co.
  3a. **S. diffùsus** Schuyler. Resembling *S. Congdonii*, the infl. more diffuse with primary rays mostly again divided; perianth bristles shorter, their teeth retrorse, quite crowded, rather than antrorse and scattered.—Mostly below 6500 ft., Humboldt Co. to Lake Co. and Tulare Co.
  4. **S. fluviátilis** (Torr.) Gray reported from Santa Cruz Mts., *Thomas*; Sonoma Co., *Baker*; and Napa Co., *Jussel.*
  5. **S. robústus** Pursh as understood by Koyama and keyed out above is found in Coastal Salt Marsh of Calif., Mex., E. N. Am. and in S. Am.
p. 1417.   6. Koyama recognizes **S. marítimus** L. var. **paludòsus** (A. Nels.) Kükenth.

[*S. paludosus* A. Nels. was in synonymy under *S. robustus* in the FLORA. *S. pacificus* Britt. ex Parish] and **S. m.** var. **tuberòsus** (Desf.) R. & S. [*S. tuberosus* Desf. in the FLORA] as varieties in the **S. marítimus** complex.—The first named is native in N. Am. and common at low elevs. in Freshwater Marsh, etc., while the second is an Old World plant natur. in Calif. and Quebec. An additional record for it in Calif. is Kern Co., *Twisselmann*.

7. **S. americànus** Pers. For Calif. Koyama recognizes two vars. as shown in the new key: Var. **longispicàtus** Britt. [*S. a.* var. *polyphyllus* (Böckeler) Beetle, in part] which he gives as from inland Calif. to inland B.C., Mex., W. Indies, S. Am.

Var. **monophýllus** (Presl) Koyama [*S. m.* Presl.] which he ascribes to coastal Calif.; n. to coastal B.C. and s. to S. Am.

8a. **S. subterminàlis** Torr. Aquatic perennial, with slender nodulose culms 3–10 dm. long; lvs. slender, channeled, 2–5 dm. long, 0.5–1 mm. wide; spikelets solitary, terminal, oblong-cylindrical, 6–10 mm. long, subtended by an erect subulate involucral lf.; fls. 6–10; scales light brown with green midveins; stamens 3; style 3-cleft to middle.—N. Del Norte Co., *Hobart,* Nevada Co., *Howell & True*; to B.C., Atlantic Coast. July–Aug.

12a. **S. saximontànus** Fern. [*S. supinus* L. var. *s.* Koyama]. Tufted annual; culms slender, terete, simple, unequal, to 4 dm. tall; basal sheaths mostly bladeless; elongate cauline blade occasional; invol. erect; spikelets 1–7, becoming cylindrical, 0.5–1.5 cm. long; scales cuspidate-acuminate, with green keel; styles 3-cleft; ak. strongly 3-angled, the subequal faces slightly convex.—Damp shores, Colo. to S. Dak., Kans., Tex., etc. Reported as in Ventura, Kern, Colusa, Glenn, and Butte cos.

p. 1418.   14. **S. acùtus** Muhl. Add as syn. *S. lacustris* ssp. *glaucus* (Smith) Hartman. So treated by Koyama, Can. J. Bot. 40: 926. 1962.

15. **S. válidus** Vahl. [Add as syn., *S. lacustris* L. ssp. *validus* (Vahl) T. Koyama, Can. J. Bot. 40: 927. 1962.]—Reported from as far south as San Francisco, *Rubtzoff* and Santa Barbara Co., *C. Smith*.

16. **S. califórnicus** (C. A. Mey.) Steud. in Napa and Sonoma cos., *Rubtzoff*.

17. **S. Cleméntis** Jones. In third line from end of description, "1–5 mm." should read "1.5 mm."

18. **S. Rollándii** Fern. [*S. pumilus* auth., not Vahl. *S. p.* ssp. *R.* Raymond.] Stoloniferous with slender scaly stolons and filiform rhizomes; culms in tufts, 5–15 cm. high; spikelet solitary, 3–4 mm. long; scales ovate, brownish; bristles 0; ak. blackish.—Calcareous places at 10,200 to 10,600 ft., Convict Lake Basin, Mono Co.; Colo. to Alta., e. Can.

HELEÓCHARIS.   The spelling **Eleócharis** is preferable. In Key after A, BB, CC:

> D. Scales spirally arranged; tubercle not 3-lobed.
>> D'. Tubercle confluent with the ak., merely conic. and not forming a distinct caps. .... 2. *H. pauciflora*
>> D'D'. Tubercle obviously differentiated from the ak., forming a distinct apical caps.
>>> E. Tubercle long-subulate, etc. as in the FLORA.

p. 1419.   1. **H. aciculàris** (L.) R. & S. var. **rádicans** (Poir.) Britton. In Sonoma Co., *Rubtzoff*, and in Marin and Mendocino cos.

2. **H. pauciflòra** (Lightf.) Link. Reported from Sonoma and Monterey cos. and the White Mts. Clapham, Tutin & Warburg in the Fl. Brit. Isles use **H. quinqueflòra** (F. X. Hartmann) Schwarz instead of *pauciflora*, but I have seen no discussion as to the reason.

p. 1420.   3. **H. párvula** (R. & S.) Link. In Napa Co., *Rubtzoff* and in Marin Co.

5. **H. montevidénsis** var. **Paríshii** Grant. $n = 5$ (Raven et al., 1965).

p. 1421.   11. J. T. Howell (Wasmann J. Biol. 22: 163.) uses **H. macrostàchya** Britton. instead of **H. palústris** (L.) R. & S. $2n = 38$ (Strandhede, 1967).

p. 1423.   HEMICÁRPHA

2. **H. occidentàlis** Gray. Reported from Greenhorn Mts., Kern Co. and Kern Plateau, Tulare Co., *Hardham*.

p. 1424.   CYPÈRUS

In Key change AA, B, C, DD, EE to:

> EE. Scales ovate to rounded, not recurved at tip.
>> F. Spikes dense, often lobate; scales ovate-orbicular, not mucronate. . . . . 8. *C. diffusus*
>> FF. Spikes loose; scales ovate, mucronate. . . . . 8a. *C. fuscus*

1. **C. nìger** var. **capitàtus** (Britton) O'Neill ranges to Humboldt and Shasta cos., *Rubtzoff.* Ascends to 5700 ft. in Lassen Nat. Park.

Var. *rivulàris* (Kunth) V. Grant. Correct name is var. **castàneus** (Pursh) Kükenthal.

p. 1425.   8. **C. diffórmis** L. Rubtzoff (Leafl. W. Bot. 10: 68) sums up records from Coast Ranges: Sonoma, Napa, Marin, San Francisco cos.

8a. **C. fúscus** L. Tufted; invol. of 2–4 divergent lvs.; umbel condensed or rayed, the spikes subcapitate; spikelets purple-brown, 3–12 mm. long, the scales ca. 1 mm. long.—Stanislaus R. at Caswell Memorial State Park; San Joaquin Co., *Rubtzoff.* Found in e. U.S.; native of Old World.

p. 1427.   KYLLÍNGA

1. **K. brevifòlia** Rottb. List as synonym *Cyperus brevifolius* Rottb.

SCHOÈNUS

1. **S. nigricáns** L. *n* = 22 (Davies, 1956).

p. 1428.   RHYNCHÓSPORA

2. Change name to **R. glomeràta** (L.) Vahl var. **mìnor** Britton. [*R. g.* var. *capitellata* Kükenthal.] Reported from Plumas Co. and region, *Rubtzoff.*

4. **R. califórnica** Gale in Marin Co. at Point Reyes.

p. 1429.   CÀREX

At end of generic description add: (*Carex,* the classical Latin name, of obscure derivation).

p. 1433.   In Key after FF, G, H, II insert:

> J. Perigynia lance-ovate, tapering gradually into a beak ca. ¼ the length of the body. At above 4000 ft., mts. of Calif.
>> 46. *C. mariposana*
> JJ. Perigynia broadly ovate, tapering abruptly into a beak almost ½ the body length.
>> 46a. *C. molesta*

p. 1434.   In Key under **Firmiculmes** change to:

> A. Culms terete or obtusely triangular, usually smooth. . . . . 86. *C. multicaulis*
> AA. Culms sharply triangular, scabrous above.
>> B. Rootstocks prolonged; spikelet solitary; pistillate scales short awn-tipped or awnless, not foliaceous. . . . . 87. *C. Geyeri*
>> BB. Rootstocks not prolonged, the plants cespitose; spikelets sometimes 2 or 3; pistillate scales ± foliaceous. . . . . 87a. *C. Tompkinsii*

p. 1436.   1. **C. capitàta** L. $2n = 50$ (Löve & Löve, 1956).
p. 1437.   3. **C. Brèweri** Boott. Occurs in the White Mts., Inyo Co.
p. 1438.   9. **C. pánsa** Bailey. Add as synonym *C. arenicola* ssp. *pansa* Koyama & Calder.

10. **C. Eléocharis** Bailey. To 13,500 ft. in the White Mts.

11. **C. simulàta** Mkze. s. to the Piute Mts., Kern Co., *Twisselmann.*

12. **C. vallícola** Dewey taken at Monitor Pass, Alpine Co.

p. 1439.   17. **C. tumulícola** Mkze. On San Clemente Id., *Raven.*

21. **C. vicària** Bailey. In Greenhorn Range, Kern Co., *Twisselmann.*

p. 1440.   23. **C. Dúdleyi** Mkze. in San Luis Obispo Co., *Hardham.*

24. **C. diandra** Schrank. $2n = 60$ (Löve & Löve, 1956).

p. 1441.   26. **C. Jònesii** Bailey. In Greenhorn Range, Kern Co., *Twisselmann.*

30. **C. dìsperma** Dewey. $2n = 70$ (Löve & Löve, 1965).

32. **C. canéscens** L. $2n = 56$ (Löve & Löve, 1956).

p. 1442.   34. **C. laeviculmis** Meinsh. In Nevada Co., *True & Howell.*
p. 1443.   38. **C. angústior** Mkze. In the Greenhorn Range, Kern Co., *Twisselmann.*

39. **C. leptopòda** Mkze. [*C. Deweyana* ssp. *l.* (Mkze.) Calder & Taylor.] In Monterey Co., *Howitt & Howell*; and San Luis Obispo Co., *Hoover.*

40. **C. Bolánderi** Olney in Monterey Co., *Howitt & Howell.*

p. 1444.　46. **C. mariposàna** Bailey. In the Greenhorn Mts., Kern Co., *Twisselmann.*

46a. **C. molésta** Mkze. Cespitose, the culms 3–10 dm. high, roughened above, brownish-black at the base; lf.-blades 1–3 dm. long, 2–3 mm. wide; spikes 4–8, gynaecandrous, in a head 2–3 cm. long, the spikes subglobose, 6–9 mm. long; scales ovate, yellowish-brown with 3-nerved green center and hyaline margins; perigynia ovate, 4.5 mm. long, rounded at the base, ± nerved, tapering abruptly into a beak almost half the length of the body; beak flat, serrulate, brownish-tipped, shallowly bidentate.—Santa Barbara, *Pollard.* From the e. and central U.S.

p. 1445.　52. **C. subfúsca** W. Boott. In the White Mts.

p. 1446.　55. **C. gracílior** Mkze. Greenhorn Range, Kern Co., *Twisselmann.*

p. 1447.　61. **C. phaeocéphala** Piper f. **Eastwoodiàna** (Stacey) F. J. Herm. [*C. E. Stacey.*] Perigynium typically broadest at or below the middle, not above. Mono Co.; to Wash., Wyo.

p. 1449.　73. **C. leptàlea** Wahl. $2n = 52$ (Löve & Löve, 1965).

p. 1450.　77. **C. globòsa** Boott. On Santa Cruz Id.

78. **C. Braìnerdii** Mkze. in the Greenhorn Range, Kern Co., *Twisselmann*; ascending to 9100 ft., Lassen Nat. Park.

80. **C. Róssii** Boott. In the White Mts.

p. 1452.　87a. **C. Tompkínsii** J. T. Howell Cespitose, the stems many, erect, acutely triangular, scabrous above, 1–4 dm. tall; lvs. of the season blade-bearing, generally 2 or 3, near base of stems or above, the sheaths cylindric, hyaline, brown-tinged at mouth, blades flat or caniculate, to 4 dm. long, 1.5–3 mm. wide; spikelets bractless, androgynous, solitary and terminal or with 1 or 2 lateral; stigmas 3; scales green with hyaline margins, awn-tipped or semi-foliaceous; perigynia 5–6 mm. long, 2-ribbed, greenish, short-beaked; ak. 4–5 mm. long.—Kings River, Fresno Co. at 3200–5500 ft.

p. 1454.　98. **C. mendocinénsis** Olney in Monterey Co., *Howitt & Howell*, and San Luis Obispo Co., *Hardham.*

101. **C. Lemmònii** W. Boott in the Greenhorn Range, Kern Co., *Twisselmann.*

p. 1455.　104. **C. luzulìna** Olney in San Luis Obispo Co., *Hardham.*

108. **C. lanuginòsa** Michx. at various stations in Kern Co., *Twisselmann.*

p. 1456.　108a. **C. lasiocárpa** Ehrh. edges of pond, west of Lake Center Public Campground, s. Plumas Co., at 6700 ft., *E. K. Balls.* Differs from *C. lanuginosa* by having lvs. filiform-convolute, 0.5–2 mm. wide (not flat with revolute margins and 2–5 mm. wide).—Wash. to Atlantic Coast; Eurasia.

111. **C. amplifòlia** Boott. Collected in Kern Co., *Twisselmann.*

112. **C. limòsa** L. $2n = 62$ (Löve & Löve, 1956); $2n = 64$ (Löve & Löve, 1965).

p. 1458.　123. **C. gymnóclada** Holm. Hermann proposes *C. scopulorum* var. *bracteosa* (Bailey) F. J. Herm. for *C. gymnoclada.*

p. 1459.　125. **C. Kellóggii** W. Boott in the Greenhorn Range, Kern Co., *Twisselmann.*

129. **C. aquátilis** Wahl. $n = 38$ (Davies, 1956); $2n = 76$ (Löve & Löve, 1956).

p. 1460.　133. **C. nudàta** W. Boott. The lowest bract is much shorter than the infl., not the culms.

p. 1461.　137. **C. spíssa** Bailey as far n. as Monterey Co., *Howitt & Howell.*

142. **C. vesicària** L. $2n = 74$ (Löve & Löve, 1965).

p. 1462.　144. **C. rostràta** Stokes $2n = 76$ (Löve & Löve, 1956)

13. Kobrèsia Willd.

Slender arctic and mountain sedges with erect culms leafy below and with spikelets few-fld., variously grouped. Scales of spikelets 1-fld., the lower fls.

usually ♀, the upper ♂. Stamens 3. Lacking perigynia and perianth-bristles, but ♀ fl. closely enfolded by the inner glume. Ovary oblong, narrowed into a short style; stigmas 2–3, linear. Ak. sessile, obtusely angled. (Von *Kobres,* a German naturalist.) Ca. 30 spp.

1. **K. myosuroìdes** (Vill.) Fiori & Paol. [*K. Bellardii* (All.) Degland]. Culms very slender, 1–4.5 dm. tall; lvs. shorter, narrow, the margins ± revolute; old sheaths fibrillose, brown; spike subtended by a short bract or bractless, usually densely fld., 1.5–3 cm. long, 3–4 mm. diam.; aks. scarcely 2 mm. long, 1 mm. thick, appressed.—At 9700 to 10,600 ft., moist places, Convict Basin, Mono Co.; to Arctic Am., Eurasia.

p. 1465. FESTÙCEAE
In Key HH, II, J, change K:

> K. Spikelets in racemes.
>> L. Racemes short, dense, over-topped by the lvs.; spikelets awnless. ..... 6a. *Sclerochloa*
>> LL. Racemes elongate, loose, ex-serted; spikelets awned or mucronate. ...... 7. *Pleuropogon*

HÓRDEAE
In B in the 8th line from the bottom of the page, the word "latter" should be "lateral" in the 1959 printing.

p. 1466. AGROSTÍDEAE
In Key AA, BB, insert before C:

> B'. Lemma firm, bearing a long straight delicate awn just below the tip; palea ca. as long as lemma. .... 53a. *Apera*
> B'B'. Lemma thin or membranous.
>> C. Glumes mostly longer, etc. as in the FLORA.

p. 1467. PANICÈAE
In Key after AA, BB, change to:

> C. Glumes awned or mucronate; apex of palea not inclosed by the lemma.
>> D. Infl. paniculate; spikelets silky. .... 86a. *Rhynchelytrum*
>> DD. Infl. of unilateral racemes along a common axis; spikelets not silky.
>>> 87. *Echinochloa*
> CC. Glumes awnless, etc. as in the FLORA.

Key after AA, BB, CC, DD, EE, change to:

> F. Racemes slender, 3–12.
>> G. Fr. flexible; 1st glume reduced, but present. 82. *Digitaria*
>> GG. Fr. rigid; 1st glume wanting. .... 82a. *Axonopus*
> FF. Racemes stout, in pairs. .... 85. *Paspalum*

ANDROPOGÒNEAE

> A. Spikelets all alike, fertile, surrounded by copious soft hairs; infl. a narrow panicle.
>> 91. *Imperata*
> AA. Spikelets unlike, the sessile perfect, the pedicellate ♂ or neuter.
>> B. Racemes of several joints.
>>> C. Fertile spikelet with a hairy-pointed callus, formed of the attached support-ing rachis joint or pedicel; awns strong, brown. .... 92b. *Heteropogon*
>>> CC. Fertile spikelet without a callus, the rachis disarticulating below the spike-let; awns slender.
>>>> D. Lower pair of spikelets like the others of the raceme. 92. *Andropogon*
>>>> DD. Lower pair of spikelets sterile, awnless; racemes in pairs on slender flexuous peduncles. .... 92a. *Hyparrhenia*

p. 1468. BB. Racemes reduced to 1 or few joints, these in a compound panicle. 93. *Sorghum*

p. 1469. BRÒMUS
1. *B. cathárticus* Vahl should be changed to **B. Willdenòvii** Kunth. (cf. Raven, Brittonia 12: 221. 1961).

p. 1470. 2. Change *B. Haenkeànus* (Presl) Kunth to **B. unioloìdes** HBK. The sp. has recently been reported from Cantil, Kern Co., *Twisselmann,* and Monterey Co., *Howitt & Howell.* 2n = 42 (Schulz-Schaeff. & Mark, 1957).

8. **B. marítimus** Hitchc. 2n = 56 (Schulz-Schaeff. & Mark, 1957).

p. 1471. 9. **B. polyánthus** Scribn. $2n = 56$ (Schulz-Schaeff. & Mark, 1957).

12. **B. vulgàris** (Hook.) Shear. Santa Cruz. Id.

p. 1472. 18. **B. eréctus** Huds. $n = 21 + 4$ (Schulz-Schaeff., 1956); $2n = 42, 56,$ 70, 112 (Hill, 1965).

19. **B. Pórteri** (Coult.) Nash in the Sierra Nevada of Tulare and Inyo cos., *Raven.*

20. **B. Richardsònii** Link. $2n = 28$ (Mitchell & Wilton, 1965).

p. 1473. 26. **B. racemòsus** L. $n = 14$ (Schulz-Schaeffer, 1956).

29. **B. arvénsis** L. Reported from Madera Co., *Raven.*

31. *B. rígidus* Roth should be changed to **B. diándrus** Roth. $n = 21$ (Schulz-Schaeffer, 1956).

p. 1474. 32. **B. stérilis** L. In Monterey Co., *Howitt & Howell.*

33. **B. rùbens** L. $2n = $ ca. 28 (Reese, 1957).

36. **B. Trìnii** E. Desv. in Gay.

p. 1476. FESTÙCA

10. **F. microstàchys** var. **símulans** (Hoov.) Hoov. has spikelets 3–6-fld. instead of 1–3 and is common on hills and plains of Kern Co. and into interior San Luis Obispo Co.

11. **F. Eastwoòdiae** Piper in the Temblor Range, Kern Co., *Twisselmann.*

p. 1477. 12. **F. Tràcyi** Hitchc. In Tuolumne Co., *Raven.*

16. **F. elátior** L. $2n = 14$ (Bowden, 1960). Change to **F. praténsis** Huds. Cf. Terrell (Brittonia 19: 129. 1967).

18. **F. califórnica** Vasey. In San Luis Obispo Co., *Hoover* and in Sierra Nevada of Eldorado Co., *Crampton.*

p. 1478. 20. **F. rùbra** L. In San Luis Obispo Co. $2n = 42$ (Jorgensen et al., 1958).

21. **F. occidentàlis** Hook. In the Greenhorn Range, Kern Co., *Twisselmann,* and in Santa Barbara Co., *Pollard* and Monterey Co., *Howitt & Howell.*

p. 1480. PUCCINÉLLIA Twisselmann reports both **P. erécta** and **P. pauciflòra** as in Kern Co.

GLYCÈRIA

2. **G. leptostàchya** Buckl. At San Francisco, *Howell & Raven.*

p. 1481. 3. **G. occidentàlis** (Piper) J. C. Nels. In San Mateo Co., *Thomas.*

4. **G. declinàta** Brebiss. In Calaveras and Stanislaus cos., *Crampton.*

6. **G. elàta** (Nash) Hitchc. In Sonoma and Marin cos., *Rubtzoff.*

6a. **Sclerochlòa** Beauv.

Low tufted annual with broad upper sheaths, folded blades and dense spikelike racemes. Spikelets subsessile, imbricate in 2 rows on 1 side of the broad thick rachis, 3-fld., the upper floret sessile. Glumes broad, the first 3-nerved, the second 7-nerved; lemmas rounded on back, with 5 prominent parallel nerves and hyaline margins. (Gr., *skleros*, hard, and *chloa*, grass).

1. **S. dura** (L.) Beauv. [*Cynosurus d.* L.] Two to 7 cm. tall; lf. blades 7–18 mm. long, 1–3 mm. wide; raceme 1–2 cm. long; spikelets 6–7 mm. long.— Adventive in Shasta V., Siskiyou Co., *Fuller.* From s. Eu.

PLEUROPÒGON

2. **P. califórnicus** (Nees) Benth. in Vasey. San Luis Obispo Co., *Hoover.*

p. 1482. 3. **P. refráctus** (Gray) Benth. ex Vasey. $2n = 18$ pairs (D. E. Anderson, 1965).

p. 1483. PÒA

In Key after BB, CC, D, EE, FF, add:

> G. Glumes lanceolate, acute, shorter than the first lemma; ligules of culm lvs. 3–5 mm. long. .... 17. *P. palustris*
> GG. Glumes narrower, acuminate, ca. as long as the first lemma; ligules very short. .... 17a. *P. nemoralis*

p. 1484. 1. **P. ánnua** L. A much used common name in Calif. is WINTERGRASS. $2n = 14$ (Hovin, 1958).

3. **P. Bigelòvii** Vasey & Scribn. In Red Rock Canyon, w. Mojave Desert, *Twisselmann.*

p. 1486.   14. **P. bulbòsa** L. ranges s. to Fresno Co. in the Sierra Nevada, *Raven;* several localities in Kern Co., *Twisselmann;* Santa Barbara Co., *Fuller;* w. Riverside Co., *Lathrop.*

15. **P. triviàlis** L. In San Francisco.

p. 1487.   17a. **P. nemoràlis** L. Culms tufted, 3–7 dm. tall; ligule very short; blades ca. 2 mm. wide; panicle 4–10 cm. long, the branches spreading; spikelets 2–5-fld., 3–5 mm. long; glumes narrow, sharply acuminate, ca. as long as the first floret; lemmas 2–3 mm. long, sparsely webbed at base, pubescent on keel and marginal nerves.—Natur. in Golden Gate Park, San Francisco. From Eu.

p. 1488.   23. **P. épilis** Scribn. From 5500 to 12,000 ft.

24. **P. nevadénsis** Vasey ex Scribn. at Isabella, Kern Co., *Twisselmann.*

BRIZA

2. **B. mìnor** L. $n = 7$ (Gould, 1958).

p. 1491.   ERAGRÓSTIS

In Key, AA, BB, C, change to:

> D. Spikelets 3–5 mm. long; lemmas 1–1.5 mm. long; pedicels mostly longer than the spikelets; surface of the grain smooth; side of grain opposite the embryo rounded. . . . . 2. *E. pilosa*
> DD. Spikelets 5–7 mm. long; lemmas ca. 2 mm. long; pedicels mostly shorter than the spikelets; surface of grain reticulate, side of grain opposite the embryo flat or grooved. . . . . 6. *E. Orcuttiana*

p. 1492.   2. **E. pilòsa** (L.) Beauv. $2n = 60$ (Tateoka, 1965).

3. **E. hypnoìdes** (Lam.) BSP. Santa Cruz Co., Sonoma and Lake cos. to Siskiyou Co., *Rubtzoff.*

4. **E. pectinàcea** (Michx.) Nees. $n = 20, 30$ (Gould, 1958).

5. **E. diffùsa** Buckl. in Sonoma Co., *Rubtzoff;* in Marin and San Francisco cos., *Howell.* $2n = 60$ (Gould, 1965).

8. *E. megastàchya* (Koel.) Link. Probably the preferable name is **E. cilianensis** (All.) E. Mosher.

9. **E. poaeoìdes** Beauv. ex R. & S. In Sonoma Co., *Rubtzoff.*

p. 1493.   14. **E. cúrvula** (Schrad.) Nees. In San Diego, Contra Costa and Solano cos., *Fuller;* in Yolo Co., *Crampton.* $2n = 14$ (Reese, 1957).

DISSANTHÈLIUM

Swallen and Tovar (Phytologia 11: 361–376. 1965) recognize 17 spp. most of them from S. Am.

p. 1496.   CORTADÈRIA

1. **C. Selloàna** (Schult.) Asch. & Graebn. Natur. at San Francisco and in the North Coast Ranges, *Howell;* a heavy infestation of 1100 acres, e. side of Big Lagoon, Humboldt Co., *Fuller.*

p. 1497.   MÉLICA

2. **M. Gèyeri** var. **aristulàta** J. T. Howell in Tehama Co., *Crampton.*

3. **M. Harfórdii** Bol. In San Luis Obispo Co., *Hoover.*

4. **M. aristàta** Thurb. ex Bol. in the Santa Lucia Mts., *Hardham.*

p. 1499.   ECTOSPÉRMA Swall., not Vaucher.

Renamed **Swallènea** Soderstrom & Decker, with **S. Alexándrae** (Swallen) Soderstrom & Decker.

TRÌDENS

Tateoka (Am. J. Bot. 48: 565–573. 1961) recognizes two genera *Tridens* R. & S. with **T. mùticus** (Torr.) Nash [$2n = 40$ (Tateoka)] and *Erioneuron* Nash with **E. pulchéllum** (HBK) Tateoka and E. pilosum (Buckl.) Nash. [$2n = 16$ (Tateoka).]

p. 1500.   NEOSTÁPFIA

1. **N. colusàna** (Davy) Davy. $2n = 40$ (Stebbins & Major, 1965).

ORCÚTTIA

Begin the Key for the 4 spp. treated in the FLORA with:

> A. Lemmas toothed at the apex; florets 10–40 in a spikelet; lodicules obsolete. (Use the key in the FLORA for spp. 1–4.)

AA. Lemmas not toothed at the apex, but erose on the margin and with a terminal mucro; florets 5–10 in a spikelet; lodicules 2, fused to the palea. . . . . 5. *O. mucronata*

p. 1501. 5. **O. mucronàta** Crampton. Culms decumbent, 2.5–12 cm. long; lvs. 1–4 cm. long, viscid; infl. 1.5–6 cm. long; spikelets 7–19, spirally arranged, 7–13 mm. long, 5–10-fld.; glumes 4–7 mm. long, unequal; lemmas coriaceous, 5–7 mm. long.—Dry lake, 12 mi. sw. of Dixon, Solano Co.

p. 1502. AGROPŶRON
In Key, AA, BB, C, DD, change EE to:

EE. Lemmas finely pubescent.
    F. Glumes acute or awn-pointed; lvs. flat to involute.
        4. *A. dasystachyum*
    FF. Glumes truncate; lvs. flat. . . . . 4a. *A. trichophorum*

In Key, AA, BB, CC, change D to:

D. Spikelets much compressed.
    E. Spikelets crowded on rachis; glumes narrowed to short awns.
        1. *A. desertorum*
    EE. Spikelets shorter than the internodes; glumes obtuse or truncate.
        6a. *A. elongatum*

1. **A. desertòrum** (Fisch.) Schult. $2n = 28$ (Sarkar, 1956). In Plumas and Mono cos., *Raven*.

4a. **A. trichóphorum** (Link) Richt. [*Triticum t.* Link.] Plants with creeping rhizomes; culms tallish; lvs. flat; spikelets pubescent, awnless; glumes several-nerved, truncate.—Reported as probably established after being seeded as TOPAR WHEATGRASS on brush-burns, Greenhorn Range, Kern Co., *Twisselmann*; Siskiyou Co., *Fuller*.

5. **A. ripàrium** Scribn. & Sm. $2n = 42$ (Tateoka, 1956).

p. 1503. 6a. **A. elongàtum** (Host) Beauv. [*Triticum e.* Host.] TALL WHEATGRASS. Not creeping, 3–10 dm. tall, glabrous; lvs. glaucous, inrolled, stiff; spike elongate, very lax; spikelets spaced, compressed, oval, 4–8-fld.; glumes obtuse or truncate, 7–9-nerved.—Established in Plumas, Lassen, and Kern cos. From the Medit. region.

7. **A. subsecúndum** (Link) Hitchc. In Tehachapi Mts., ne. of Lebec, *Twisselmann*.

10. **A. Scríbneri** Vasey. $2n = 28$ (Tateoka, 1956).

13. **A. saxícola** (Scribn. & Sm.) Piper is considered to be a hybrid by F. Douglas Wilson.

p. 1504. 15. **A. × Sáundersii** (Vasey) Hitchc. is also a hybrid, between *A. trachycaulum* (Link) Malte and *Sitanion Hystrix* (Nutt.) J. G. Smith. It is reported by *Raven* from the Sierra Nevada of Alpine, Tuolumne, Madera, Fresno, Tulare, Mono, and Inyo cos.

ÉLYMUS

1. **E. cáput-medùsae** L. is recorded from Solano, Alameda, Sacramento, San Joaquin, Tulare, and Fresno cos. McKell, Robison and Major use the name *Taeniatherum asperum* (Simonkai) Nevski for plants referred to **E. cáput-medùsae** by Am. auth.

p. 1505. 2. **E. móllis** (Trin ex Spreng. $2n = 18$ (Löve & Löve, 1956). Ranges s. to San Luis Obispo Co., *Hoover*.

3. **E. móllis** Trin. ex Spreng. × **E. triticoìdes** Buckl. for *E. vancouverensis* Vasey nothomorph *californicus* Bowden.

5. **E. pacíficus** Gould in San Luis Obispo Co., *Hoover*.

p. 1506. SITÀNION
Insert literature citation: Wilson, F. D. Revision of Sitanion. Brittonia 15: 303–323. 1963.
Use this Key:

A. Spikelets 3 at each node of the rachis; florets of central spikelet fertile, those of lateral spikelets reduced, rudimentary. Siskiyou Co. . . . . 5. *S. hordeoides*
AA. Spikelets usually 2 at each node of the rachis, if 3, at least some florets of lateral spikelets fertile.

B. Lowermost floret of 1 or both spikelets at each rachis-node sterile and reduced to
    a subulate or lanceolate structure, giving the appearance of extra glume segms.
C. Glumes entire or bifid. . . . . 3. *S. Hystrix*
CC. Glumes 3–many-cleft; awns of the lemmas exceeding those of the glumes.
                                                                                   2. *S. jubatum*
BB. Lowermost floret fertile, not reduced.
C. Glumes subulate, entire; awns of the glumes exceeding those of the lemmas.
                                                                                   4. *S. longifolium*
CC. Glumes usually lanceolate, entire or 2–several-cleft; awns of the lemmas ex-
    ceeding those of the glumes. . . . . 1. *"S."* × *Hansenii*

3. **S. Hystrix** (Nutt.) J. G. Smith. Delete *S. californicum* and *S. longifolium*
from the synonyms. At least 1 glume of each node of the rachis 2-cleft; awns
of the glumes exceeding those of the lemmas.—E. of the Sierra Nevada, deserts from Modoc Co. to Riverside Co.; to B.C., S. Dak.

Var. **califórnicum** (J. G. Smith) F. D. Wilson. [*S. c.* J. G. Smith. *S. minus*
var. *c.* Jtn.] Glumes entire; awns of the lemmas exceeding those of the glumes.
—Mts., s. Calif. to B.C., Mont., Utah.

4. **S. longifòlium** J. G. Smith. Plants 2.5–6 dm. tall, usually loosely cespitose; culms slender to robust, erect to spreading; blades 2–5 mm. wide, usually
glabrous above; spikes 7–15 cm. long; spikelets mostly 2 at a node, few-
several-fld.; glumes entire, usually 1-nerved, subulate, with spreading setaceous
awns 5–12 cm. long; lemmas 7–12 mm. long, the central nerve extending into
a stout spreading, setaceous awn 5–10 cm. long.—At 2000–10,000 ft., s. Calif.
to S. Dak., Tex., Mex.

5. **S. hordeoìdes** Suksd. Plants 1–2 dm. tall, loosely cespitose; sheaths puberulent to villous; blades 1–4 mm. wide; spikes 3–6 cm. long, dense; spikelets
3 at a node, the central spikelets usually with 2 sterile lateral florets and 1 fertile terminal one; glumes subulate to narrowly lanceolate, extending into
slender scabrous awns 1.5–5 cm. long; lemmas obscurely 5-nerved, ca. 10
mm. long.—Dry rocky places, Siskiyou Co., to Wash., Ida.

p. 1507.   AÈGILOPS
1. **A. ovàta** L. The Glenn Co. reference in the FLORA should have been Wil-
lits, Mendocino Co., according to *Fuller.*
3. **A. triunciàlis** L. The rachis does not disarticulate.

p. 1509.   HÓRDEUM
5. *H. Hýstrix* Roth should be changed to **H. geniculàtum** Allioni.
8. *H. Stébbinsii* Covas should be changed to **H. gláucum** Steud.
10. In **H. vulgàre** L. all spikelets produce large seed. In a cult. Barley **H.
dístichon** L. which is reported as adventive in Monterey Co.; the spike is 2-
rowed, not 4- or 6-rowed. In it the lateral spikelets are sterile.

p. 1510.   LÒLIUM
2. **L. multiflòrum** Lam. var. **mùticum** (DC.) Volkart reported from Monterey Co., *Howitt & Howell* and from San Francisco, *Raven.* It differs from the
sp. in having all lemmas awnless, instead of at least the upper awned. Other
San Francisco collections, with branched panicles, are var. **ràmosum** Guss.,
Howell.

PARÁPHOLIS
1. **P. incúrva** (L.) C. E. Hubb. $n = 21$ (Gould, 1958).

SCRIBNÈRIA
1. **S. Bolánderi** (Rhurb.) Hack. $2n = 26$ (Stebbins & Major, 1965).—Reported from Santa Barbara Co., *Raven;* Kern Co., *Twisselmann.*

p. 1511.   SCHÍSMUS
S. barbàtus (L.) Thell. and **S. arábicus** Nees are both recorded from Monterey Co., *Howitt & Howell.* For both spp., $n = 6$ (Gould, 1958).

KOELÈRIA
1. **K. cristàta** (L.) Pers. is an illegitimate name. Apparently **K. macrántha**
(Ledeb.) Spreng. may be used for our plant (Voss, Rhodora 68: 441. 1966).
$n = 7$ (Tateoka, 1955); $2n = 14$ (Bowden, 1960).

p. 1512.   SPHENÓPHOLIS
Citation: Erdman, K. S. Taxonomy of the genus Sphenopholis. Iowa State Jour. Sci. 39: 289–336. 1965.
1. **S. obtusàta** (Michx.) Scribn. $2n = 14$ (Erdman, 1965).
TRISÈTUM
2. **T. spicàtum** (L.) Richt. $2n = 28$ (Tateoka, 1954).
3. **T. cérnuum** ssp. **canéscens** (Buckl.) Calder & Taylor.—Found in the Greenhorn Mts., Kern Co., *Twisselmann,* and in San Luis Obispo Co., *Hoover.*

p. 1513.   DESCHÁMPSIA
2. **D. elongàta** (Hook.) Munro ex Benth. $2n = 26$ (Bowden, 1960).
4. **D. cespitòsa** (L.) Beauv. for original spelling. $2n = 26, 27, 28$ (Bowden, 1960). Reported from Kern Plateau, Kern Co., *Twisselmann;* Mt. Pinos, *Hoffmann.*

p. 1514.   Ssp. **holicifórmis** (Presl) W. E. Lawr. extends s. to San Luis Obispo Co., *Hoover.*
AÌRA
2. **A. caryophyllèa** L. $2n = 14, 28$ (Böcher & Larsen, 1958).
3. **A. élegans** Willd. ex Gaudin, $2n = 14$ (Böcher & Larsen, 1958).
AVÈNA
1. **A. barbàta** Brot. $2n = 28$ (Martinoli, 1955).
2. **A. fátua** L. Grows to a height of 1.9 m.

p. 1515.   HÓLCUS
1. **H. lanàtus** L. To 2 m. tall.
2. **H. móllis** L. $2n = 28, 35, 42, 49$ (Jones, 1958).

p. 1516.   DANTHÒNIA
1. **D. intermèdia** Vasey. $2n = $ ca. 98 (Taylor, 1967).
3. **D. califórnica** Bol. ranges s. to San Luis Obispo Co., *Hoover.*

p. 1517.   CALAMAGRÓSTIS
5. **C. ophítidis** (J. T. Howell) Nygren. The synonym should be *C. purpurascens* var. *ophitidis* J. T. Howell.
6. **C. rubéscens** Buckl. ranges s. to Monterey Co., *Howitt & Howell,* and to San Luis Obispo Co., *Hoover.* Santa Cruz Id., *Blakely & Muller.*

p. 1518.   7. **C. nutkaénsis** (Presl.) Steud. has been reported from San Luis Obispo Co., *Hoover.*
10. Change the name of *C. canadensis* var. *Langsdorfii* (Link) Inman to *C. c.* var. **scàbra** (Presl) Hitchc. and add Mt. Lassen area for its distribution.

p. 1519.   ### 53a. Apèra Adans.

Near *Agrostis.* Annual, with compound panicle, the lemma chartaceous, terete, shortly bifid, with a well developed awn from the sinus. Three spp. Eurasia.
1. **A. interrúpta** (L.) Beauv. Low, tufted, 1.5–6 dm. tall; lvs. $\pm$ convolute, smooth, narrow, short; ligule to 5 mm. long, truncate; panicle 3–18 cm. long, narrow, $\pm$ interrupted; spikelets 1.5–2 mm. long.—Found 2.6 mi. w. of Alturas, Modoc Co.; introd. from Eu.
AGRÓSTIS
In Key, under AA, BB, CC, D, E, change to:

> F.   Lemmas 2 mm. long or less.
>   G.   The culms spreading; panicles strict, greenish; lemmas with a minute awn or the midnerve ending below the apex. Coastal. (See also var. *marinensis.*)
>   15. *A. Blasdalei*
>   GG. The culms erect; panicles narrow but loose, purple; lemmas awnless, the midnerve reaching the apex. Montane.
>   16. *A. variabilis*
> FF. Lemmas 2.5 mm. long or more; awn ca. 2 mm. long. N. Coastal. . . . . 16a. *A. clivicola*

p. 1520.   1. **A. avenàcea** Gmel. *Raven* records it from Eldorado Co.
              4. **A. stolonífera** L. var. **màjor** (Gaud.) Farwell. [*A. alba* auth. *A. gigantea*
              Roth.] for REDTOP and var. **palústris** (Huds.) Farwell for CREEPING BENT.
              5. **A. ténuis** Sibth. $2n = 28, 32, 34$ (Bowden, 1960).
p. 1521.   12. **A. lépida** Hitchc.—Occurs in n. Fresno Co., *Raven.*
              15. **A. Blasdàlei** Hitchc. var. **marinénsis** Crampton. Glumes 3–4 mm. long;
              lemmas 2.5–2.8 mm. long.—Coast of Marin Co.
              16a. **A. clivícola** Crampton (Brittonia 19: 174. 1967). Perennial; culms
              tufted, glabrous, 1–3.5 dm. long, more or less prostrate; panicle dense, 2–7
              cm. long; glumes 2.8–4 mm. long, the awns to 0.5 mm. long; lemmas 2.5–3
              mm. long, scabrous over the back; $2n = 42$.—Coastal bluffs, Mendocino and
              Sonoma cos.
              Var. **púnta-reyesénsis** Crampton. Culms erect; lf.-blades thinnish, pointed;
              $2n = 42$.—Marin and Sonoma cos.
p. 1522.   18. *A. califórnica* Trin. Change to **A. densiflora** Vasey (cf. Chambers, Ma-
              droño 18: 251. 1966).
              20. **A. scàbra** Willd. $2n = 42$ (Bowden, 1960).

              CÍNNA
              1. **C. latifòlia** (Trev.) Griseb. $2n = 28$ (Tateoka, 1954).
p. 1523.   ALOPÉCURUS
              3. **A. aequàlis** Sobol. $2n = 7$ pairs (D. E. Anderson, 1965).
              Var. **sonoménsis** Rubtzoff. More robust and erect than the sp.; lf. blades to
              7.5 mm. wide; panicle 2.5–9 cm. long, 4–8 mm. wide; awn exserted 1–2.5 mm.
              —Moist places, Marin and Sonoma cos.
              7. **A. carolinianus** Walt. In Merced and Madera cos., *Rubtzoff.*
p. 1524.   POLYPÒGON
              2. **P. marítimus** Willd. *Rubtzoff* finds this quite widespread in Calif.
              3. **P. interrúptus** HBK. Rubtzoff apparently refers most Calif. material for-
              merly identified as this sp. to **P. austràlis** Brongn. It differs from *P. i.* in a
              shorter ligule, to 2 mm. long, shorter blades, lax more purplish panicle and
              slender ± tangled hairs.—Originally from S. Am. It has been found in
              Orange, Riverside, San Bernardino, Inyo cos. and from Stanislaus to Butte
              cos. and from Sonoma to Humboldt cos. Also in Monterey Co., *Howitt* and
              Howell, and Santa Clara and Ventura cos.
p. 1525.   PHLÈUM
              2. **P. alpìnum** L. Add *P. commutatum* Gaud. as a synonym. In the North
              Coast Ranges, the sp. comes s. as far as San Francisco Bay.
p. 1526.   MUHLENBÉRGIA
              In Key after BB, insert:

              B′.   Culms decumbent and rooting at the nodes; glumes minute, the first glume
                     sometimes wanting. .... 12a. *M. Schreberi*
              B′B′. Culms erect or spreading, but not rooting at the nodes;
              C.   Second glume 3-toothed, etc. as in the FLORA.

p. 1526.   4. **M. asperifòlia** (Nees & Mey.) Parodi. $n = 10$ (Pohl & Mitchell, 1965).
              6. **M. Richardsònis** (Trin.) Rydb. Reported by Twisselmann from Mt.
              Pinos and Piute Mts., Kern Co.
p. 1527.   9. **M. andìna** (Nutt.) Hitchc. in Napa Co., *Howell.* $n = 10$ (Pohl & Mitch-
              ell, 1965).
              11. **M. mexicàna** (L.) Trin. f. **ambígua** (Torr.) Fern. with conspicuously
              awned lemmas, should be used instead of f. *setiglumis* (Wats.) Fern. and
              occurs in Mendocino, Humboldt, Butte, and Plumas cos., *Rubtzoff.*
              12. **M. califórnica** Vasey. $n = 40$ (Pohl & Mitchell, 1965).
              12a. **M. Schrèberi** Gmel. Branches 1–3 dm. long; blades flat, to 6 cm. long,
              2–4 mm. wide; panicles slender, lax, nodding, 5–15 cm. long; glumes minute,
              the first often obsolete, the second 0.1–0.2 mm. long; lemma 2 mm. long,
              awn 2–5 mm. long. $n = 20$ (Pohl & Mitchell, 1965).—Introd. on property of
              Felix Gillet Nursery, Nevada City, Nevada Co., *Fuller.* From e. N. Am.

p. 1528.   SPORÓBOLUS
Insert at beginning of Key:

0. Plants annual. .... 6. *S. vaginiflorus*
00. Plants perennial.
    A.   Glumes subequal, much shorter etc. as in the FLORA. Spp. 1–5.

    1. **S. contráctus** Hitchc. In Stanislaus and San Joaquin cos., *Fuller*.
    3. **S. cryptándrus** (Torr.) Gray. at Andrews Camp, Bishop Creek, Inyo Co., at 9000 ft. and 5 mi. s. of Coleville, Mono Co., *Raven*; in Yolo and Solano cos., *Crampton*. $n = 19, 36$ (Gould, 1958); $2n = 36$ (Bowden, 1960).

p. 1529.   6. **S. vaginiflòrus** (Torr.) Wood. Annual, 2–4 dm. high; blades slender, subinvolute; panicles mostly not more than 3 cm. long; glumes acute, subequal, 3–5 mm. long; lemmas as long as glumes or longer, acute to acuminate, sparsely pubescent.—Reported from Nevada and Shasta cos., *Raven*. Native of e. U.S.

HELEÓCHLOA

    1. **H. schoenoìdes** (L.) Host. Additional records are: Kern Co. (Lake Isabella) and San Luis Obispo Co., *Twisselmann*; Los Angeles Co. (Bouquet Canyon) *Raven*; Monterey Co., *Howitt & Howell*; Tulare Co., *Twisselmann*.

p. 1530.   ORYZÓPSIS
    B. L. Johnson (Am. J. Bot. 47: 736–742. 1960) discusses a number of hybrids between *Oryzopsis hymenoides* (R. & S.) Ricker and *Stipa speciosa* Trin. and (in Am. J. Bot. 50: 228–234. 1963) a hybrid between *O. hymenoides* and *S. pinetorum* Jones from Inyo Mts.

p. 1531.   STÌPA
In Key after A, BB, C, DD, EE, FF, GG, H, change I to:

    I.   Hairs on upper part of lemma longer than those below; awn with rather short hairs.
        J.   Lemma more than 2.3 times as long as the palea; culms glabrous below the nodes; sheaths sparsely villous, sometimes glabrous at the throat; awn-hairs 0.2–1 mm. long. ..... 12. *S. californica*
        JJ. Lemma less than 2.3 times as long as the palea; culms scabrous below the nodes; sheaths glabrous at the throat; awn-hairs 0.5–1.5 mm. long. ... 12a. *S. nevadensis*

In Key after AA, BB, CC, change D to:

    D.   Mature lemma brownish.
        E.   Lemma 8–12 mm. long, ± sparsely pubescent; awn 10–15 cm. long. Common native. .... 4. *S. comata*
        EE. Lemma 3.5–6 mm. long, pubescent in lines; awn 1.1–1.8 cm. long. Rare introduction. .... 4a. *S. brachychaeta*

    1. **S. speciòsa** Trin. & Rupr. N. to Fresno Co. in the Sierra Nevada.
    2. **S. Stillmánii** Bol. *Howell* reports as in Shasta, Tehama, Plumas, and Nevada cos.

p. 1532.   3. **S. coronàta** Thurb. in Wats. In Napa Co., *Rubtzoff*.
    4. **S. comàta** Trin. & Rupr. To 11,300 ft. on the e. side of the Sierra Nevada, *Raven*.
    4a. **S. brachychaèta** Godr. Densely cespitose perennial to 1 m. tall; blades firm, flat or loosely involute; panicle narrow, open, the few spikelets on slender pedicels; glumes 6–8 mm. long; lemma 3.5–6 mm. long, brown, pubescent in lines; awn 1.1–1.8 cm. long.—Reported from s. edge of Fresno and near Camarillo, Ventura Co., *Fuller*. Native of Argentina.
    8. **S. Thurberiàna** Piper. Reported from Cuyama Valley, Ventura Co., *Clifton Smith*; ranges n. to Wash., Ida.
    9. **S. Élmeri** Piper & Brodie; 10. **S. occidentalis** Thurb.; etc. J. Maze (Leafl. W. Bot. 10: 159–160. 1965) presents a different key by which to distinguish spp. in this complex:

A. Awn pubescent, at least at the base, plumose or subplumose.
    B. Hairs of the first segm. of the awn subequal to or exceeding those at the tip of the lemma; transition from pubescence of lemma to that of awn gradual.
        C. Plant more than 4 dm. tall. .... 9. *S. Elmeri*
        CC. Plant less than 4 dm. tall. .... 11. *S. occidentalis*
    BB. Hairs of the first segm. of the awn shorter than those at the tip of the lemma; transition from pubescence of lemma to that of awn abrupt.
        C. Palea ca. half as long as lemma; floret less than 2.2 times as long as palea, the hairs at tip of palea mostly ca. 1 mm. long; glabrous area on the inside curve of the callus obtuse to acute and usually not well extended toward the lemma, callus tip shorter and more acute than that of *S. californica*, callus less than 1 mm. long. .... 12a. *S. nevadensis*
        CC. Palea mostly less than half as long as lemma; floret more than 2.2 times as long as palea; hairs at tip of palea mostly less than 1 mm. long, or glabrous area on the inside curve of the callus more acuminate and well extended toward the lemma, callus tip usually longer and more acuminate than that of *S. nevadensis*; callus ca. 1 mm. long. .... 12. *S. californica*
AA. Awn scabridulous to hirtellous.
    B. Lemma with few, if any, longer hairs at the tip, the hairs not spreading, or glabrous area on the inside curve of the callus short-acute and not well extended toward the lemma. .... 14. *S. columbiana*
    BB. Lemma with many distinctly longer hairs at the tip, the hairs usually spreading; the glabrous area on the inside curve of the callus long-acute and well extended toward the lemma; glabrous tip of the callus acuminate. ..... 12. *S. californica*

p. 1533.   12. **S. califórnica** Merr. & Davy. Shirley Meadows, Kern Co., *Twisselmann*.
        12a. **S. nevadénsis** B. L. Johnson. Culms often in tufts, 4–8 dm. tall, scabrous below the nodes; sheaths glabrous or nearly so, glabrous at throat; ligule ca. 0.5 mm. long; cauline lvs. 1–2.5 dm. long, 1–3 mm. wide, becoming involute, ± puberulent above, glabrous below; panicle narrow, 1–2.5 dm. long; glumes 7–10 mm. long; lemma 5–6.5 mm. long, 1.7–2.3 times as long as the palea, sparsely villous, the summit hairs ca. 1.5 mm. long; awn 2–3.5 cm. long, twice geniculate, plumose on first and second segms., awn hairs 0.5–1.5 mm. long; $2n = 68$.—E. slope of the Sierra Nevada, Modoc Co. to Kern Co., to Ida., Nev.
        14. **S. columbiàna** Macoun. $n = 18$ (Johnson, 1962).
        15. **S. Lettermánii** Vasey restricted by Johnson to San Bernardino Mts. $n = 16$ (Johnson, 1962).

p. 1534.   18. **S. pinetòrum** Jones. Eldorado to Tulare and Inyo cos., *Raven*.
p. 1535.   ARÍSTIDA
        3. **A adscensiònis** L. Known also from San Luis Obispo Co., Santa Barbara Co., San Diego Co.
        5. **A. divaricàta** Humb. & Bonpl. ex Willd. $n = 11$ (Gould, 1958).
        9. **A. purpùrea** Nutt. $n = 11$ (Gould, 1958).
        11. **A. Fendleriàna** Steud. $n = 33$ (Gould, 1958).

p. 1536.   HILÀRIA
        2. **H. Jàmesii** (Torr.) Benth. $2n = 18$ pairs.
        3. **H. Belángeri** (Steud.) Nash. A slender stoloniferous plant 1–3 dm. tall, with bearded nodes; spikes 2–3 cm. long.—Reported as se. Calif.; to Tex., n. Mex. *Wiggins*.
        LEPTOCHLÒA
        2. **L. fasciculàris** (Lam.) Gray in Monterey Co., *Howitt & Howell* and in Sonoma Co., *Rubtzoff*, as well as Santa Barbara Co.
        3. **L. uninérvia** Hitchc. & Chase. $n = 10$ (Gould, 1958).

p. 1537.   4. **L. víscida** (Scribn.) Beal. Differing from the 3 spp. treated in the FLORA in having lemmas 2 mm. long, viscid on back; panicle usually less than 10 cm. long, tinged purple; sheaths scabrous.—Reported from Kern Co., *Twisselmann*; ranging to Tex., n. Mex.
        ELEUSINE
        2. **E. tristàchya** (Lam.) Lam. [*Cynosurus t.* Lam.] Differing from *E. indica* by the fewer and shorter spikes (1–3 in number, 1–2.5 cm. long, 8–10 mm. thick).—Reported from 2.5 mi. n. of Clements, San Joaquin Co., *Fuller*. Introd. from Africa.
        DACTYLOCLÈNIUM

1. **D. aegýptium** (L.) Beauv. 2n = 40 (Tateoka, 1965). Taken at Bonsall, San Diego Co., *Dixon in 1965*.

CÝNODON
1. **C. dáctylon** not Dactylon. 2n = 40 (Tateoka, 1954).

p. 1538. SPARTÌNA
Change Key to:

A. Blades mostly more than 8 mm. wide; spikes closely approximate forming a cylindric
    infl. Coastal marshes and dunes. .... 1. *S. foliosa*
AA. Blades less than 5 mm. wide; spikes distinct, appressed or spreading.
    B. Blades usually flat; glumes conspicuously hispid-ciliate on the keels; spikes sev-
        eral, appressed. Interior alkaline meadows. .... 2. *S. gracilis*
    BB. Blades usually involute; glumes scabrous on the keels; spikes few, ascending or
        spreading. Southampton Bay. .... 3. *S. patens*

3. **S. pàtens** (Ait.) Muhl. SALTMEADOW CORDGRASS. Culms slender, usually less than 1 m. tall, with long slender rhizomes; blades mostly involute, less than 3 mm. wide; spikes 2 to several, 2–5 cm. long, rather remote on the axis; spikelets 8–12 mm. long; first glume ca. half as long as the floret, the second longer than the lemma; lemma 5–7 mm. long, emarginate.—Reported from Southampton Bay in a marsh, nw. of Benicia, Solano Co., *Mall*; e. U.S.

p. 1539. CHLÒRIS
1. **C. distichophýlla** Lag. 2n = 40 (Huynh, 1965).
2. **C. Gayàna** Kunth. 2n = 40 (Tateoka, 1965).
3. **C. virgàta** Sw. Reported from near Hilts, Siskiyou Co., *Fuller*.

p. 1540. BOUTELOÙA
2. **B. curtipéndula** (Michx.) Torr. n = 10 (Gould, 1958). Gould and Kapadia (Brittonia 16: 203. 1965) refer California material to var. **caéspitosa** Gould & Kapadia as more stiffly erect than in the sp. Crampton reports the sp. as from Yolo Co.
3. **B. radicòsa** (Fourn.) Griffiths. 2n = 60 (Gould, 1965).
4. **B. barbàta** Lag. 2n = 20 (Gould, 1965).
6. **B. hirsùta** Lag. n = 10, 23 (Gould, 1958); 2n = 46, ca. 52 (Gould, 1965).
7. **B. grácilis** (HBK) Lag. Reported from the Goleta campus of the University of California, *Ernst*. 2n = 20, 40, 60 (Gould, 1965).
9. **B. trífida** Thurb. 2n = 20 (Gould, 1965).

p. 1541. HIEROCHLÒE
1. **H. occidentàlis** Buckl. 2n = 21 pairs (D. E. Anderson, 1965).

ANTHOXÁNTHUM
1. **A. odoràtum** L. 2n = 28 (Tateoka, 1954); 2n = 20 (Gray, 1965).

EHRHÁRTA
2. Add **E. calycìna** Sm. Spikelets 7–8 mm. long; sterile lemmas thinly silky-villous; fertile lemma silky on the nerves.—Reported from San Luis Obispo Co., *Twisselmann,* and Ventura Co., *Pollard*. Introd. from S. Afr.

PHÁLARIS
Introduce after generic description: Anderson, D. E. Taxonomy and distribution of the genus Phalaris. Iowa State Jour. Sci. 36: 1–96. 1961.

p. 1542. In next to last line of Key, "2–6 mm." should read "2–6 cm."
1. **P. paradóxa** L. 2n = 14 (Ambastha, 1956).
2. **P. califórnica** H. & A. In synonymy *P. amethystina* not *A. amethystina*. 2n = 28 (Ambastha, 1956).
3. **P. arundinàcea** L. 2n = 28 (Ambastha, 1956).
4. *P. tuberòsa* L. var. *stenoptera* (Hack.) Hitchc. Anderson uses **P. aquática** L. Howell (Leafl. W. Bot. 10: 40–41. 1963) uses *P. stenóptera* Hack. and reports it as widespread in Calif.
6. **P. canariénsis** L. 2n = 12 (Löve & Löve, 1956).

p. 1543. 9. **P. caroliniàna** Walt. 2n = 14 (Ambastha, 1956).
10. **P. angústa** Nees ex Trin. 2n = 14 (Ambastha, 1956). Taken in Sonoma Co., *M. Baker*.

DIGITÀRIA

Swallen (Wiggins, Fl. Sonoran Desert 1: 282. 1964) recognizes **D. ad-scéndens** (HBK) Henr. as a weed and distinguishes it from **D. sanguinàlis** (L.) Scop. by having the second glume two-thirds as long as the spikelet; fr. pale (instead of 2nd glume half as long as spikelet; fr. lead-colored). He has the former ranging w. to Calif., the latter w. to Texas. *D. adscendens* grows to 1.5 m. tall, not 1–6 (–9) dm., as in the text.

p. 1544.   82a. **Axonòpus** Beauv.

Stoloniferous or tufted perennials, rarely annuals. Blades usually flat or folded. Racemes slender, spikelike, digitate or racemose along the main axis. Spikelets depressed-biconvex, oblong, usually obtuse, solitary, subsessile, alternate, in 2 rows on one side of a 3-angled rachis. First glume wanting; second glume and sterile lemma equal; fertile lemma and palea indurate, the lemma oblong-elliptic, usually obtuse. (Gr. *axon*, axis, and *pous*, foot.)

1. **A. compréssus** (Sw.) Beauv. Stoloniferous; culms compressed, 1.5–5 dm. long; blades 8–25 cm. long, 8–12 mm. wide; raceme-spikes 2–5, mostly 4–8 cm. long; spikelets 2.2–2.5 (–2.8) mm. long, pilose.—Reported as occasional lawn weed, although sometimes planted for lawns. Se. U.S. to S. Am.

ERIOCHLÒA

1. **E. grácilis** (Fourn.) Hitchc. In Kern Co., *Twisselmann.*
2. **E. aristàta** Vasey. $2n = 36$ (Gould, 1965).

p. 1545.   PASPÀLUM

1. **P. dístichum** L. $2n = 60$ (de Wet, 1958).
2. **P. dilatàtum** Poir. $2n = 50$ (Tateoka, 1955).

PÁNICUM

In Key, after A, BB, CC, D, change E to:

E.   Blades glabrous on both surfaces.
    F.   Ligule a ring of hairs 4–5 mm. long. . . . . 3. *P. Lindheimeri*
    FF. Ligule obsolete. . . . . 3a. *P. agrostoides*
EE. Blades pubescent, at least on lower surface.
    F.   Plants velvety-pubescent. . . . . 4. *P. thermale*
    FF. Plants ± pubescent, but not velvety.
        G.   Vernal blades pubescent above.
           H and HH as in the FLORA.
        GG. Vernal blades glabrous above. . . . . 7. *P. occidentale*

p. 1546.   3a. **P. agrostoìdes** Spreng. In dense clumps 5–10 dm. tall; lf. blades 2–5 dm. long, 5–12 mm. wide, flat; panicles terminal and axillary, 1–3 dm. long; pedicels 1- to several-haired near summit; spikelets reddish, ca. 2 mm. long.— Reported from Calif.; e. U.S.; central Am.

p. 1546.   9. **P. arizónicum** Scribn. & Merr. In Monterey Co., *Howitt & Howell.*

10. **P. dichotomiflòrum** Michx. $n = 27$ (Gould, 1958). Additional records are Monterey Co., *Howitt & Howell*; Nevada Co., Stanislaus Co., *Fuller.* Widely distributed in the state, *Rubtzoff.*

11. **P. capillàre** L. is probably in California, especially as a weed in San Francisco. It differs from the var. **occidentale** Rydb. in having longer, more pubescent blades; panicles less exserted and narrower; spikelets 2–2.5 mm. long.

p. 1547.   12. **P. Hillmánii** Chase. In Yolo and Solano cos., *Crampton.*

86a. **Rhynchelýtrum** Nees

Perennials or annuals, with rather open panicles of silky spikelets, these on short capillary pedicels. First glume minute, villous; second glume and sterile lemma equal, gibbous below, raised on a stipe above the first glume, emarginate, short-awned, covered, except toward the slightly spreading apex, with long silky hairs, the palea well developed. Lemma cartilaginous, boat-shaped.

A genus of several spp. (Greek, *rhynchos,* beak, and *elytron,* scale, referring to the beaked second glume and sterile lemma.)

    1. **R. ròseum** (Nees) Stapf and Hubb. [*Tricholaena rosea* Nees.] NATAL GRASS. Perennial, ca. 1 m. tall; blade flat, 2–5 mm. wide; panicle rosy to pink, 1–1.5 dm. long, with slender ascending branches; spikelets 5 mm. long. Abundant weed at La Mesa, San Diego Co., *T. C. Fuller;* natur. from S. Afr.

ECHINOCHLÒA

    1. **E. crusgálli** (L.) Beauv. $n = 36$ (Gould, 1958).

    2. **E. colònum** (L.) Link. $2n = 54$ (Tateoka, 1965).—Reported from Palo Alto, Santa Clara Co.

    3. **E. oryzícola** (Vasinger) Vasinger var. **mùtica** Vasinger. Spikelets 5 mm. long, awnless.—Rice fields near Biggs, Butte Co.; originally from Eurasia.

SETÀRIA

After generic description cite: Rominger, J. M. Taxonomy of Setaria in North America. Ill. Biol. Mon. 29: 1–132. 1962.

p. 1548.   In Key to **Setaria,** after AA, BB add:

> C. Upper surface of lvs. scabrous; spikelets 1.8–2.2 mm. long; panicles at maturity nodding from apex. . . . . 6. *S. viridis*
> CC. Upper surface of lf. blades pilose or strigose; spikelets 2.5–3 mm. long; panicles at maturity nodding from near the base. . . . . 7. *S. Faberi*

    1. Change *S. gláuca* (L.) Beauv. to **S. lutéscens** (Weigel) Hubb.

    2. **S. geniculàta** (Lam.) Beauv. $2n = 36, 72$ (Gould, 1965).

    3. **S. sphacelàta** (Schumacher) Stapf & Hubb. $2n = 36$ (de Wet, 1954); $2n = 18$ (de Wet, 1958).

    4. *S. Cárnei* Hitchc. Rominger says that the Fresno specimen so identified is S. verticillàta (L.) Beauv.

    7. **S. Fàberi** Herrm. Annual, 5–20 dm. tall; lf. blades scabrous and soft hairy on upper surface; panicles arching and drooping from near the base, 6–20 cm. long; spikelets 2.5–3 mm. long, subtended by 3 (1–6) bristles, each ca. 1 cm. long.—Reported as adventive in Marin Co., *Howell;* Solano Co., *Crampton;* and Los Angeles Co., *Fuller.*

PENNISÈTUM

    1. **P. clandestìnum** Hochst. ex Chiov. $2n = 36$ (Narayan, 1955). Reported from San Francisco, Alameda, and Shasta cos.

    2. **P. villòsum** R. Br. Renamed as *Cenchrus longisetus* M. C. Johnston.

p. 1549.   3. **P. setàceum** (Forsk.) Chiov. Occurs in Monterey Co., *Howitt & Howell.*

CÉNCHRUS

Cite as a reference: De Lisle, D. G. Taxonomy and distribution of the genus Cenchrus. Iowa State Jour. Sci. 37: 259–351. 1963.

In Key change *C. pauciflorus* to *C. incertus* and add *C. longispinus:*

> A. Invol. with a ring of slender bristles at base; spikelets usually 4 in each bur.
>   1. *C. echinatus*
> AA. Invol. with no ring of slender bristles at base; spikelets usually 2 in each bur.
>   B. Spines broader at base, less than 45 in number, 2–5 mm. long. . . 2. *C. incertus*
>   BB. Spines slender, usually more than 50 in number, 3.5–7 mm. long.
>   3. *C. longispinus*

    1. **C. echinàtus** L. $2n = 68$ (Tateoka, 1955). $2n = 70$ (Gould, 1965). In Imperial Co., *DeLisle;* Solano Co., *Fuller.*

    2. **C. incértus** M. A. Curtis [*C. pauciflorus* Benth.] $2n = 34$ (Tateoka, 1955). Solano Co., *Crampton;* Daggett, San Bernardino Co., *Fuller.*

    3. **C. longispìnus** (Hack. in Kneucker) Fern. [*C. echinatus* f. *l.* Hack. in Kneucker.] Forming large clumps with many branches; culms terete, 1–9 dm. tall; sheaths pilose on margins and at throat; ligule a rim of ciliate hairs 0.7–1.7 mm. long; blades 6–18 cm. long; infl. compact, 4–10 cm. long; burs ± globose, 8–12 mm. long; spines slender, 3.5–7 mm. long; spikelets 2–3 in a bur, 6–8 mm. long; $n = 17$.—Reported from Merced, Riverside, Solano, Yolo, Lassen, and Monterey cos. Native of e. U.S.

IMPERÀTA
1. **I. brevifòlia** Vasey. Found as far n. as Centerville, Fresno Co., *Fuller*.

p. 1550.   ANDROPÒGON
3. **A. virgínicus** L. from Shasta, Butte and Yuba cos., s. to Fresno Co., *Fuller*.

5. **A. saccharoìdes** Sw. is reported from s. Calif. eastward by Swallen in Wiggins, Fl. Sonoran Desert 1: 299. 1964, differing from *A. barbinodis* by having numerous racemes on a relatively long axis (not few on a short axis), panicle long-exserted; nodes glabrous or appressed-hispid (not densely bearded); spikelets sessile, 4 mm. long (not 5–6 mm.).

Var. **Torreyànus** (Steud.) Hack.—Near Fairfield, Solano Co., *Crampton*.

92a. Hyparrhènia Anderss. ex Stapf

Tall perennials, the pairs of racemes and their spathes ± crowded, forming a large elongate infl. Spikelets in pairs, those of the lower pairs alike, sterile and awnless; fertile spikelets 1–few in each raceme, terete or flattened on the back, the base usually elongate into a sharp callus. Fertile lemma with a strong geniculate awn.

1. **H. hírta** (L.) Stapf. [*Andropogon h.* L.] To ca. 1 m. tall; blades to 3 mm. wide, ± involute, flexuous; racemes whitish or grayish, silky-villous.—Reported from Los Angeles, *Raven*. From the Old World.

92b. Heteropògon Pers.

Annual or perennial, with flat or folded blades and usually solitary terminal racemes. Lower few pairs of spikelets alike, ♂, awnless; remaining sessile spikelets fertile, long-awned; pedicellate spikelets ♂ like lower ones; rachis continuous below, bearing fertile spikelets above, disarticulating at base of each joint, the joint forming a sharp barbed callus below fertile spikelet; glumes of fertile spikelet dark brown, the 1st enclosing the 2nd; lemmas hyaline, fertile one with a long stout twisted geniculate awn. (Greek, *heteros*, different, and *pogon*, beard, referring to the awnless ♂ and awned ♀ spikelets.)

1. **H. contórtus** (L.) Beauv. ex Roem. & Schult. [*Andropogon c.* L.] Perennial, tufted, 2–8 dm. tall, glabrous, with a few flowering branches at upper nodes; blades 5–15 cm. long, 3–7 mm. wide, scabrous; raceme usually long-exserted, 4–7 cm. long; 1st glume hirsute with spreading hairs; awns 5–12 cm. long, hirsute; spikelet ca. 1 cm. long.—Dehesa School, San Diego Co., *Gander*; n. Imperial Co., *Wheeler*; Ariz. to Texas and south.

SÓRGHUM
Fuller collected 3 additional spp. of *Sorghum* from near the Experimental Farm near Bard, Imperial Co. One of these, **S. sudanénse** (L.) Pers., has been reported from the w. side of the San Joaquin Valley in Kern Co., *Twisselmann*. It is an annual, 2–3 m. tall; lf.-blades 1.5–3 dm. long, 8–12 mm. wide; panicle erect, loose, 1.5–3 dm. long, the branches subverticillate. Escaped from cult. as a hay and pasture grass.

Another, **S. virgàtum** (Hack.) Stapf was taken by *Fuller* 1.5 mi. sw. of Bard, also n. of Indio, Riverside Co. It is a tall annual with a narrow slender open panicle and narrowly lanceolate green finely awned spikelets.

The third, **S. lanceolàtum** Stapf was also from 1.5 mi. sw. of Bard, Imperial Co. It is a robust annual to 1.5 m. tall; blades 3–6 dm. long, 2–3.5 cm. wide; panicle 2.5–4 dm. long with ascending branches; rachis joints and pedicels ciliate; spikelets ca. 6 mm. long, silky-pubescent; awn ca. 1 cm. long. From trop. Afr.

CORRECTIONS TO THE INDEX OF THE FLORA

p. 1594. Aesculus, 994

p. 1595. Allium
lacunosum, 1378

p. 1599. Arbutus
Menziesii, not
italicized.

p. 1600. Artemisia
1238 after vari-
ous spp. should
be 1236
Artemiastrum
should be
Artemisiastrum,
1236

p. 1603. Barbarea
orthoceras, not
orthoceras

p. 1604. *Bermudiana*
should precede
Bernardia

p. 1605. Change order to:
Brachyris
Bracken
Brake
Brandegea
Brasenia
Brassica
Braya
Brevoortia
Breweria
Brewerina
Brickellia
Bride, Mourning-
Brier, Sweet-
Briza
Brizopyrum
Brodiaea
Bryanthus,
on p. 1605
after Brush

p. 1608. Campanula
prenanthoides,
1063
Cardionema,
not italicized

p. 1610. Ceanothus
cordulatus, 978

p. 1612. Chicory, 1288

p. 1614. Clarkia
deflexa, 942

p. 1615. Coleogyne
ramosissima, 782

p. 1617. Crypsis
niliaca,
not niliacea
Cryptantha
pterocarya, 567
Purpusii, 568

p. 1621. Eastwoodia, 1099

p. 1622. Ephedra
viridis, 67

p. 1627. Eupatorium
occidentale, 1268

p. 1629. Gastridium, 1525

p. 1632. Gnaphalium
decurrens, 1260

p. 1633. Gymnosteris,
add:
minuscula, 474
nudicaulis, 474

p. 1634. Heleochloa
schoenoides,
1529

p. 1637. Hymenoclea
monogyra, 1102
Salsola, 1102

p. 1639. Koeberlinia
spinosa, 174

p. 1641. Liguliflorae, 1286
Ligusticum
Grayii, 1014
Pringlei, 1014

p. 1643. Lonicera
involucrata, 1050
flavescens, 1051
Ledebourii,
1051

p. 1644. Lotus
junceus,
not italicized
Lunaria
annua, 241
Lupinus
Benthamii,
not italicized

p. 1647. *Mammillaria*,
not italicized

p. 1649. *Microcala*,
not italicized

p. 1652. Nemophila
macrocarpa and
maculata should
be above
Menziesii
Neostapfia
colusana
misspelled

p. 1653. Oenothera
Jepsonii, p. 946

p. 1659. Phragmites
should precede
Phyla

p. 1661. Poa bulbosa,
1486

p. 1670. Scrophularia
californica,
not california

p. 1671. Senecio
petrocallis, 1250

p. 1672. Snow Plant, 436
Solomon's-Seal,
False, 1330

p. 1676. Thelesperma,
1095
Thlaspi should
precede Thorn,
Box-Thorn
Cotton- through
Thysanocarpus
(p. 1677) should
precede Tillaea.

p. 1677. Trifolium
californicum,
838

p. 1678. Macraei, 838
Trisetum
spicatum
not italicized

p. 1679. Vancouveria
to come after
Valerianella

p. 1680. Vicia
californica, 895
madrensis, 895

p. 1681. Zigadenus
Fremontii, 1334
inezianus, 1334

Index to the Supplement

Names in italics are largely those in italics in the text. Common names that are hyphenated or consist of more than one word, such as Poison-Oak and Blue Oak, are to be sought under the second word, in this case Oak. Compound names spelled as a single word, like Fireweed and Watermelon, are listed under the initial letter.